THE COMPLETE
FURSEY

Two Novels
THE UNFORTUNATE FURSEY
and
THE RETURN OF FURSEY

by

MERVYN WALL

WOLFHOUND PRESS

Originally published by The Pilot Press as two novels, *The Unfortunate Fursey* (1946) and *The Return of Fursey* (1948).

WOLFHOUND PRESS
68 Mountjoy Square, Dublin 1.

British Library Cataloguing in Publication Data
Wall, Mervyn
        The complete Fursey
            I. Title II. Wall, Mervyn. The unfortunate
            Fursey III. Wall, Mervyn. The return of Fursey
        823'.914[F]   PR6045.A3255

ISBN 0-86327-074-3
ISBN 0-86327-093-X Pbk

This book is published with the assistance of
The Arts Council (An Chomhairle Ealaíon)
Dublin, Ireland.

Cover Design by Denis Brown
Printed by Billings and Son Ltd.

CONTENTS

THE UNFORTUNATE
FURSEY

TO

DENIS DEVLIN

remembering many a lively evening

CHAPTER I

IT is related in the Annals that for the first four centuries after its foundation by the blessed Kieran the monastic settlement of Clonmacnoise enjoyed a singular immunity from the visitation of imps and ghouls, night fiends, goblins and all sorts of hellish phantoms which not unseldom appear to men. Within the sound of its bells the dark operations of magic were unknown, for no witch, sorcerer or charmer could abide the sanctified air. Other religious settlements were sadly plagued by disembodied spirits, demons, lemuses and fauns snorting and snuffling most fiendishly in the darker corners of the corridors and cells, and it was not unusual for a monk to be seriously injured or lamed as a result of their mischiefs and devilments. Philomaths of the profoundest erudition century after century poring over the great elephant folios in the library, shook their heads and warned their brethren that they could not expect to be always immune from such visitants, and that if the Prince of Darkness did but once gain a footing, he would be aflame with the thwarted malice of centuries. But the monks put their trust in the blessed Kieran and in their own sanctity, and it may have been their presumption in this regard that at last opened the door to the pestilential demons which towards the close of the tenth century thronged to Clonmacnoise from their horrible and shadowy dens.

The holy place had its first indication that its defences had been breached when one evening in early April Father Killian, who had the care of the monastery brewery, emerged from his place of work to take the air for a few minutes before returning to the main building for vespers. He had worked diligently all day, and the night air was pleasing to his heated face.   It was a dark night, and he experienced some difficulty in finding his way between the cells and huts to the palisade which surrounded the settlement.   When he reached it at last he stood for a time looking across the fields towards the river invisible in the darkness.   It was very quiet : nothing was to be heard but the regular grunting of a monk in a nearby cell, who was plying his discipline with more than usual determination.   Suddenly the moon came from behind a cloud, the river flashed silver, there was a blast of pestilential wind, and Father Killian became aware of a huge swarthy caco-demon sitting on the palisade some paces from where he stood. The face of this hideous spectre was turned back to front, and it was crunching and eating red hot coals and other dangerous matters with its teeth.

Father Killian, knowing that it was always ominous to see such a creature and that it was best not curiously to meddle, would have taken to his heels if only his legs had obeyed him, but they were paralysed with terror, which was by no means allayed when the hellish goblin, swinging itself suddenly from the palisade, took up a position beside him, and in an ingratiating manner began to tempt him to deny God and curse the Abbot.   When the startled monk found his voice it was to begin a devout recitation of the psalms, whereupon the demon seized him by the throat in a fearful grip and well-nigh throttled him.   He lifted Father Killian and flung him against the base of the round tower thirty yards away, and then letting out a hideous yell the creature vanished in a foul black smoke, leaving behind him so intolerably stinking and malignant a scent as is beyond all imagination and expression.

The fiend's parting scream brought the monks from their cells like a swarm of bees, and compressing their nostrils between their forefingers and thumbs by way of protection against the horrid and noisome stench, they made their way through the murky smoke to carry the unconscious Killian back to the monastery.

Two hours later the Abbot Marcus, returning to Clonmacnoise by boat from a day's fishing on Lough Ree, found the settlement in turmoil. The entire community crowded around him as he took his chair in the chapter house, and the white-faced Killian was carried in and propped against a wall where the Abbot could see him with convenience. The Abbot listened with some impatience to the chatter of the affrighted monks before sternly dismissing them to their beds ; and then, having ascertained that Father Killian was capable of speech, he helped him to a chair and slowly drew the story from him.

" Hm ! " said the Abbot, " how can you be certain that it was not the false impression of a timid and fretful imagination ? "

Father Killian assured him that it was not, and showed his bruises and the mark of the fiend's nails upon his throat.

" I still don't believe it," said the Abbot ; but seeing the indignation in the monk's face, he added charitably :

" You are the best brewer we have ever had in Clonmacnoise, but I have thought of late that from excess of zeal you are inclined to overwork. That might perhaps account for your hallucination. I think I will take you out of the brewery and put you in charge of the poultry, where you will find the work more agreeable to your present nervous state." And the Abbot Marcus, who was renowned far and wide for his kindness, assisted the still dazed Killian across to his cell and into bed, and left him with a promise to remember him in his prayers.

On the following morning a dish of broken food was put into Killian's hand, and he was led into the poultry house, while the brewery was committed to the care of a father of noted piety, who many years before had made a vow never to drink anything but water. The Abbot assembled the community and lectured them gravely on their childishness and their lack of faith in the blessed Kieran. When he had brought his address to a firm and dignified finish, the monks and novices dispersed to their daily tasks somewhat reassured, though an inclination to glance over their shoulders remained with them during the day.

About the hour of sunset a sudden shower of fish, which fell from the heavens like hail, occasioned the Abbot certain disquiet. During the night hoarse coughs and deep sighs were heard in the passages, followed by the barking and baying of giant dogs. On the following morning an octogenarian monk made his way into the Abbot's presence with the help of two sticks to complain of the presence in his cell during the night of an evil spirit in the form of a beautiful harlot, bravely dressed, who with mincing gait and lewd gestures had tempted him to fornication. This sequence of inexplicable events forced the Abbot to the conclusion that the monastery was badly haunted.

During the day he read up the subject in the library with the help of the apprehensive custodian, and at nightfall every monk, student and novice was assembled in the great church. As he faced them and looked at their white faces strained and tired from lack of sleep, the Abbot felt an immense pity for his spiritual children. A shudder passed through the community as he took for his text the words from the thirteenth chapter of Isaiah : " Fauns, Satyrs and the hairy ones shall dance in their palaces."

" The day of battle is at hand," began the Abbot. " The Evil One has gained entrance to the holy city of Clonmacnoise." He went on to warn them of the sinuous cunning of the Fiend, who has a myriad devices at his command, and whose minions might be expected to appear in the guise of goats, hares or horned owls. If in their cells they were to hear most lamentable moan and outcry proceeding from some invisible source, they might shrewdly suspect a manifestation. If an evil spirit did manifest itself, they should be armed to address and speak to it, and should adjure the spectre in the name of God, if it were of God, to speak ; if not, to begone. " Should a ghastly apparition suddenly confront you, be not over-confident in yourselves and presumptuously daring, but fervently recommend yourselves to God. A valiant warrior of Christ is always armed with the buckler of faith and the breastplate of hope. Dread particularly the fiend who appears in another guise, fascinating your senses and deluding you with glamour. A stoup of holy water is most healthful and efficacious, and a sure protection against the malice and attacks of unclean spirits." At the conclusion of the sermon holy water and books of exorcism were distributed to all.

The monks went slowly to their cells, their minds filled with apprehension. Before long, restless spirits could be heard groaning and sighing in the passages. About midnight the first explosion occurred. Father Leo had observed a pale, bleeding wraith, which crooned softly as it attempted to draw and switch away the quilt and blankets from his bed. As he did not deem its answer to his adjuration satisfactory, he gave it a slash of holy water, which caused it to explode and disappear through the ceiling in a sheet of flame, setting fire to the thatch in its passage upwards. An unearthly silence followed ; but before long other distant rumblings were heard, and soon the monastery was filled with smoke, noise and the smell of sulphur.

When the bell rang for matins the monks came from their cells a little haggard and shaken, but with renewed confidence. Everywhere that the enemy had manifested himself he had been defeated. Father Sampson had spent the night struggling with an incubus, but as Sampson had been a wrestler at the court of the King of Thomond before he entered the cloister, he had been well able for his adversary. Brother Patrick had been caused annoyance by a huge black dog, hideous to look upon, barking at him from a corner of his cell. As Patrick had been too terrified to reach for the holy water, the demon had remained until the crowing of the first cock ; but the lay brother had suffered no inconvenience other than loss of sleep ; and Brother Patrick remarked philosophically : "I wouldn't have slept in any case." Other monks had been scandalised by the presence of damsels of excessive comeliness, who had succeeded in divesting themselves of the greater part of their clothing before the fathers could find the right page in the books of exorcism. A suave gentleman of swarthy aspect, thought to be the Prince of Darkness himself, had actually had the audacity to try to tempt the Master of Novices and had got very much the worse of the encounter.

The Abbot, who again spent the morning in the Library and was beginning to find the subject interesting, assembled the community once more and warned them of the further evil sleights and tricks the Fiend might be expected to have at his command. He admonished them particularly to beware of complacency, an injunction which most of the brethren were inclined to think unnecessary. During the afternoon the Abbot was grieved to receive applications from many of his monks for permission to leave the monastery for varying periods in order to visit sick relatives and aged parents whom the applicants accused themselves of having sinfully neglected for many years. He sternly turned down all such representations, and the applicants set themselves to the business of learning the exorcisms and adjurations by heart, and looked to the oncoming night with doleful foreboding.

For fifteen successive days Clonmacnoise was haunted horribly. It became commonplace for a monk on turning a corner to be confronted by a demon who saluted him with cuffs and blows. Hydras, scorpions, ounces and pards frequented the cells, and serpents filled the passages with their hissings and angry sibilations. The nights were hideous with a horrid hubbub, a clattering of wrenching doors, and the howls and shrieks of invisible beings.

On the sixteenth day a sullen deputation of elderly monks awaited on the Abbot.

" It's not the look of the demons I mind," said Father Crustaceous. "A sentence or two of Latin soon disperses them. It's the lack of sleep."

" I don't mind the ones on two legs or even four," said Father Placidus, " but I can't abide loathly worms and dragons."

" The long and short of it," said another hard-bitten veteran, " is that we're of opinion that it's time for you in your capacity as Abbot to take these hellish sprites and bind them to the bottom of Lough Ree."

There was a general grunt of assent. The Abbot did not appear to have heard the last remark.

"The learned Gaspar Diefenbach has written at length on the subject," he murmured absently.

"There is a sort of feeling in the monastery," said Father Crustaceous grimly, "that our affliction by these fearful demons may be due to a lack of proper sanctity in high places."

The Abbot's fingers played nervously with a heavy folio of Cornelius Atticus.

"I will not do anything with unbecoming haste," he said shortly. "I must give some time to reflection and prayer."

Muttering, the deputation shuffled out of the cell.

Two days later, before the Abbot had completed his meditations, the haunting suddenly ceased. A free and balmy air pervaded Clonmacnoise; an expression of relief, almost of gaiety, manifested itself in every face, the monks went about their work with a lighter tread. Credit was generously given to the Abbot, for it was believed that the deliverance was due to his prayers. No doubt he had taken the matter up very seriously with the blessed Kieran, who, after all, could scarcely turn a deaf ear to the representations of his own abbot ; and, of course, everyone knew how powerful was the influence exercised by Kieran in Heaven. In anything touching Clonmacnoise he was sure to be called in for consultation, it would be discourteous to ignore him when great decisions were to be taken affecting his own foundation. The Abbot, though he said little, seemed to be satisfied that he had managed things very well with Heaven, so that it was with considerable chagrin that he listened to the halting story of a wretched lay brother, who three days later threw himself on his knees at the Abbot's feet.

Brother Fursey possessed the virtue of Holy Simplicity in such a high degree that he was considered unfit for any work other than paring edible roots in the monastery kitchen, and even at that, it could not be truthfully claimed that he excelled. The cook, a man of many responsibilities, was known on occasion to have been so wrought upon by Brother Fursey's simplicity as to threaten him with a ladle. The lay brother never answered back, partly because in the excess of his humility he believed himself to be the least of men, and partly because of an impediment in his speech which rendered him tongue-tied when in a state of excitement or fright. So it came to pass that for three whole days the wretched lay brother kept his alarming knowledge to himself through sheer terror at the thought of having to face the Abbot. While all Clonmacnoise believed that the satanic hordes had taken their departure, one man alone knew that they had not.

When the settlement had first been plagued by demons, Brother Fursey, in common with everyone else, had been strongly moved to perturbation and alarm, but when night after night had passed, and the first week had crept into the second, without his having been maltreated or belaboured, or even seeing a demon in the shape of beast or bird, he happily concluded that his soul was too mean to excite the avarice of Hell. So while the rest of the community sweated and prayed, Brother Fursey, convinced of his own worthlessness, slept blissfully beneath his blankets; but on the very first night during which the others were untroubled by devilish manifestations, the door of Brother Fursey's cell was suddenly and violently flung open. The lay brother started into a sitting position and fixed his eyes on the open doorway with some misgiving, for he knew that it was unlucky for the door of a chamber to open of its own accord and nobody to enter. He had been sitting thus for some time when an ungainly creature of the gryphon family ambled in from the corridor and, casting a disdainful glance at the startled monk, sat down in the centre of the floor. It wheezed once or twice as if its wind were broken, and gloomily contemplated the resultant shower of sparks which fell in every corner of the cell. Appalled at such a foul sight, Brother Fursey fell back against his pillows. When he roused himself again, he felt that he

was like to lose his wits, for a seemingly endless procession of
four- and six-legged creatures of most uninviting aspect was
shuffling in through the doorway and disposing themselves
about the cell. An incubus followed, and clambering on to
the bed, seated itself without much apparent enthusiasm
astride on Brother Fursey's chest. The lay brother was by
this time so nigh driven frantic by fear that he scarcely
noticed the galaxy of undraped females of surpassing loveliness
who assembled in a corner and appeared to be exchanging
gossip while they tidied up their hair. Lastly there entered
a black gentleman who walked with a slight limp. He carefully
closed the door behind him and, advancing to the head of
the bed, saluted the lay brother politely. Brother Fursey's
brain simmered in his head as he tried to remember the form
of adjuration, but the only words that he could bring to
mind were those of the Abbot's injunction : " Be not over-
confident in yourself and presumptuously daring." The sable
gentleman signed to the incubus to give place, whereupon,
grunting horribly, it slid off Brother Fursey's chest and,
waddling across the room on its bandy legs, seated itself
astride the prie-dieu. The dark stranger sat on the side of
the bed and addressed the monk with affability.

" You have no occasion to be alarmed," he said. " You
must regard this as a friendly visit."

Brother Fursey's eyes rolled agonisingly towards the stoup
of holy water on the adjoining table.

" Now, now," said the Devil, shaking his head reprovingly,
" you mustn't do that. Even if you can nerve your arm to
stretch it forth from beneath the bedclothes, I would point
out that in the past fortnight myself and the children have
acquired considerable dexterity in skipping out of the way of
a slash of that nasty, disagreeable stuff, especially when it is
cast by a shaky hand. Now," he continued, " I expect
that you are mildly exercised as to the reason for this seemingly
discourteous interruption of your sleeping hours. We had
no choice, Brother Fursey, we had no choice. Never in all

my experience as a devil have I encountered such obstinate sanctity as exists in this monastery. The boys are half-blinded with holy water and completely worn out. They need a rest, a little while to recuperate before returning to the fight, newly armed with the experience they have gained, the next time to succeed and to wipe out forever this sickly plague-spot of womanish men and chanting monkdom." Here the archfiend grated his teeth horribly, and lightenings danced in his eyes ; but he glanced down in a manner by no means unfriendly at the wisp of hair and the two button-like eyes above the quilt, which was all that could be seen of Brother Fursey.

" To compress the matter into a nutshell," continued His Highness, " I admit that my forces have been worsted in the first encounter, but I am not the sort of demon to retire with my tail between my legs and meekly allow the victory to my opponents. My troops are in need of rest and re-armament, that is all. What with the smell of incense, the splashing of holy water and the sound of the Latin language, there is no safety for any of us in this settlement elsewhere than in your cell, where due to the happy chance of your having an impediment in your speech, we are in no danger of being suddenly ejected, by a string of Latin or a shrewd adjuration, into the outer air, which is a different sort of place entirely. If I were to withdraw my legions altogether for recuperation to a clime more salubrious and more welcome to their natures, that dull fellow you have for abbot, would be up to some game such as the sevenfold circuit of the bounds of the settlement with chantings and bells so as to render our return difficult, if not altogether impossible. I intend keeping a foothold in Clonmacnoise until I clear it of its pale inhabitants. Your cell is our sanctuary. You, my dear Fursey, are our bridgehead."

For a few moments there was silence broken only by the chattering of the monk's teeth. Then a choking sound became audible from beneath the quilt. The black gentleman withdrew a pace with some distaste.

" I beg of you," he said coldly, " to give over your attempts at prayer. You know well that your fright is such as to render you incapable of the formation of a single syllable. We are both men of the world, and a ready acceptance of the position will do much credit to your commonsense and make for mutual respect. And now, to show you that I am not ungenerous, but am willing to repay your hospitality, I should like to do something for you. Purely as a matter of accounting and to keep my books straight, I shall, of course, require your soul in exchange. It's not a very valuable soul, its market value would be small ; but you won't find me haggling over the price. Are you perhaps a lover of beauty ? "

The demon waved his hand, and a queue of desirable females began to move monotonously across the cell from the door to the far wall, where they disappeared through the plaster. The monk gave vent to a deep groan and closed his eyes tightly. When he re-opened them with due caution his visitor was regarding him with professional interest.

" You have been a long time in a world of wattled huts and whitewashed cells," he said. " Do you never long for the freedom you once had, to climb the hills and move through the woods just as you please ? The breeze was pleasant when you were a boy, the forests were full of mystery, and you had a great liking for paddling your feet in the fords of rivers. All the length of a summer day you had to yourself, with no one to say ' Fursey, do this,' or ' Fursey, do that '."

Immediately a bird call was heard and the gurgling of streams. A silvan sounded a few hesitant notes on a rustic pipe, and the cell became full of heavenly fragrance and sweet odours. The demon studied the lay brother's reactions in his staring eyes and twitching forehead. It was all he could see of the monk, who had the bedclothes drawn up to the bridge of his nose.

" I'm afraid your tastes are vulgar," said the fiend with some disappointment. " What about a mighty reputation as a warrior ? "

Brother Fursey became aware of the clash and clamour of battle, the heartening burst of trumpets, and the brave flash of coloured cloaks as swords were wielded. At this point the lay-brother lost consciousness, for his was a timorous nature, and he had always been adverse to violence.

For three days the wretched Fursey crept about the monastery as in a trance. He spoiled hundreds of edible roots and pared large slices of flesh from his thumbs. He would certainly have fallen foul of Brother Cook but for the latter's exceeding good humour resultant on the departure of a poltergeist which had made itself at home in his cell and whose least prank had been to heave him out of bed several times during the night. It was only at the close of the third day that Brother Fursey gathered together his wits and the remnants of his courage. He came faltering into the Abbot's presence and knelt at his feet. It took the lay-brother a long time to stammer out his story. The Abbot heard him in silence sitting brooding in his great chair. At length he arose, uttered a sigh ; and raising Fursey, bade him return to the kitchen. Then he summoned the elder fathers to council and when they had assembled, he went down on his knees before them.

" I accuse myself," he said, " of spiritual pride. In my foolish presumption I imagined that my wretched prayers had been efficacious. The clearance of the greater part of the settlement from fiendish visitants has, in fact, been due to the stalwart piety of you, my fathers, and of the rest of the community." Then not wishing to cause his monks further embarrassment by the sight of their abbot so humbling himself before them, he got to his feet and resumed the abbatical chair. Alarm, and then consternation, manifested itself on every face as he related the lay-brother's story. There was some toothless whispering among the fathers and a great nodding of bald heads, then Father Crustaceous spoke.

" None of us is without sin," he said, " and a man's sins concern only himself and Heaven. Let us proceed at once to consider how Brother Fursey may best be relieved of this intolerable burden, and these execrable fiends be dispersed and scattered for once and for all. No doubt your lordship can now make arrangements to surround and lead them into captivity, preparatory to binding them securely to the bottom of Lough Ree."

The Abbot coughed.

" I am but a poor sinner," he said, " in sanctity the least among you. Many a man excelling me by far in piety has in the course of such an operation been torn into small pieces, and the pieces dispersed no man knows where."

" If such should be your fate," said Father Placidus, " you would be assured of a martyr's crown. Your saintly successor would certainly not omit to plead at Rome the cause for your canonisation."

" These matters are not easily put into execution," remarked the Abbot diffidently.

" It should at least be attempted," said Father Crustaceous.

" But how will the monastery benefit by my demise and subsequent canonisation, if the suggested operation be not efficacious in scattering the dread sprites that infest it ? My saintly successor would be in an even worse plight with the horrid example of my failure before him."

The Master of Novices rose to his feet. " Fathers," he said, " this discussion is getting us nowhere. I am responsible for the spiritual care and well-being of our novices and students. I cannot but rejoice that the female demons who have displayed themselves with such disregard for decency in the cells of our impressionable youth, now restrict their disgraceful activities to one cell only, and that cell the cell of a lay-brother so grounded in piety as to be indifferent to their hellish charms. Let us leave well alone. Brother Fursey is winning for himself a celestial seat. Would you deprive him of it ? Who knows but that the sufferings which he is at present enduring, may not result in his speedy demise and assumption to his Heavenly reward ? He seems to me to be a man of poor constitution. With Fursey's happy translation

Heavenwards, the Archfiend will no longer have a foothold in Clonmacnoise."

" Is there not a danger," asked Father Placidus, " that Brother Fursey, being subjected to such an assembly of the batteries of Hell, may before his constitution fails him, succumb to the unhallowed suggestions of the Evil One, and even form a compact with him detrimental to this holy foundation ? "

" But," said the Novice Master, " I understand from our lord the Abbot that this lay-brother is a man of such resolution and so charged with the seven virtues, that he laughs to scorn the most insidious temptations that Hell has been able to devise."

" That is generally true," said the Abbot. " According to what Brother Fursey has related to me, only one suggestion of the Fiend appeared to him to have been even sensible. With more than diabolical cunning the Father of Lies represented to Brother Fursey the attractiveness of murdering Brother Cook by creeping on him unawares and tipping him into the cauldron of Tuesday soup. But as soon as this devilish suggestion was insinuated into Fursey's mind, his mental agony was such that he for once succeeded in bursting the bonds which impede his speech, and he called aloud on the blessed Kieran for aid, which aid was forthcoming with such little delay that the desire to kill faded instantly from Fursey's mind beneath the outpouring of grace which drowned and overwhelmed his soul. I think we may safely assume that now that Brother Fursey is aware of this chink in his armour, he will be forearmed to resist any infernal promptings in this regard to which he may be subjected."

" Nevertheless," said Father Placidus " a word to Brother Cook would perhaps be not amiss. He should not turn his back to Brother Fursey, and it would be no harm to remove any choppers that may be lying around the kitchen."

"A good cook is hard to come by," muttered Father Crustaceous.

" It is agreed then," said the Master of Novices, " that the heroic Fursey continue to hold at bay the powers of darkness until his happy demise (which will deprive the Archfiend of his only foothold in Clonmacnoise) or until the blessed Kieran intervenes powerfully on our behalf, whichever be the shorter. In the meantime the community should address itself urgently to prayer."

"And," added Father Crustaceous, " our lord the Abbot will no doubt make every effort to increase in sanctity, and in the intervals of his fastings and scourgings he will continue in his studies as to how demons are best fastened to the bottoms of lakes. Is that the position ? "

" That is the position," said the Abbot shortly, and he dismissed the council.

When Brother Cook was informed of the grievous temptation to which his helpmate was exposed, he generously urged that it was not fitting that a man of Fursey's piety should be called upon to perform the menial tasks of the kitchen. The Abbot, however, insisted that Brother Fursey continue his offices among the edible roots, whereupon the Cook respectfully petitioned for a transfer to the poultry house, where Father Killian, who had never fully recovered from his grim experience, was not doing as well as might be desired. The Abbot curtly refused, and there was much grumbling in the monastery at the deterioration in the cooking, due to Brother Cook's difficulty in keeping his mind on his work, and the fact that he spent most of his time with his back to the wall watching Brother Fursey.

A week passed, and a certain uneasiness began to pervade the settlement. It was true that Brother Fursey's hair was now white, but he showed no signs of dissolution ; and it was not doubted but that the imps and ghouls were steadily recruiting their strength for a renewal of the assault. Every morning he was questioned by the Abbot as to the previous night's experiences, and he stammered out his story to the best of his ability. On Thursday he had been offered the crown and robes of the King of Cashel ; on Friday efforts had

been made to beguile him with melifluous verse and the promise
of a reputation as a man of letters. On Saturday he had to
be carried on a stretcher from his cell to the refectory ; for
Satan, losing all patience at the unfortunate lay-brother's
lack of interest in a shower of gold, had handed him over to
four poltergeists to work their will on him : but by nightfall
Brother Fursey had sufficiently recovered to be able to limp
back to his cell with the aid of a borrowed crutch. The
monks began to be horribly alarmed.

Father Crustaceous sucked hard at his one remaining tooth.

" There's nothing for it," he said. " Father Abbot must
set about binding them to the bottom of Lough Ree. What's
he hesitating about ? Is he afraid they'll spoil the fishing ? "

The old men rose with one accord and stumped and hobbled
to the Abbot's cell.

" I won't do it," said the Abbot violently. " That's final.
But," and he fixed his eyes on Father Crustaceous, " I have
under consideration the allotting of the holy task to a father
of greater sanctity than myself."

Father Crustaceous' mouth fell open. There was an uncomfortable silence, which was broken by the suave voice of
the Master of Novices.

" I imagine matters can be arranged more suitably," he
said, " and with satisfaction to all. We must expel Brother
Fursey from Clonmacnoise before the horrid strangers that
frequent his cell, feel that they are strong enough once more
to assail us. When Fursey is gone, their foothold will be
gone. There is no time to lose."

Every face brightened.

" Do you think it quite fair ? " began the Abbot.

" Is he not a harbourer of demons ? " asked Father Placius
hotly.

" Fair or not," said the Master of Novices, " we must
consider the good of the greater number. Remember our
innocent, but perhaps imaginative, novices subject at any
moment to the onset of a bevy of undraped dancing girls."

Father Crustaceous uttered a pious ejaculation.

"So be it," said the Abbot, and he turned away.

Within a short space the astonished Fursey found himself led to the great gate that opens on The Pilgrims' Way. The Master of Novices pointed out to him his road and indicated that he was never to return. Brother Fursey wept and held on to the other's cloak, but the Novice Master broke his hold, and left him with his blessing and the present of a second crutch.

On the side of the hill Fursey sat down in the heather and turned his red, swollen eyes to where the towers and cells of Clonmacnoise lay cluttered in a little heap beside the river. Lucifer came and stood beside him.

"If it would afford you any satisfaction," said that personage, "I will rive one of the round towers with a ball of fire. I regret that I am not allowed to damage the churches or cells."

"No," said the ex-monk, who now that there was no urgent necessity for him to speak, found that he could do so with reasonable fluency. "I wish you'd go away. You're the cause of all this," and he burst into a fresh fit of weeping.

The Devil hesitated. "What are you going to do?" he asked.

"What can I do?" moaned Fursey. "No religious settlement will admit me with the reputation I've acquired."

"The world is a fine broad place," said the Devil.

"What is there in it?" asked the ex-monk. "I looked at it long ago and left it."

"There are women, riches, fame and sometimes happiness."

Fursey raised his voice in a howl. "Are they there for a white-haired old man with a broken hip?"

"I'm sorry about the hip," said the Devil. "I assure you there was no personal ill-feeling."

"Have you not shown me such numbers of luscious and agreeable females that henceforth all women that I shall meet, must seem to me hideous and in the highest degree undesirable? What are the little wealth and distinction that must be wrested from the world, to me who have rejected

showers of gold and the thrones of kings ? Demon, you have
undone me.''

Lucifer regarded him not unsympathetically.

'' You should have come over to my side in the beginning,''
he said. '' I'd have made you abbot of that place, and we'd
have wrecked it together.''

The ex-monk emitted a dolorous moan.

'' Give over this unmanly plaining,'' said the Devil with
some impatience, but Fursey's only answer was : '' What will
become of me ? What will become of me ? ''

'' To live, a human being must eat,'' remarked the Devil
sagely. '' The best thing you can do is to go down to the
city of Cashel and there secure for yourself employment
suitable for you having regard to your age, sex, physique,
education, normal occupation, place of residence and family
circumstances.''

'' I'll have to go to Cashel anyway,'' replied Fursey. '' It's
the only place this road leads to.''

'' Cashel is a fine big city,'' said the Devil meditatively.
'' It has a hundred and twenty-two wattled huts as well as
the King's House and the new thatched palace the Bishop
has built for himself. You'd be assured of employment in
such a teeming centre of population.''

'' The trouble is that I'm not much good at anything except
washing and paring edible roots,'' replied Fursey. '' They
never trained me to anything else.''

'' Nonsense,'' said the Devil encouragingly. '' Surely a man
of your ability could milk a cow without pulling the teats off
her.''

'' I suppose so,'' said Fursey without much conviction.

'' Well, come on,'' said the Archfiend. '' What are we
waiting for ? ''

'' I trust that you are not coming with me ? '' said Brother
Fursey, his voice betraying some anxiety. '' I'd prefer you
wouldn't, if you don't mind.''

'' I have no choice,'' said the Devil. ''As you yourself
indicated just now, Cashel is the only place to which this road

leads. So of necessity myself and the boys will bear you company. They're waiting below around the bend of the road, a whole acre of them, an acre of the choicest and most variegated demons that have ever been brought together in this holy land of Ireland. You will travel in style, with an entourage the Emperor of Constantinople cannot boast of. Besides, I have a little business in Cashel. An acquaintance of mine is being subjected to ill-treatment in that city, and I must see if something cannot be done to alleviate her distress. She's a very fine old lady. Fifty years ago there wasn't a handsomer woman in the territory. She's a little broken in the wind now, I'll admit, and somewhat spavined. You must make her acquaintance, my dear Fursey. I have no doubt but that the two of you will find that you have much in common."

The ex-monk groaned as he placed his crutches beneath his aching armpits and painfully made his way to the road, while the Devil strolled beside him discoursing affably on the beauty of the countryside, the gentle greenness of field and tree, the flaming yellow gorse and the hawthorn in pink and white blossom. As they walked along the crooked road towards the bend where it curled over the hill, the vast sky, woolly with cloud, shed its mild sunlight down upon them.

" It's the first day of May," said the Devil. " I must admit that it's good to be alive."

He was silent for a moment, listening to the stumping and grinding of Fursey's crutches on the stony road and the heavy breathing of the ex-monk who was inexperienced in such work. Then his face darkened.

" The old lady is being most foully ill-treated," he said, " by a villainous oaf of a bishop, a most uninviting fellow, gaunt and hungry-looking, with a smell of grave-mould off his breath that would turn your stomach. I don't fancy him at all. Himself and the King are intent on burning her as a witch. Did you ever hear the like ? " said the Devil, and a hard note crept into his voice. " If there's one thing I can't stand," he said, " it's superstition."

CHAPTER II

ON a morning of sprightly sunshine and breeze a friar of huge stature came along the southern road towards Cashel. The dust that powdered his sandals and robe indicated that he had come a long way. He had a mop of wiry ginger hair, which seemed pale in contrast to the fiery red of his face. Indeed, only for his dress, which proclaimed him a man of God, the flaming hue of his countenance and his nose blossoming in the centre of it, might have led one to believe that he was addicted to the pleasures of the table and to the sorry joy that is derived from the consumption of strong drink. It would have been an unjust judgment ; for the mighty fires that raged in Father Furiosus proceeded from love of God and the desire to smite at Evil wherever it might raise its ugly head. He was a man of powerful frame ; and you had but to observe the great knotted fist clutching a heavy blackthorn stick, to have it borne in powerfully upon you that the Church Militant was no empty phrase.

At the wicker gate in the palisade he brushed aside the guard who diffidently enquired his name and business, and proceeded on his way without deigning to reply ; but he had only advanced a few paces into the city when a rabble of dogs came tumbling from the alleys and doorways, and precipitated themselves in his direction, snarling hideously. Scrubby and raffish curs who were investigating distant rubbish heaps, hearing the din that betokened a stranger within the gates, immediately abandoned their researches and came tearing towards him with bared fangs. The guard at the gate and those citizens who were in the immediate vicinity, hurriedly took refuge in the neighbouring cabins, from which they peered in morbid expectancy of seeing the newcomer torn to pieces. But the older and more case-hardened canines pulled up suddenly in full career, for a second glance at the broad-shouldered friar lightly swinging his blackthorn stick as he strode confidently on his way, seemed to persuade them that they had misconstrued the situation. They circled him once or twice and grudgingly wagged their tails as if to convince him that their actions had been motivated merely by friendly curiosity ; but a few of the younger and less experienced dogs came within his reach growling fiercely, until the friar, without pausing in his stride, with a few deft backhanders of his blackthorn, scattered them in all directions yowling piteously.

As Father Furiosus made his way among the hundred-and-twenty huts that constituted the city, he noted appreciatively the signs of prosperity and happiness on every side of him, the peat smoke billowing from the doorways of the cabins, the crowing of the city's cocks and the tuneful grunting of its pigs. In a couple of minutes he had traversed the settlement and found himself at the northern gate. Here he paused and raised his finger to indicate to the armed guard that he wished to converse with him. The soldier came running to his side, bowing abjectly.

" Tell me, fellow," said the friar, nodding towards a fine new building which stood on a slight eminence, " is that the palace of your wise and enlightened monarch, the mighty Cormac Silkenbeard ? "

" Oh no, sir," replied the soldier, " may it please your reverence, that's the new palace which good Bishop Flanagan has built for himself."

Father Furiosus turned to admire the edifice. It was a building of generous proportions, thatched with the best of ·seasoned reeds and fronted by a pair of bronze doors so wide that four churchmen could walk through abreast without undue difficulty.

" It actually has what they call an ' upstairs '," volunteered the soldier with considerable awe in his voice, " the first ' upstairs ' that was ever in Ireland. It means, as it were, that there are two houses on top of one another. There are rooms up there in the air where you can walk about if you want to."

"Dear me," said the friar sententiously. "One of these days science will certainly over-reach itself. And does not certain danger attend the ascent?"

"They say not, your Holiness," replied the soldier. "The Bishop does have a class of ladder of the finest polished elm-wood, which brings you to the 'upstairs' through a hole in the roof."

"It's a fine building," said the friar, adding thoughtlessly: "It must have cost a power of wealth to build."

"Yes," said the soldier with a slight sigh.

The friar turned and indicated a large building at some distance.

"And I suppose that's the King's House?"

"It is," replied the soldier.

"That's all, my man," said the friar, dismissing his informant, who with a grovelling bow ran back to his post.

For a moment or two Father Furiosus contemplated the King's House, its thatch decayed and diseased, and one of its walls supported by a manure heap. He smiled slightly, then he turned his steps to the incline which led to the Bishop's Palace, reflecting as he went that it was well to assert at all times and in all things the superiority of the Church to the State.

The great bronze doors of the Palace were opened by an Anglo-Saxon slave boy, who on hearing the friar's name and condition, ushered him into a spacious hall strewn with sweet-smelling rushes. The Bishop, he explained, was out in the stockyard at the back of the palace inspecting the episcopal herds, but would be informed at once of the friar's arrival.

Father Furiosus had not long to wait before the lean figure of the Bishop slid through a doorway, and advancing noise-lessly across the hall, held out his hand for his visitor to kiss. When the friar arose from his knees he was graciously waved to a seat on a bench that ran along the wall. After the exchange of the usual civilities about the weather, the Bishop politely enquired whether the friar had lunched.

"Indeed, no," replied Father Furiosus with a sigh that seemed to come from the hollow depths of his stomach. "I have but even now arrived in your splendid and interesting city."

"Then you must lunch with me," said the Bishop. "I am about to partake of my mid-day collation. I keep but a poor table : perhaps that is fitting in a man of God. I trust that you will honour me by sharing my humble meal."

Father Furiosus protested that food was a thing to which he seldom gave a thought, but he arose with alacrity and followed the Bishop into an inner room. They seated themselves, and at a command from the Bishop discreet serving-men placed before them two quart-pots of ale and a jelly of smelts.

"I trust that you have at least breakfasted," said the Bishop.

"I did," replied the friar, "but sparingly. In a cave on the road about ten miles to the south there lives a gentle anchorite with whom I stopped to exchange the time of day. We passed a pleasant hour in godly conversation. He pressed me to partake of a couple of his crusts and obligingly smashed them for me with his mallet."

"It's all very well for the anchorites," said the Bishop. "They use up none of their energies sitting at the mouths of their caves all day, but a man like yourself who has to be about God's work, needs more solid sustenance. Eat up, there is a second course. A dish of lampreys is to follow."

The grateful friar needed no second invitation. As they ate and drank in silence, Father Furiosus was enabled to study Bishop Flanagan, whose reputation as a man of God was only second to his own.

Those who did not like the Bishop, whispered of him that he was a man from whom every graceful attribute seemed to have been withheld by Nature. He was spare and stringy, and his Adam's apple was in constant motion in his scraggy throat. His underlip was loose and twitched as he looked at you, but it was not from nervousness, for the way he held his head and the unrelenting gaze of his eyes close placed above the long thin nose, betokened his pride in his exalted rank and his determination to exact from all the respect which was his due. The odour of sanctity was clearly discernible from his breath and person.

When the dish of lampreys had been carried in by two undersized serfs the Bishop replenished his ale-pot and leaned across the table towards the friar.

"Father Furiosus," he said, "I want you to know how honoured I am to have under my roof-tree a man of your great reputation and sanctity."

The face of Father Furiosus clouded, as it always did when he heard himself praised. It came to him that he should not have drunk his second quart of ale so rapidly, for there was a tear in his eye for which he could not account. However, he bent towards the Bishop and answered huskily:

"Please don't say that, your lordship. I know that I have quite unworthily acquired such a reputation, but it never fails to grieve me to hear such sentiments expressed. I am at once overwhelmed with the consciousness that there does not walk the roads of Ireland a more depraved sinner than myself."

"Tut, tut," said the Bishop, "how can you say that?"

"Listen," said the friar vehemently, clutching Bishop Flanagan's arm. "When I was young I led a most wicked and dissolute life. I blasphemed God and cursed my parents, and gave myself over to every infamy. I was a wrestler at the court of the King of Thomond. I rejoiced in circuses and the godless company of acrobats. Thank God, I kept myself free from the taint of women; but in all else I was a lost soul. I was a gambler, a drunkard and a singer of songs. I rejoiced in poetry. But on the day of my greatest triumph when I broke the back of Torgall the Dane, God spoke to me, and I heard Him even above the applause of that wild court. 'Vanity of vanities,' He said, 'and all in vanity.' I heard

Him, but I heeded Him not. But that evening when the moon was out I was approached by a lively and engaging female with an invitation to take a walk with her along a country road. By ourselves actually, and by moonlight! Then did I know indeed that I was trembling on the brink of Hell, and I fled from that court, first to the hills, and then to the monastery at Glendaloch. But you probably know the rest."

The friar flung his great bulk back into his chair despondently.

" You didn't stay," said the Bishop gently.

" They wouldn't keep me," said the friar. "A little dispute with the cook about the porridge being cold one morning. Unfortunately I crippled him."

" It was a pity," said the Bishop.

" It was the same in every monastery I entered," continued Father Furiosus gloomily. " My ungovernable temper was my ruin. In Bangor I deprived the doorkeeper of the one eye he had, and I killed a scullion in Clonfert. I pleaded with the Abbot that his skull was thin, but they turned me out."

The friar seemed sunk in intolerable dolour until the Bishop replenished his tankard.

" God's ways are not our ways," said Bishop Flanagan, " perhaps it was for the best. See all the good that you have been enabled to do."

" Yes," said Father Furiosus, rousing himself to drink deeply. " I became a wandering friar, and as God has given me a spirit that fears neither man, dog nor devil, I have perhaps done some little good. I make my way from settlement to settlement wherever I think my services may be needed, and I assure you it is a sturdy demon or necromancer that can stand against me. I have become expert in demonology and in detecting the darker acts of sorcery. On my way from town to town I clear the lovers from the ditches and the doorways, but that's in the nature of a sideline."

" Nevertheless, even if it be but a sideline, you have done a man's part in preventing the hateful passion of love from spreading throughout this land."

" I have a strong arm, thank God," said the friar.

" Where have you come from now ? " asked the Bishop.

" From the town of Cork ," replied the friar.

" Business, I suppose ? "

" Yes," said the friar, " a bad case of werewolves. Some thirty citizens had disappeared leaving no evidence of whither they might have betaken themselves. A heap of skeletons, picked clean of flesh, was found in the backyard of a town councillor. This, as you may imagine, gave rise to suspicion, and I had him watched. It transpired that three town councillors were involved. Every evening at sundown the spirit of the wolf took possession of them, and they repaired to the forest. They were small, paunchy men, and to see them coursing through the woods, naked and on all fours, was a remarkable sight."

" It must have been," remarked the Bishop. " What did you do with them eventually ? "

" We hunted them with hounds and spearmen, and deprived them of their lives," replied Father Furiosus gloomily. " It's the only thing to do with a werewolf."

" Is there no way," asked the Bishop, " whereby a werewolf may be detected in the early stages of his affliction ? "

" Yes," replied the friar, " when a man first becomes a werewolf, he often betrays himself by going out and fighting with all the town dogs. I don't know if that perhaps happened before my arrival. The people of Cork are singularly uncouth, and such behaviour might not have been deemed in any way extraordinary."

The Bishop arose from the table and led the way back to the hall.

" I hope," he said, " you will be able to stay a couple of days in Cashel. We have need of your services here."

" I was on my way to Clonmacnoise," replied the friar, " which, I hear, is much abused by disembodied spirits and satanic creatures of the craftier sort, and I had looked forward to greeting again an old fellow-wrestler at the Thomond Court, a Father Sampson, who is now a monk in that monastery; but hearing that Cashel was enduring sundry molestations and the worst horrors of witchcraft, I turned aside to place my experience in such matters at your lordship's disposal. In what way are you troubled here in Cashel? Is it by wily imps teasing the besotted natives or have strange and terrible happenings come about through the detestable workings of a witch? Tell me all. Do not fear that your lordship will alarm me. I am hardened by many a fight with the Evil One and by many a lonely midnight prayer."

" I am walking over to the King's House," said the Bishop. " If you will accompany me, I shall relate to you the story of our afflictions."

They passed out through the bronze doors, out into the pleasant sunlight. As they walked down the hill towards the litter of huts, groups of townspeople, when they saw the Bishop, removed their hats and even fell on their knees, while little children ceased their play and crept out of sight.

" You must know," began Bishop Flanagan, " that our minds have recently been exercised by certain untoward happenings which gave rise to the conviction that there were sorcerers in the neighbourhood. For many nights King Cormac Silkenbeard had been deprived of his rest by the hideous caterwauling of a platoon of cats, who mustered on the roofs surrounding the royal dwelling, and there raised a clamour so uncouth and deformed that it was speedily doubted whether their behaviour did not proceed from the operation of a powerful spell. On the fourth night, King Cormac told me, he had drunken deeply of brown ale in an endeavour to forget his cares; and, enraged by the persistence of the persecution to which he was being subjected, he seized his sword and rushed out into the garden in his night attire. To his horror he beheld several felines engaged in what appeared to be animated conversation, while on the wall sat a brindled tom of monstrous size with gleaming eyes and large white eyeballs, who grinned sarcastically at the King and waved his paw in derision.   There could be no further doubt but that these were enchanted cats ; and on my advice, two conjurors and a ventriloquist who had come to the town for the annual fair, were immediately seized.   As they persisted obstinately in denial, they were put to the question."

"With favourable results ? " asked the friar, whose professional interest was aroused.

"Yes," said the Bishop with satisfaction.   "After three days application of the best available monkish tortures, they agreed to admit anything.   Further proof of their guilt was afforded by the fact that no sooner had they been apprehended by the King's men, than the enchanted cats ceased to trouble the royal repose."

Father Furiosus nodded approvingly.   "It's a well-known fact," he said, "attested by all the Fathers of the Church, that when the officers of justice lay their hands upon a sorcerer, he is at that moment bereft of his execrable powers."

"Unfortunately," said the Bishop, "the two conjurors and the ventriloquist, having been crippled in the course of the judicial examination, had to be carried to the stake.   The burning was a colourful ceremony, but I should have wished that they could have walked."

"It's more impressive certainly," agreed the friar.

The Bishop's face darkened, and his underlip twitched alarmingly.

"But evil powers did not cease to trouble us," he said. "Not long afterwards, the city was subjected to a plague of fleas whose inordinate fierceness and voracity far exceeded the experience of the oldest inhabitant.   They appeared to make a particular set on me and on the canons of the Chapter ; and this impiety, together with their exceeding briskness in evading capture, convinced me that their activities were not of nature, but proceeded from the damned art of witchcraft."

Father Furiosus nodded gravely while the Bishop scratched his buttock reminiscently.

" I had two mathematicians burnt," continued the Bishop, " but it did little to abate this strange and grievous vexation. Next, an army of mice started to march up and down the streets of the town in an orderly company without stragglers. You can imagine our alarm, for we knew that such an extraordinary purposeful march could not but presage evil. Such persistent persecution, we felt, could only be the result of spells of peculiar malignancy. We were concerting further measures when once more the King was struck at, this time through the medium of enchanted beer. His secretary set down in writing an exact record of the King's experiences, and it is at present in my possession. King Cormac one evening after supper innocently consumed six quarts of a particularly delectable ale, and was at once filled with vague and disagreeable sensations. He sat for a long while gnawing his beard while his terrified servants hurried over to my palace in search of spiritual aid. When I arrived with my book of exorcisms the unfortunate man had begun to laugh and frolic, and was shouting the most villainous and the lewdest language that ever man heard. Under exhortation his sportiveness abated ; he sunk down in a swoon of gladness and lay a great while like as he had been dead. His limbs being rendered unserviceable by the malignant potency of the spell, he had to be carried to his couch by six servitors, where he lay unconscious while a choir of monks in the corner of the room chanted throughout the night the psalm, '*Ad Deum cum tribubarer*.' Under this treatment he recovered towards morning ; but marvellous to relate, remembered nought of his frenzy."

Father Furiosus shook his head gravely. " Faith," he said, " is the best buckler against such invasions. Is King Cormac perhaps a man in his mode of life indifferent to heavenly things, and careless of the well-being of the Church ? Does he contribute regularly to the support of his pastors ? "

" Indeed, yes," said the Bishop, " he is a faithful son of the Church, who never fails to enrich with a tithe of one-third of the spoils of war the abbeys and religious settlements of his kingdom, so that they have grown to an exceeding sleekness, reflecting the highest credit on him."

"He seems to be a right and proper prince," said Furiosus meditatively. "It would appear that we must look elsewhere for the cause of these stubborn manifestations. I am not inclined to believe that they proceed from the malice of demons : firstly, because they are not in character ; and secondly, because I have information that all the demons in Hell are at present at Clonmacnoise, where some weeks ago they succeeded in penetrating the defences raised by the prayers of the Blessed Kieran, and where they are exercising every species of wile and violence to win the good monks from their duty. Are there any other ventriloquists, mathematicians, acrobats, charmers or reciters of poetry in the neighbourhood ? If you wish I will institute an inquisition of likely persons. As you know, I am licensed by the Synod of Kells to search for conjurors."

"No," said the Bishop, who had been waiting impatiently for the friar to have done, "they have all fled. But," and the Bishop's underlip vibrated with satisfaction, "I believe I have in custody the *fons et origo* of this dismal and abhorred business."

"Indeed," said the friar, somewhat crestfallen.

"Yes," said Bishop Flanagan, "four days ago the sexton of Kilcock Churchyard, a worthy fellow, came to me and laid information denouncing as a witch an impoverished hag of advanced age, known locally as The Gray Mare, who resides within a stone's throw of the sexton's house. He had frequently seen her at night out on the hillside struggling with a cat ; and recently, while he was watching her over the fence which separates their land, her body changed, horns appeared on her head, and she went on all fours like an animal. He has also, he avers, seen her changed into a horse and walking on her hindlegs ; but it was not until last week that his suspicions were really aroused by the sight of her astride a broomstick, on which she ambled and galloped through the air, flying by his house with such velocity that the wind of her passing did raise much of the thatch from his roof."

" Hm," said Father Furiosus, " it has all the signs of a bad case of sorcery. I trust there is no reason to suspect that the sexton in laying the charge was actuated by malice ? "

" Well," admitted the Bishop somewhat reluctantly, " I understand that there is some dispute between the two, something about a boundary fence and a trespassing goat ; but the sexton is a worthy man, and he was very positive in his accusations."

" How did you proceed ? "

" We seized the witch and formally accused her of being a companion of hellhounds, a caller and a conjuror of wicked and damned spirits."

" How did she react to these charges ? "

" She at once lodged a countercharge against the sexton, accusing him of being a damnifying sorcerer himself ; but, at his own request, his legs were examined by the canons of the Chapter, and his knees being found horny with frequent praying, he was immediately acquitted."

" Yes," said the friar, stroking his red jowl thoughtfully, " things look bad for this woman you call The Gray Mare. Did you put her to the torture ? "

" No," said the Bishop regretfully. " She is old and frail, so that we were in fear lest she should die before the day appointed for her burning. We did, however, walk her up and down for three days in the approved manner, thus depriving her of sleep and rest ; and in relays we continuously questioned her, but it was of little avail. Under this treatment she admits everything we suggest, but no sooner is she permitted to sit down than she speedily retracts it all. Indeed, she is a witch full of craftiness and wile." The Bishop's eye gleamed fanatically, and his voice became shrill. The friar watched the jerking underlip fascinated.

" But we will tie her to a strong stake of faggots," said the Bishop, his voice rising almost to a scream, " and we will

burn her, as is right ; and from her mouth will be seen to
issue a swarm of sorceries and lies and other hideous devilries."

Father Furiosus waited respectfully for the Bishop's anger
to abate before he again spoke.

" When is the burning ? " he asked.

The Bishop's face darkened.

" I regret to say that the date is not yet fixed. Some of
the canons of the Chapter, quite foolishly it seems to me,
still entertain doubt as to her guilt. They seem to be not
altogether convinced of the sexton's bona fides on account of
the dispute about the trespassing goat. So I have reluctantly
consented that one more trial be màde of her. We are going
to swim her this afternoon in a pool in the River Suir two
miles from the town."

" An excellent test approved by every writer on the subject," said the friar, rubbing his large red fists with satisfaction.
" If the water rejects her ; that is, if she floats, it is sure proof
that she is a witch. If she sinks, God has plainly manifested
that she is innocent."

" You wouldn't be so punctilious about the fine points of
the matter," said the Bishop sourly, " if you had been subjected to the attentions of a myriad of enchanted fleas of a
dexterity and agility altogether out of the course of nature.
However, here we are at the house of the noble Cormac
Silkenbeard."

The Bishop knocked at the door with his pastoral staff.
It was opened at once by a serving boy whose face fell at
sight of the churchman.

" Is your royal master within ? " enquired Bishop Flanagan.

The youth did not reply, but seemed to be experiencing the
liveliest consternation.

The Bishop gave him a sharp look and pushed by him into
the royal kitchen. Father Furiosus followed.

It was a spacious room furnished with several spits and a
shining array of bronze vessels ; but what riveted the friar's
gaze was the extraordinary sight of an aged gentleman,
apparently naked, sitting bolt upright in a species of orna-

mental bath set in the centre of the earthen floor. The tub was so short that the old gentleman had of necessity his knees drawn up to his chin. An immense silky grey beard concealed most of his person. He was chortling, evidently in huge enjoyment of a stream of warm water which a servingman poured from a watering-can on to his bald head. His back was to the door, so that the first indication he had of the presence of visitors was when the Bishop accosted him with a voice of thunder.

"What is this I see?" demanded Bishop Flanagan, "in the Royal House of Cashel, a scene reminiscent of the worst excesses of the Roman Empire!"

The serving-men retreated hurriedly from the room, and a blush of shame could be seen creeping down the back of the monarch.

"Get out of that at once," commanded the Bishop harshly.

"I can't," said the King feebly. "I'm jammed. It's rather short, and I do have to be lifted out."

"This is a grievous sight," continued the Bishop harshly. "I bring to visit you a stranger, a powerful man of God. I tell him the King of Cashel is a man of beautiful thoughts and pregnant principles, and what does he see in the Royal House—every evidence of lax, unrestrained and vicious living."

The King's hand shook as he made a weak attempt to spread his beard so as to cover as much of his naked chest as possible.

"Where did you get that device of the devil?" demanded the Bishop.

"It was sold to me by a travelling salesman from the Eastern World," replied the monarch humbly. "He had a fine share of talk, and he tempted me by urging that all the best people in the Byzantine Empire have them installed."

"Yes," thundered the Bishop. "And where is the Byzantine Empire now? Rotten with heresies! You didn't think of that?"

" No," replied Cormac, " I didn't think of that. I'm only a poor king," he added plaintively, " broken with the years and surrounded by damnifying witches trying to bring about my final undoing."

" The first thing is to remove you from that slough of sin," said Bishop Flanagan. " Father Furiosus, maybe you can be of use here."

" Certainly," said the sturdy friar, rolling back his sleeves. He grasped Cormac under the armpits and lifted him without difficulty from the bath. He held the king in the air for a few moments expecting him to stretch out his legs and stand, but Cormac kept his knees up to his chin, his legs still cramped by the sudden fright induced by the arrival of the Bishop. The friar placed him gently in a sitting position on the floor. Bishop Flanagan kept his eyes modestly averted until a towel had been draped around the monarch.

" I cannot understand," commented the Bishop, " how a man of your upbringing, education and position can be unaware of the heinousness of such conduct. It was in the effeminate steam of the bath-house that the strength and resolution of Rome evaporated, leaving her a prey to the barbarian. God has made the human body to exude natural oils and vapours, and you would defy the divine economy and undo His work by impiously washing them off. I tremble for your immortal soul, Cormac. Indeed, I do not know if anything less than excommunication will meet the case."

At the sound of the dread word King Cormac was gripped by a fit of trembling.

" I confess my sin," he said abjectly. " Perhaps a small offering to the Church, maybe two bullocks—— ? "

" Forgiveness is not a commodity that can be bought," replied the Bishop haughtily. " Nor is it wise for a sinner to be niggardly with God."

The King groaned. " *Four* bullocks," he suggested. " They will be driven over to your stockade before sundown."

" Well," said Bishop Flanagan, " I don't wish to be hard on you, particularly as you have recently been subjected to operations of a magical character far from pleasant. I shall send over the absolution when the four bullocks are delivered. You must surrender the bath, of course, that we may burn it with due ceremony."

" I am most willing to follow any course your Holiness indicates," replied King Cormac humbly. " May I now be permitted to resume my clothing ? This earthen floor is grievously chilly and unfriendly to the buttocks."

" Yes," said Bishop Flanagan, " and when that office is performed, you may join us in the sun-room."

The Bishop led the way from the kitchen, down a passage, and through several spacious apartments. He and Furiosus met nobody. This very much surprised the friar, who had expected to see the entire personnel thronging around the Bishop to receive his blessing and to beg the favour of kissing the good man's hand ; but instead, Furiosus was conscious of gently closing doors and dim footfalls, as if the inmates were most anxious to keep out of sight. There was silence in every corner of the Royal House, but it was not the silence of a deserted place ; it was the tingling stillness in which one feels that behind every door human beings are standing motionless, almost afraid to breathe. Father Furiosus shook his red mane angrily. He was a straightforward, downright man ; and these fancies disturbed him.

On the floor of the sun-room sat two of King Cormac's daughters. The younger was stringing a set of multi-coloured beads, and the stones, jasper, amethyst and cornelian, lay heaped in her lap. Her sister had let down her hair. It was of the colour of gorse and lay tumbled in brilliant profusion over her shoulders. Squatting back daintily on her slender haunches, she was combing it with long, rhythmic strokes. Bishop Flanagan started on seeing the two girls, and instinctively averted his eyes ; but Father Furiosus, who had as much sense of beauty as one of the royal bullocks that was shortly to change its allegiance, stared stolidly at the spectacle.

An important feminine conversation was in progress.

" You glanced at him," giggled the girl who was stringing
the beads.

" I did not," replied her sister, tossing back her yellow head.

" I tell you I saw you. You glanced across when you
thought he wasn't looking."

" And I tell you again that I didn't."

The dialogue lost itself in a series of titters, which terminated
abruptly when Golden Head, glancing around, caught sight
of the Bishop and the friar standing in the doorway. Her
face grew scarlet. She dropped the comb and, springing to
her feet, bundled her hair into a silken cap, which she hurriedly
pulled down over her ears. Her sister, no less alarmed,
grabbed her handful of stones, dropping one or two in her
haste ; and rose to her feet. They curtsied deeply as Bishop
Flanagan walked into the room. He gave them a curt nod,
and then seemed to lose himself in thought until an irregular
lump of amethyst gave him a purple wink from the floor. He
touched it with his foot.

" You've dropped one of your baubles," he said harshly.

The girl stooped hastily to pick it up, and she and her
sister slipped unobtrusively from the room. The Bishop took
four paces across to the wall and then turned to gaze gravely
at Father Furiosus.

" This is serious," he said at length.

The friar looked at him enquiringly.

The Bishop's eyes had narrowed, and his Adam's apple was
in motion in his throat.

" You heard what they were talking about ? " he asked
darkly.

" No," replied the friar.

" Men ! " said the Bishop. He seated himself carefully,
keeping his eyes fixed on Father Furiosus, who sat down too
and waited for enlightenment.

Bishop Flanagan's brow was furrowed, and his face had
the set expression of a shepherd who discerns in a thicket the
grey snout of a wolf. His grip tightened on his pastoral staff.
He rose to his feet again and began to walk to and fro.

" I must talk to their father," he said weightedly. " It's high time those girls were married or in a cloister. The eldest is seventeen."

Father Furiosus grappled with the problem.

" Do you think they'd make good nuns ? " he asked at length.

" I do not," said the Bishop. " Marriage is the only thing for it. Fortunately, I know of several elderly, stolid farmers with some share of the world's goods. I'll make a list of four or five, and the girls can have their choice. Women are feather-brained creatures and are apt to make difficulties unless they are allowed the exercise of a choice. I'm sure I don't know why, but it's an undeniable fact."

Furiosus sat back lost in admiration of his companion's organising ability.

The Bishop gave vent to a long-drawn sigh.

" Did it ever occur to you to wonder why God created women ? " he asked. " It's the one thing that tempts me at times to doubt His infinite goodness and wisdom."

The friar shrugged his shoulders and exhaled noisily to demonstrate that this was a problem far beyond his limited perceptions.

" It's a thing that I've long since given up trying to understand," he replied. " I assume with a blind faith that they are in the world for the trial and affliction of man, that his entry into another sphere may be the more glorious for the temptations that he has successfully withstood in this."

" It was a hard measure," muttered the Bishop. " God's hand was heavy on mankind the day that He created woman."

" Are you afflicted much by the antics of women in this neighbourhood ? " enquired Furiosus politely.

" The situation was bad when I came here first," said the Bishop, " but I cleaned up the city pretty quickly. Why, it was actually the practice of merchants to display articles of women's underwear on their stalls during the monthly fairs, to the grave detriment of morals."

" That was bad," said the friar. " Some of these merchants have no care that such garments powerfully affect youth, giving rise to unmentionable thoughts and desires."

" Exactly," said the Bishop. " However, I organised the pious, God-fearing women of the settlement. They went in a body to the merchants and threatened to withdraw their custom unless such raiment was kept under cover and not displayed before the gaze of men."

" Excellent," said the friar.

" Love-making was also rife, but the threat of ecclesiastical censure generally proved sufficient."

" I find a blackthorn stick and a stout arm most effective," said Father Furiosus diffidently ; " but then I am not favoured with your lordship's eloquence and your powers of excom-munication."

" In extreme cases of failure to conform, in this as in other things, I have recourse to the civil authority, who deprives the offender of his livelihood," replied the Bishop. " I'm proud to say that there isn't in all the land a cleaner or more God-fearing diocese than this."

" I can well believe you," said the friar.

The two men of God sat for a little while in silence. The friar's gaze wandered around the room. Beneath one of the benches lay a couple of beads from a necklace, and in the centre of the floor were the broken fragments of a comb on which the Bishop had trodden in his striding to and fro. It was a pleasant three-walled room. The fourth side was open to a tiny garden of grass and half-a-dozen apple trees. The room was built facing south so that full advantage might be taken of the sunlight, with which it was now agreeably flooded. The furniture was simple, a few benches and stools. There were no hangings to be injured by rain or rough weather. It was only when the skies were mild that the room was used at all. The friar noticed these things and listened dreamily to the birds that hopped from branch to branch of the apple trees, letting fall their little tuneful notes and whistlings. A wagtail fluttered through the air and alighted at the Bishop's feet.

" Birds," said the Bishop suddenly.

" Yes, your lordship," said Father Furiosus, arousing himself from his thoughts.

" Next to women," said Bishop Flanagan, " there is nothing more productive of evil than birds."

" Indeed," said the friar, rather surprised. " I'm rather fond of them."

Bishop Flanagan bent a disapproving gaze upon his companion. " Then you are wrong," he said roughly. " Birds are inciters to laziness and easy living. They work not, neither do they spin. Their silly singing is a distraction to good men at their prayers and meditations. The very waywardness of birds is an encouragement to man to take pleasure in the deceitful beauty of this world instead of fastening his gaze upon his heavenly home. I'm surprised at you, Father Furiosus. I tell you we can never be too much on our guard against these things that appeal to our senses. Besotted poets are always bleating about birds and bird-song. Isn't that enough ? "

" I suppose you're right," agreed the friar grudgingly.

" Of course I'm right," replied the Bishop severely " I've had every tree around my palace cut down. Until I did so, I had no peace from their incessant chirruping."

The wagtail took a little run of half-a-dozen steps, wagged his tail up and down for a second or two, then raised it almost vertically, disclosing to the Bishop's gaze a little feathered backside. He cocked his eye as if to see how the Bishop was taking it, before fluttering away into the trees.

Bishop Flanagan's face grew red. " Did you see that ? " he said savagely. " Deliberate disrespect for a Prince of the Church ! Maybe now you'll believe in the depravity of birds."

Before Father Furiosus could think of an answer King Cormac entered the room. Now that he was clothed in his royal robes of saffron and blue he appeared to greater advantage. The golden circlet of Cashel environed his bald head,

and he carried himself with greater assurance, almost as if
he and the Bishop were equals. He was not a tall man : in
fact he was stumpy ; but he was broad-shouldered and
sturdy, and he held himself well for his age. One hand
rested on the handle of a short iron sword strapped to his
side, while the other played in and out of his immense snowy
beard. Sometimes he fingered the silky tip at waist level ;
at other times, when he fondled his chin, his hand and arm
were lost to sight as far as the elbow.

" God save all here," said the King courteously.

" God save you kindly," answered the two ecclesiastics.
Cormac dropped on one knee and kissed the Bishop's ring.

" When we met previously this morning," said the Bishop,
" the occasion did not seem to me suitable for the formal
introduction of Father Furiosus, who, as a scarifier of conjurors and demons, is at the summit of his profession."

Cormac withdrew his hand from his beard and held it out
to the friar, who gripped it in his huge freckled fist.

" It's an honour," murmured the King ; and going to the
door he clapped his hands. Four slaves entered at once,
bearing three foaming pots of mead and a reserve basin lest
anyone should crave a second helping. The Bishop and the
friar immediately addressed themselves to the consumption of
this delectable beverage. By the time each had emptied his
second pot the conversation had become general. The final
arrangements for the witch-dipping, which was the business
that had brought the Bishop to the Royal House, were
speedily disposed of. Father Furiosus related as an item of
gossip how in the recent war in the east the King of Hungary
had put into the field a battalion of vampires recruited in
his Transyllvanian dominions. They had wrought great
havoc among the Byzantine troops in the mountainous Danube
country, until the Emperor formed a special shock brigade
armed with small wooden crosses, sharpened stakes and
mallets ; and sent them into battle with a baggage train
composed exclusively of cartloads of garlic. The opposing
forces had at first experienced difficulty in making contact

with one another, by reason of the marked disinclination of the Imperial troops to fight otherwise than by day, while the unholy legions of Hungary only came out at night. But, God be praised, the warriors of the Christian Emperor had at last prevailed, due to their superior mobility ; the vampire soldiery being much encumbered in their forays by the necessity of bringing their coffins with them, in which to bivouac between sunrise and sunset.

The King nodded his head sagely. " Mobility is of the first importance in mountain warfare," he said. " By the way," he continued, turning to the Bishop, " has your lordship heard this strange rumour of the motley company that has been seen on the northern road, and which appears to be coming towards Cashel ? "

" I have not," said the Bishop, somewhat nettled that anyone should have news before himself.

" They say that a collection of grotesque animals such as have never before been seen in these parts, is on its way hither. It seems to be some sort of gigantic circus. It is led by a gentleman in black, probably the ringmaster, and by a man in the habit of a monk who proceeds with the aid of crutches."

" The habit of a monk ! " ejaculated Father Furiosus. " Surely your informant is mistaken. Probably the gentleman referred to is of foreign extraction ; and his alien clothing has given rise to the error. No doubt he is the capitalist who finances the undertaking. I have seen such menageries at the great fair at Tara."

" Circuses are a great occasion of sin," said the Bishop. " Does rumour report whether there are women travelling with this gang of mountebanks ? "

The King coughed diffidently and looked as if he wished he hadn't introduced the subject.

" Well, yes," he said hesitantly. " In fact, my informant stated that they were present in large numbers."

" You're holding something back," said Bishop Flanagan sternly.

" I don't wish to offend your lordship's ears," said Cormac, looking rather frightened, " but it's said that many of the women in the troop are insufficiently clad considering the rigours of this climate ; in fact, that many of them have no apparent clothing at all."

There was silence except for the loud beating of the King's heart. Then the Bishop threw himself back in his chair.

" Stuff and nonsense ! " he said. " Who told you that fantastic story ? "

" A travelling gipsy woman who came around to the back-door this morning to beg for a bite of bread. She insisted that she had seen the concourse herself."

" A woman ! " Father Furiosus laughed suddenly and relaxed his giant limbs. " I never knew a lying story that was not traceable to a woman. King Cormac, I'm afraid you're a very gullible man. You'll find that there's nothing more than a band of tinkers with a dancing bear and, maybe, a couple of performing dogs."

" No doubt, no doubt," said the King, much relieved at the easing of the tension.

Bishop Flanagan permitted himself a rasping laugh as he bent over to pour the dregs of the mead from the basin into his mug.

" The very idea ! " he said. " Women without clothes in my diocese ! "

*   *   *

It was late in the afternoon when a solemn procession of monks and laymen left Cashel by the northern gate and moved slowly along the road towards the bend in the River Suir two miles beyond the town. At the point where the river curved there was a deep pool only a stone's throw from the hut in which The Gray Mare was said to have practised her dark sorceries. The procession was headed by a column of hooded monks walking two by two and chanting hymns of the most doleful character imaginable. The funereal responses to each sombre anthem filled everyone with mournful thoughts

of dissolution and doom. The very birds stopped their play-
acting in the trees and huddled together to watch the gloomy
train of humans who moved slowly forward as if fatalistically
impelled, trampling with unnoticing, indifferent feet the wild
pansies and primroses and all the tiny flowering things on the
grassy edges of the track. The general body of clergy followed,
red-faced, burly men with an occasional gaunt ascetic among
them. Close behind came the canons of the Chapter, rotund
and mostly out of breath. Father Furiosus walked alone,
his blackthorn under his arm, seemingly impatient of the slow
pace of the procession. Then, preceded by a choir of youthful
ecclesiastics singing " *Ecce Sacerdos Magnus*," came the
Bishop, distributing blessings every few yards to the onlookers
left and right. A high cart followed, in which sat the notorious
Gray Mare, tied hand and foot. The cart was surrounded
by twenty-six marching soldiers, the entire armed forces of
Cashel. Behind it rode King Cormac in his war chariot ;
and a long line of similar chariots followed, bearing the great
men of his kingdom, famous warriors, rich landowners and
the two members of his Civil Service. A large concourse of
persons of low birth came after, out-of-step and quite incapable
of keeping in rank. The procession tailed off in a horde of
children and barking dogs.

The Gray Mare, a very old, spent and decrepit hag, perched
high in her cart, seemed to be experiencing a certain feminine
pleasure from the fact that she was the centre of attention.
She leered at nearly every group of onlookers standing by the
roadside, and shouted a greeting, addressing them all as
acquaintances, which might perhaps have been excused in
her as she was very nearly blind. Those whom she hailed did
not at all appreciate her friendliness, but crossed themselves
hurriedly and hastened to explain to one another that they
had never seen her before in their lives. It was thought very
ill of her to display levity in the course of a religious ceremony
of such antiquity and importance. It was contrary to all
custom : witches and conjurors in such a situation invariably
comported themselves with the greatest seriousness. Old

men shook their heads. It was a great mistake, they said, not to have put her to the torture. It would have induced in her a frame of mind more in keeping with the occasion. And accompanied by the clangour of the handbells carried by the clergy and the lugubrious chanting of the monks, Church and State in awful solemnity wound their way in a long, thin serpent under the fresh green of the trees, along the stony track, and across the Maytime fields, while the object of it all sat high above them, grinning and cackling half-wittedly, and to all appearance having the time of her life.

The spot appointed for the witch-dipping was at a point where the river curved forming a tranquil backwater. There was an open field capable of accommodating a large number of spectators. The proximity of the thatched cabin where The Gray Mare had lived made the spot selected for her trial peculiarly appropriate. The fields rose from the river's edge to a low line of hill, so that from this point the road ascended and crept over the summit about two hundred yards away, where it was lost to sight.

A crowd of countrypeople had already assembled along the river bank, and as the procession wound into the field, they fell on their knees, bowing their heads to receive the Bishop's blessing. When he had passed, they sprang to their feet and greeted The Gray Mare's cart with catcalls and a shower of sods and stones, most of which struck the surrounding soldiery. When the two horses drawing King Cormac's chariot cantered into the field with the gallant monarch standing erect, his white beard streaming behind him in the breeze, a great shout of welcome went up. While the monks and secular clergy formed themselves into two squares facing one another, a high chair covered with purple and cloth of gold was placed in the centre to accommodate the person of the Bishop. He seated himself, and the canons of the Chapter draped themselves in a semi-circle behind him. A small chair had been set up for the King, and he took his seat surrounded by the officials of his household, his secretary, the commander of his armed forces, the master of the kitchen and the royal door-keeper. Four slaves stood in readiness to run messages. Some paces away sat the Civil Service on two small stools which they had had the forethought to bring with them. The landowners and the few warriors who had survived the wars of the reign, stood alongside. The general public was kept at a respectful distance, and six of the soldiers guarding The Gray Mare were detached to keep them in order with the butts of their spears. The Gray Mare herself, now that she found herself at the water's edge, seemed to have lost a great deal of her light-heartedness. She sat on the grass muttering to herself and rubbing her wrists and ankles, which had been untied by direction of Father Furiosus. The friar had been authorised to conduct the proceedings in virtue of his long experience of such matters and as a graceful compliment to him as a visitor to the city.

The ceremony began with prayer, at the conclusion of which Bishop Flanagan imparted his blessing to all. Then the elder of the Civil service arose and read the indictment from a series of wax tablets. These were passed up to him as required by his junior from a heavy box in which they were neatly filed. The Gray Mare was asked whether she pleaded Guilty or Not Guilty, but no answer was forthcoming as she had impiously fallen asleep during the prayers with which the ceremony had opened. All efforts to awake her proved unavailing, and Father Furiosus explained that it was in no way to be deemed obstinacy and held against her, but was no doubt due to the fact that she had not been permitted to sleep during the previous three days and nights while the judicial examination was in progress. A sigh of relief arose from the crowd, who had feared for a moment that she was already dead, thus cheating them of their entertainment. Father Furiosus directed that a plea of Not Guilty should be entered; the Civil Service sharpened a fine stake of wood with his hunting knife and made the entry in a neat hand on a fresh wax tablet. A short argument developed at this point: the Bishop intervening to urge that

the silence of the accused should be construed as an admission
of her guilt, that the dipping should be abandoned as unnecessary, and The Gray Mare carried back immediately to the
town for judicial burning. The Bishop's suggestion found
great favour with the crowd, who expressed their agreement
at the top of their voices until most of them were hoarse, but
Father Furiosus was able to quote numerous passages from
the Fathers to prove that his procedure was correct. The
Bishop sat back in his chair, an unusual flush in his sallow
face. The friar then addressed the crowd and indicated that
he would break the back of the next man or woman who
impiously interrupted the proceedings. He returned to his
place and bowed to Bishop Flanagan, who with a slight movement of his hand directed that the ceremony should continue.
The friar, thereupon, delivered an oration on the damnable
nature of witchcraft, pointing out that it was laid down by
Moses that no witch should be permitted to live. He under-
lined his discourse with numerous quotations from the Scrip-
tures and from the Fathers of the Church proving the existence
of witches and setting out the proper methods for their disposal. He concluded by explaining clearly the nature of the
present proceedings, and reminded his audience in forceful
words that The Gray Mare was not yet a proven witch. She
was merely undergoing trial. They had adopted a sure method
of ascertaining whether or not she was guilty, a method proved
on countless occasions, a method never known to fail. If,
when thrown into the water, the water rejected her ; that is,
if she floated, it was certain proof that she was a witch, and
she would be handed over for burning to the secular arm, as
the Church itself never polluted its hands with blood. If, on
the other hand, she visibly and truly sank, it was proof of her
innocence ; and she would be released to return to her home
without a stain on her character. The friar concluded his
peroration with a stern command to the crowd to maintain
order and not become excited. His speech made a powerful
impression, and the atmosphere was tense as he turned to
supervise the final proceeding.

As it wasn't deemed fair to throw The Gray Mare into the water in her present somnolent condition, she was awakened with difficulty by the judicious prodding of the soldiers' spears. Father Furiosus then ordered that she be stripped to her shift ; but while this was under way, an unexpected difficulty arose : it was discovered that she didn't wear one. After much sifting of his memory for a precedent, the friar consented to her being immersed in such clothes as she had on, a careful search having first been made to ensure that she had no heavy stones concealed so as to defeat the ends of justice. Her shoes were removed and her hands and feet tied crossways, the right hand to the left foot and vice versa. During these preparations some of her old spirit seemed to revive, and she laughed immoderately, complaining in a cracked voice that the soldiers were tickling her. Finally a rope was tied around her waist. Two soldiers were given the loose end and instructed to hold it tightly, so as to be able to pull her out again when directed to do so.

At a command from the friar she was lifted by brawny arms, a queer little bundle with her grey hair streaming behind her. On no one of the hundreds of faces that were bent upon her, was there sympathy apparent. Every face expressed the same feelings— loathing and strong religious emotion. As Father Furiosus with sure dramatic instinct delayed the final command, the tension became so palpable as to be almost unbearable. All at once he raised his two arms high above his head. The crowd held its breath.

" Now ! " he shouted, bringing his arms suddenly down to his sides. The soldiers swung back and heaved. The crowd drew in their breath with a loud penetrating hiss as The Gray Mare flew through the air, rolling over and over. The Bishop and the King had risen to their feet, and every neck was craned as she struck the surface of the water with a mighty splash. She immediately disappeared from sight.

A disappointed howl arose from the crowd.

" She's sunk ! "

Indeed, there didn't seem to be much doubt about it. Father Furiosus counted a hundred. There was still no sign of The Gray Mare.

"Pull her out," commanded the friar. "God has clearly demonstrated that she's innocent."

"Wait," said the Bishop. "Give her a bit longer. It's better to make sure."

Father Furiosus gave him a quick look. "I'm not going to have murder on my soul," he said roughly. "Pull her out."

The two soldiers bent their weight upon the rope to the accompaniment of hoots and angry shouts from the crowd. She seemed to be a long way down, for there was still no sign of her.

"Pull harder," shouted the friar savagely, and he gripped the rope himself. The howling of the crowd arose in a crescendo, and they broke their ranks, knocking over the few soldiers who tried to restrain them. Men and women rushed to the river bank, picking up stones as they ran.

"Get back," shouted the friar furiously, as he strained at the rope.

The Gray Mare's head suddenly broke the surface. Her mouth opened, a stream of water came out, followed by a feeble curse.

At that moment a sudden terrified cry pierced the air.

"Look at the hill!" someone screamed.

So insistent was the cry that everyone turned. About two hundred yards away where the road wound over the hill, stood two figures, one a graceful man clothed in black and the other a monk leaning on a pair of crutches. It was not these two that had caused the alarm, but a motley crowd of dreadful creatures that were topping the rise for hundreds of yards on either side of the road. Cacodemons, black and grey, lumbered along. Minotaurs, leopards and hippogriffs came into sight peacefully cropping the grass in the neighbouring fields. Centaurs cantered back and forward. A legion of imps came leap-frogging across the rise. Furies and vultures flew from tree to tree. A moving sea of scorpions crept along the shallow ditches, interspersed here and there with a brace of cockatrices or a hippogiraffe.

For one moment the human beings by the river bank stood petrified. Then someone raised a shout :

" The demons from Clonmacnoise ! "

Immediate panic ensued. The rope that held The Gray Mare was dropped, and she sank once more to the bottom. Soldiers and people ran blindly in all directions, some in their frenzy were so foolish as to run into the river. Bishop Flanagan was one of the first to fly. He sprang into the royal chariot with such agility and determination that he knocked the unfortunate Cormac out the far side. The Bishop seized the reins and would have left the King behind only for the devotion of two slaves who bundled Cormac back again just as the Bishop made off in crazy career across the fields. Chariots were driven into ditches and gates, and a score of serfs and underlings were trampled underfoot. Father Furiosus made a gallant attempt to stay the panic, until he observed on his left an outflanking movement by a squadron of poltergeists, variegated in hue, but mostly yellow and green ; and from seven to nine feet in height. From their drooping shoulders their long arms swung obscenely, the fingers nearly touching the ground. Their faces were creased with unholy smiles. Father Furiosus took one look at this hideous apparition, and jumped into the last chariot. In the space of two minutes there was no one in sight. Even those who had been bruised and wounded by the horses' hooves made their escape, some on their hands and knees, with astounding alacrity.

Brother Fursey stood in the middle of the road propped up by his crutches, and gaped down at the extraordinary spectacle. At one moment the road and fields seemed to be full

of people running madly in all directions, the next moment
there was no one to be seen. While he was trying to understand this remarkable phenomenon, the Devil touched him
gently on the arm.

" At this point," he said, " our ways part, but I want you
to know what a pleasure it has been to have made your
acquaintance ; and I want to thank you again for your company, which has done so much to relieve the tedium of the
journey. I will not flatter you by saying that you are in any
way remarkable as a conversationalist, but I can assure you
that I have rarely met a better listener."

He took Fursey's listless hand and shook it warmly.

" I am speaking no more than the truth, my dear Fursey,
when I say that I have acquired a great affection and genuine
regard for you. If at any time I can do anything for you,
you have only to call on me. I am to be found in the flesh
in the Devil's Glen in Wicklow, where myself and the boys
are now repairing for a much needed rest. One last thing
before I go—I want to direct your attention to the fact that
an unfortunate fellow creature of yours is at this moment in
process of drowning in that pool in the river where you saw
all those people. I need say no more—you are a man and
a Christian."

Brother Fursey turned and found himself alone. Nowhere
could he see even one of the ghastly host that had accompanied him for the previous three days. The fields and hills
were deserted. He could hardly believe his good fortune.
A great lump came in his throat and nearly choked him. He
hurried forward with tears of thankfulness streaming from his
eyes, but the scraping and thumping of his crutches seemed
to him to beat out in rhythm the Fiend's parting words :
" You are a man and a Christian—a fellow creature is drowning." A loud sob came from his throat as he realised vaguely
that some duty had been laid upon him when his one desire
was to get as far away as possible. He didn't know what
was required of him, nor did he wish to give the matter any

thought. In his hurry his crutch slipped among the loose
stones on the road, and he fell heavily. As he lay sprawling,
groping blindly for the crutch, the words came into his mind
again : "A fellow creature is drowning." He clambered
painfully to his feet, hesitated and groaned aloud ; then
turning towards the river, he made his way slowly across the
fields. Soon he was standing on the trampled grass at the
edge.

CHAPTER III

FURSEY stood motionless, gazing out over the flood of brown, bog-stained water that moved by impassively. At this point a narrow mudbank extended into the river forming a backwater in which the water circled ever so slowly, eddying slightly as it rejoined the main stream. Nothing was to be heard but the tiny flap-flapping of the wavelets against the bank on which he stood.

"There's nothing here at all," he said to himself. "This is very remarkable."

His eye fell suddenly on a rope lying along the grass, and trailing over the bank into the river. Beyond the rope a stream of bubbles rose delicately and broke on the surface of the water. This seemed to him even more remarkable, so he hurried over and began to haul in the rope. It was heavy work, especially when one was trying at the same time to maintain an upright position on a pair of crutches; so after he had tripped himself twice, he abandoned the crutches and, seating himself on the grass, pulled at the rope as if his life depended on it. He was greatly amazed when a little old woman tied in a ball, bobbed up on to the surface and came drifting towards him. At first he couldn't reach her; but he hit on the expedient of passing the armpit of one of the crutches over her head, and so by hooking her under the chin, he was able to yank her up on to the bank. His strong, rough fingers quickly untied the ropes that bound her feet and hands. She lay to all appearances dead, and the ex-monk, not knowing what to do, gazed down at her in mingled pity and horror. He did not for a moment doubt but that this was more of the Devil's work, and he was swept by a flood of fierce indignation against that suave personage.

All at once he remembered an incident that had occurred at Clonmacnoise the previous year. On the feast day of the blessed Kieran, after the usual banquet at which ale and mead had been consumed in great quantities, little Brother Patrick had insisted on going for a walk along the bank of the River Shannon. The great river flowed past the settlement, and the diminutive monk insisted that he wanted to look at the full moon, which, he said, reminded him of his mother. Brother Fursey and a few laughing lay-brothers went with him. It was a good thing they did, for the voluble Patrick had not gone very far before he fell into the river. His frightened brethren managed to fish him out and carry him back unconscious to the monastery. Father Sampson, who was knowledgeable in such matters, had immediately swept them all aside and, seizing the damp and bedraggled Patrick, had flung him across the gatepost where he worked on the lay-brother's back with a see-saw motion to the vast admiration of the group of half-tipsy monks. In a few minutes Brother Patrick had come back to life, laughing uproariously and still talking about his mother.

The recollection of this event had no sooner crept across Fursey's mind than he seized The Gray Mare and laid her across a granite boulder so that her head and legs hung down on either side. After a moment's thought he placed his hands carefully on her back below the ribs, and began to exert pressure, rhythmically swaying himself back and forward on his crutches. Nothing happened for a long time. Fursey's difficulty was to remain awake. He had not had a full night's rest since the awful evening when the legions of Hell had first ambled into his cell at Clonmacnoise ; and the see-saw motion of artificial respiration induced sleepiness. Twice he tumbled backwards, but he picked himself up and resumed his good work without even pausing to examine his bruises. At long last he was rewarded by a low cry from the old woman. He redoubled his efforts, and she began to

scream. Fursey paused and carefully turned her over. She
was a strange sight with her old grey locks plastered to her
head. She looked up at him with bleary eyes.

" I'll admit anything you want," she gasped. " Why don't
you burn me and have done with it ? "

While Fursey was wondering what this strange speech
could mean, she lapsed once more into unconsciousness. He
began immediately to chafe her hands and feet vigorously.
When he looked at her face again he was delighted to see
that her eyes were open and were fixed upon him. He began
to laugh immoderately.

" What are you trying to do ? " she asked savagely. " Rub
the skin off me ? "

This surprised Fursey greatly, and he was looking down in
wonder at his large rough hands when she struggled feebly
into a sitting position and aimed a blow at him. The startled
Fursey retreated a few paces and stood looking at her with
dump reproach. A lump came into his throat ; he felt that
his eyes were about to fill with tears : he bowed his head, and
turning, started to hobble away. A cracked voice called
after him :

" Where are you going ? "

Fursey turned. " I don't know," he answered.

" Who are you ? " she asked.

" Just a stranger who brought you out of the water and
back to life."

The Gray Mare turned this over in her mind for a few
moments, and when she spoke again, her voice was more
gentle.

" You're some class of a monk ? "

" No. I was once, but not now."

" They thrun you out ? " queried The Gray Mare.

" Yes," answered Fursey, the pink blood gliding into his
cheeks.

The old woman emitted a throaty cackle.

" Was it creepin' after some high-steppin' young female
you were ? "

"Certainly not," replied Fursey indignantly. When he remembered all the high-stepping young female demons that had crept after him, his indignation increased.

"Certainly not," he repeated. "Nothing of the sort."

The Gray Mare seemed to have lost interest in his affairs. She was peering short-sightedly to left and right.

"Are they all gone?" she asked in a loud whisper.

"I don't understand," said Fursey. "There's no one here, if that's what you mean."

"Dirty pack of murderers," muttered the old woman. "They'd have left me to drown."

"Well, you're not drowned," said Fursey. "May God and the blessed Kieran have you in their keeping," and he turned away once more.

"Mister monk," called out the old woman.

"Yes?"

"You can't leave me here to catch my death of cold in my damp habiliments," she said coaxingly. "You've a kind face, mister man. Do me another kindness, and I won't forget it to you. Would you ever carry me up to my little house beyond on the hill? I doubt if I could get there by myself, I'm that weak."

"Certainly," said Fursey.

It was a nightmare journey. It is bad enough to have to climb a hill on crutches, but it is infinitely worse to have to do so with an old woman on one's back. The Gray Mare seemed to think it was all a great game. She belaboured Fursey with her fists pretending he was a horse, all the time crowing and cackling and exhorting him to "gee-up." The unfortunate Fursey stumbled on his way, gasping and grunting, sometimes choking and sometimes weeping from sheer misery. At length he stood at her door: how he got there he never knew.

"Carry me in," commanded the old woman.

Fursey ducked his head and struggled in through the low doorway. It was an ordinary kind of cabin with a great hole in the centre of the roof to let out the smoke. The Gray

Mare slid off his back and leaned against the table, her wet
garments clinging to her skinny frame. She shivered violently
as she began to speak. Fursey did not hear what she said.
He half-closed his eyes as the walls of the room swayed
sickeningly : he saw the floor coming up to meet him, and
he was conscious of falling heavily.

When he awoke he was in darkness and lying on a hard
pallet covered by a ragged blanket ; but he did not mind how
hard his bed was, provided he was allowed to lie still and
rest his aching legs and back. He was conscious of distant
crooning and muttering : while he was wondering about it
vaguely, he fell asleep again. And so for an interminable
period he slept and awoke and dozed, blissfully at peace.
He was fully awakened at last when a door was opened, and
the light from another room fell across his face. The Gray
Mare was standing in the doorway grinning in at him.

" Are you awake, mister man ? " she croaked.

" Yes," said Fursey, sitting up. " I'm awake."

" Maybe you're hungry and would like something to eat ? "

" Yes," said Fursey eagerly. " I'm hungry."

" Well, come and get it," she said, and she went back into
the far room.

Fursey got off the bed wonderfully refreshed, and followed
her. It was only when he was standing by the table in the
outer room that he remembered that he had forgotten his
crutches. He staggered and held on to the table with both
hands.

" What's wrong with you ? " queried The Gray Mare.
" You're not going to go unconscious on me again ? "

" I've forgotten my crutches," said Fursey. " I can't
walk without them."

" Nonsense," replied the old woman. " You've just walked
in here without them. You don't need crutches."

" I assure you that I do," replied Fursey earnestly. " My
hip was smashed by a poltergeist."

" Arrah what," said the old lady, " the lad only sprained
it. I cured you while you slept. You did me a kindness,

and I told you I wouldn't forget it to you. Just try, and you'll see that you're able to walk."

Fursey was accustomed to obedience, so he immediately relaxed his grip on the table and essayed a few steps across the floor. To his huge delight he found that he could walk. To convince himself of the genuineness of this astounding miracle he started to run up and down the kitchen.

"I can walk," he cried. "I can walk."

"Stop running," said the old woman. "You'll upset the pot. Sit down there and have something to eat. You should be hungry. You slept the whole night through and most of to-day. It's already late in the afternoon."

As Fursey seated himself he observed on the table what appeared to be a small wax image of a man. The light from the smoke hole in the roof fell directly upon it, so that he could see it clearly. A little tuft of white hair was tied to the head, and it was partly wrapped in a piece of thick brown material similar to the habit he was wearing. A dead snail pierced by a thorn lay on its hip. While Fursey was still gazing at the image The Gray Mare suddenly snapped it from the table and turned her back. A moment later she went to the fire and threw something in. Then she kneaded the image between her skeleton-thin hands until it was just a lump of shapeless wax, which she put away carefully on a shelf. She seated herself at the table opposite Fursey and sneezed once or twice. In answer to his polite enquiry, she explained that she had caught cold as a result of her immersion in the river. Fursey looked from her to the bare board between them and then back at her again, wondering with a sinking heart whether there was any food in the house. She seemed to guess his thoughts.

"What would you like to eat?" she asked.

"Whatever you're having yourself," replied the ex-monk politely.

The Gray Mare stretched up her hand, and Fursey noticed for the first time a rope which hung from the rafters. Raising his eyes he saw that the end of it hung loosely over a beam in the roof. The Gray Mare jerked the rope three times, and to Fursey's astonishment a flagon of ale, two loaves of bread and four pounds of choice beef slid down the rope, apparently from nowhere, and settled themselves in a neat pile on the table. While he was still gaping up at the rafters, thinking that it was a very inconvenient place to keep the larder, The Gray Mare arose and, going to a hole in the wall, took out a couple of wooden goblets, which she brought over to the table. She shook a family of red spiders out of one of them and placed it in front of Fursey. The spiders ran hell-for-leather over the table in all directions, but she recovered them without difficulty and carefully stowed them away in an old stocking that hung from a hook in the wall. Fursey realised with a sigh that he had lived so long in the cloister that he was quite unaccustomed to the ways of ordinary people, so he carefully suppressed any manifestation of surprise.

Before long they were eating and drinking merrily. Fursey thought she was the pleasantest person he had ever met. Women as they had existed in his imagination, and as he had seen them from afar, were creatures endowed with an evil comeliness in order to tempt men ; but this amiable old lady was so hideous that she was not like a woman at all. He could converse easily with her and found it pleasant to do so, as conversation with a woman was a new experience for him. Never, he felt, had he met such kindliness and understanding in a human being. Before he had finished his first goblet of ale, he had told her of his incredible experiences in Clonmacnoise and his resultant misfortunes. She listened with the greatest interest, punctuating his monologue occasionally with a murmur of sympathy or with a violent sneeze.

" One of the things I wonder at most," he said, " is the fact that while I was in Clonmacnoise I had the most awkward impediment in my speech ; but now it's gone, and I can speak with reasonable fluency."

The Gray Mare nodded her head sagely.

" That's easily accounted for," she said. " The impediment was frightened out of you. You went through so much that it's doubtful if anything can ever frighten you again."

It made him uncomfortable, however, to hear her uttering harsh words about his late brethren in Clonmacnoise, as she did on hearing how he had been finally expelled from the monastery. He shifted uneasily on his stool, knowing that it was unlucky to speak ill of the clergy. In any case it was the demons who were to blame. In this strange world things like that just happen to a man ; no one can help it. What else could the monks do but get rid of him ? He was glad when she launched into a mumbling and toothless account of her own trials and sufferings.

He was appalled at human depravity when he heard of the bitter enmity which the sexton of the neighbouring churchyard bore her on account of such a small matter as a wandering goat. He crossed himself when she assured him that the sexton was undoubtedly a sorcerer. He could scarcely believe his ears when she told him how the wicked sexton had actually had the effrontery to denounce her to the authorities for crimes which he had himself committed. He became frightened when he heard how human beings had " walked " her up and down for three days and nights without sleep, how human beings had taken her and thrown her into the river, and how human beings, even when her innocence had been fully demonstrated, had nevertheless picked up stones to kill her. It frightened him to think of the kind of world it was in which he must in future live, and he longed to be back in the quiet and safety of the cloister. It was with an aching heart that he told himself that he must put Clonmacnoise forever out of his thoughts.

The Gray Mare was muttering to herself as she gathered a little pile of crumbs together with her skinny fingers.

" And you were really innocent all the time ? " asked Fursey.

She shot a quick look at him.

" Didn't you find me at the bottom of the river," she replied gratingly. " Isn't that sure proof that I'm not a witch ? "

" Yes," said Fursey. " I've always heard that that's sure proof."

She started up suddenly.

" The sexton," she said. " He'll be renewing his attack, and here I am wasting my time gabbling, instead of making preparations to meet him."

She hurried over to the fire and began to stir a huge pot that hung over the embers. Then she lifted down a cob-webbed jar from the shelf and, taking from it a handful of amber grains, she threw them into the liquid, which began at once to bubble and spit angrily. Bending over the cauldron she began a low chant. At that moment there was a clatter of horses' hooves on the track outside the door.

" Hallo there ! " shouted a loud voice.

" Who's that ? " hissed the old woman.

Fursey went to the door and opened it. Three horsemen had reined their steeds on the road about fifty paces from the door. To his astonishment Fursey recognised the Abbot Marcus, who was being helped from his horse by a huge red-faced friar. On a bony nag sat an ecclesiastic in the dress of a bishop. He was gaunt and sallow, and he gazed at Fursey sourly. At a little distance stood a band of serving men loaded down with books of exorcism, bells and stoups of holy water. They were looking thoroughly frightened, as if they might take to their heels at any moment.

The first thought that came into Fursey's mind was that the Abbot Marcus had come for him to take him back to Clonmacnoise. He ran down the road and flung himself on his knees at the Abbot's feet. Marcus raised his hand and laid it gently on Fursey's head in blessing. The ex-monk gripped the Abbot's robe and gazed up at the grave face, lined with study. The far-away eyes that were bent on him were kind.

" You're going to take me back ? " said Fursey.

The Abbot turned away his face.

" Get up, Fursey," he said.

Fursey rose to his feet and glanced from one to the other. The big friar was looking at him with great interest, but the Bishop's eyes were as cold as ice, and a sneer was trembling about his mouth. Fursey instinctively knew that in the trio he had only one friend. He turned again to the Abbot Marcus.

" Father Abbot, are you not going to let me go back ? "

The Abbot's eyes shifted uncomfortably. " No," he said at last.

Fursey stood an abject figure, looking from one to the other. Then he looked at the road and up at the wide sky. He saw everything blurred and dim through a film of tears.

" Come now, my man," said the Bishop bitingly. " Weeping won't help you. I am too good a judge of human nature not to know reality from fake."

" Please, my lord bishop," interposed the Abbot. " I've already explained to you the circumstances under which Fursey left Clonmacnoise. I made it clear that he was in no way to blame."

" Where are the demons he was consorting with yesterday?" snapped the Bishop. " Let him tell us that."

" They're gone," said Fursey.

" Gone where ? " asked the Bishop quickly, as if to startle Fursey into an admission.

" I don't know. They just disappeared."

There was a moment's silence, then Father Furiosus interposed.

" They're certainly not here now," he said mildly. " We've rung bells and sprinkled holy water over an area of two square miles. No demon could stand up to that."

" Did you see any sign of an old woman ? " asked the Bishop.

" Yes," replied Fursey surprised. " I pulled an old woman out of the river, and brought her up here to the house. She's in there now."

He turned and pointed to the little cabin behind him.

" What did you do that for ? " asked the Bishop sharply. " Why did you have to meddle ? "

" Because," interjected the Abbot with some heat in his voice, " it was what any Christian would be expected to do."

" Even if the object of his misplaced charity was a witch ? " queried the Bishop.

" She's not a witch," said Father Furiosus with some exasperation. " God clearly demonstrated that she was innocent."

The Bishop was silent, but he continued to watch Fursey with baleful eyes.

" Father Abbot," pleaded Fursey, " let me go back with you to the monastery.."

" That is impossible," said the Abbot with finality. " You must understand, my poor Fursey, that the gates of Clonmacnoise and every other religious settlement are closed against you. Be reasonable, Fursey. For nearly two weeks you have consorted with demons. For all we know you may have even formed friendships. No abbot could risk taking you in. These goblins that you know would be likely to return to renew the acquaintance. The fact that you appear to have recovered the free use of your speech and are in a position to challenge them, is no safeguard. That would be a small impediment to imps and demons of the wilier sort. In any case, if I took you back to Clonmacnoise, it's very likely that the whole community would leave in a body."

" I see," said Fursey, hanging his head.

A sudden thought seemed to strike Bishop Flanagan.

" Where did you spend the night ? " he asked sharply.

" In the cottage," replied Fursey.

" With the Gray Mare ? "

" With the old woman," answered Fursey innocently.

A sharp intake of breath was heard from Father Furiosus. The thunderclouds gathered on the Bishop's forehead.

" The two of you were alone ? " he asked in tones of doom.

" Yes," said Fursey haltingly.

" In my diocese ! " said the Bishop in a horrified whisper. "An unmarried man and woman spend the night together in the one house without chaperon, and he stands there and has the effrontery to tell me so to my face ! Do you know, my man," he continued, his voice rising to a shout, " that what you have done is a reserved sin in this diocese ? What do you think of such conduct, Father Furiosus ? "

Furiosus had tightened his grip on his blackthorn, and he was looking at Fursey menacingly from beneath his ginger eyebrows.

" He must marry the woman," said Furiosus.

" Of course he must," replied the Bishop. " There's no other way to avert the scandal."

" Marry ? " said Fursey faintly.

" And if he doesn't," continued the Bishop, "I'll put a penance on him that will cripple him in this life and in the next."

" Let us discuss this new turn of events," said the Abbot. " Oblige us, Fursey, by stepping aside for a few moments."

Fursey walked some paces down the road and leaned against a tree for support. Meanwhile the three ecclesiastics approached more closely to one another and conversed in grave whispers.

" It mightn't be a bad idea at all," said Abbot Marcus. " The plight of this wretched man weighs somewhat on my conscience, and I should like to see him fixed in life. No monastery will admit him, and as he hasn't the wit to earn a living, he will certainly starve on the roadside unless something is done for him. Moreover," he added thoughtfully, " you tell me that this woman, tho' not a witch, is nevertheless a great sinner who never goes to Mass. Union with such a godly man as Fursey cannot but have a profound effect on

her character.   By good example he is very likely to win her
back to God and Holy Church."

Father Furiosus seemed impressed.

" Yes," he said, " and you have told us that this Brother
Fursey is a man of notable piety.   He can, therefore, be
trusted to report to the authorities should she at any time be
tempted to engage in the black art."

" This is all irrelevant," said the Bishop hotly.   " I would
remind you that I am in authority in this diocese.   The point
is simply this—that the unfortunate woman has been compromised by this blackguard, and that wrong can only be
righted by marriage.   He must marry her.   I insist."

" There is no need to raise your voice," said the Abbot
coldly.   " We are all agreed, tho' perhaps for different
reasons."

He turned to where Fursey was leaning against the tree
gaping vacantly out over the countryside, and called him by
name, but Fursey did not appear to hear.   He had been
trying to assemble his thoughts so as to understand what was
about to happen to him, but his mind insisted on remaining
an obstinate and tumultuous blank.   Father Furiosus went
down the road and taking Fursey by the arm, led him back to
where the others were standing.

" Now listen carefully, Fursey," began the Abbot kindly.
" We are all agreed that you must marry this lady.   It is
your duty, because by your incautious behaviour you have
cast a reflection on her honour.   From a material point of
view you will be making a good match.   She appears to have
a tidy little property, and you will enjoy economic security
for the rest of your life."

" She has only a broken-down cabin and a goat," replied
Fursey bleakly.

The Abbot looked at him severely.

" I didn't expect to find in one of my monks a sordid greed
for material goods," he replied.

" But I'm a monk," said Fursey, his voice rising in an
hysterical squeal.   " I can't marry."

" Your vows are simple vows," said the Abbot smoothly, " and it's in my power to release you. I shall immediately do so ; it would be most unfair to hold you to them."

" But she is far from comely," objected Fursey feebly.

" I'm surprised at you," said the Abbot. " There will be all the less temptation to desires of the flesh."

" It's better to marry than to burn," said the Bishop.

" But I don't feel myself burning," said Fursey.

" Don't be impertinent," said the Bishop. " It's all settled."

Fursey looked up appealingly at Abbot Marcus.

" What will I do ? " he asked.

" Do as I say, marry her," replied the Abbot, " and may God bless you both."

Fursey bowed his head.

" Whatever you say, Father Abbot," he muttered brokenly. " I suppose it's for the best."

" Now we must tell the woman," said Furiosus.

There was a moment's hesitation as none of the ecclesiastics was anxious to approach a cottage which had been held in such abominable repute. At last Father Furiosus went and called on The Gray Mare to come out. She had been watching the proceedings from the dark interior of her cottage inasfar as her defective eyesight would permit, and she now emerged hesitantly. She glanced to left and right as if considering flight, but Father Furiosus took her gently by the arm and began to lead her down the road, assuring her with a rough kindness that she had nothing to be afraid of. As she came hobbling towards them, the Bishop retreated a pace and made the sign of the cross in the dust of the road with the point of his pastoral staff. She stood before them, a frail bowed figure, making a smacking sound as she sucked at her toothless gums. She looked down at the cross traced in the dust, then up at the Bishop malevolently.

" Haven't youse done enough to me ? " she asked bitterly.

Father Furiosus hastened to explain that byegones were byegones and that they were all meeting on a friendly footing. He propounded the proposition to her. At first she was incredulous ; but when she realised that he was in earnest, she was overcome by a fit of cackling. She threw a gamey eye across at the blushing Fursey.

" So the rascal wants to marry me," she croaked. " He's not a bad-looking fellow, with his white head and his young face."

" I'm forty," said Fursey, hoping dimly to dam her rising enthusiasm.

" Sure that's only young," she replied. " You'd be useful around the house, milking the goat and the like."

" Well, what do you say ? " enquired Abbot Marcus.

" It's not what I'd call a romantic wooing," she replied, " but I suppose we could do our courting afterwards. It will always keep."

She gave Fursey a girlish nudge with her elbow. A wintry smile flickered across his face.

" Well, are you agreed ? " asked the Bishop impatiently.

" Yes," said The Gray Mare. " I'll try anything once."

" Well, go down on your knees," said the Bishop.

The Gray Mare was helped into the required position by Father Furiosus. She complained of her rheumatics, and requested him to stand by to help her up again. Two serving men were summoned to act as witnesses. The Gray Mare delayed the ceremony for some minutes by her insistence on combing her hair with her long, skinny fingers, and by her efforts to get it to curl over each ear. The Abbot formally released Fursey from his vows, stumbling occasionally over the words, for he was embarrassed by Fursey's dumb, dog-like gaze that was rivetted all the time on his face. Then the Bishop approached and placing The Gray Mare's lank claw

in Fursey's plump fist, he read through the marriage ceremony in clipped and hurried Latin. The little band of
serving men had drawn near to watch the proceedings. A
bird yelped an occasional note from the single rowan tree
standing before The Gray Mare's cabin ; and the red sun, half
below the distant slate-grey mountains, rolled his last laughing
beams on the happy couple.

CHAPTER IV

FURSEY and The Gray Mare stood on the road until the ecclesiastics and their followers were out of sight. As the beating of the horses' hooves died away into the grey of the evening, Fursey shuddered, suddenly conscious of his desolation and loneliness. The Gray Mare was pensive as she took his arm and hobbled back with him to her cabin. When they entered the kitchen she wheezed once or twice like an old cat whose day is nearly done.

"There'll be no time for love-making this evening," she croaked.

Very much relieved, Fursey took a stool and seated himself as far away as possible from his bride. He wished he were alone and had time to think. In the monk's habit he was still wearing, he had discovered a square hole from which a piece of cloth had been neatly cut, a piece of cloth very similar to the scrap of material he had seen earlier in the evening wrapped around the wax image on the table.

Her voice grated in on his thoughts.

"That fellow Cuthbert will be down on top of us in no time," she said. "We must prepare to defend ourselves."

"Who's Cuthbert?" asked Fursey.

"Didn't I tell you already?" snapped The Gray Mare. "Cuthbert is the sexton of Kilcock Churchyard: his house is not three hundred yards away; you can see it from the door."

"Is he not friendly disposed?" queried Fursey anxiously.

The Gray Mare was busy stirring the seething contents of the cauldron, but she turned to glance malevolently at her husband.

" Friendly disposed ! " she snarled. " What class of a fool
am I wedded to ? Didn't I tell you how he denounced me to
the Bishop and tried to have me massacred ? Do you imagine
he's going to give up just because he failed the first time. I
tell you there'll be dirty work to-night."

" Maybe if it were suggested to him to let byegones be
byegones," said Fursey faintly, " brotherly love and all that."

" Yah ! " replied the old woman. " Cuthbert's a spry lad
at weaving the spells. I tell you he's the crookedest sorcerer
in the whole territory. Jealousy, that's what's at the bottom
of it. He has an unfair advantage," she muttered half to
herself, " with that graveyard under his control, full of unbaptised babes and murderers' bones, to draw on just as he
pleases. Where are you going ? "

" I thought I'd like a breath of fresh air," replied Fursey feebly.

" Go along inside and tidy up the room beyond," ordered
The Gray Mare. " You're a distraction to me here."

Fursey obeyed without a word. There wasn't much tidying
to be done, the only furniture being the pallet on which he
had slept, and a stool. He began tidying these without much
enthusiasm, while all the time the one thought kept grinding
around and around in his head. Could it be that the churchmen were wrong, and that she was a witch after all ? He
had often heard that witches made wax images of people,
either to cure or destroy them. The piece cut from his habit
in conjunction with the miraculous cure of his lameness, most
disagreeably affected his imagination. Moreover, he didn't
like the general trend of her conversation, nor did he like the
look of that cauldron over the fire, which spat and foamed
every time you went near it. His long experience in the
kitchen at Clonmacnoise made him doubt whether the brew
was fit for human consumption ; it certainly did not look like
soup. His apprehension increased a few minutes later, when
in the course of his tidying, he discovered a box of toads under
his bed. He sat down on the stool to think, but his thoughts
were interrupted by the sound of conversation from the outer
room. His heart bounded at the thought of perhaps seeing

and talking to another normal human being like himself, and he arose and stepped quickly across to the door ; but when he entered the other room he stood petrified. The Gray Mare was frantically stirring the cauldron with what appeared to be a human thigh bone, and there was a dim shape, a large black object, very ill-defined, squatting on the hearth. As Fursey came into the room it was in process of vanishing. He stared where it had been, but he could see nothing ; so that he speedily doubted if the uncertain light had not deceived his eyes. Then it occurred to him that maybe it was one of the Clonmacnoise demons dogging his footsteps to spy on him. He stood with a beating heart until The Gray Mare caught sight of him.

" Make yourself useful," she shrilled. " Go out and milk the goat before it gets dark."

Fursey hastily picked up the wooden pail which she indicated with a sweep of her arm. He hurried through the doorway, relieved to be out of the cottage in the fresh cool air of the evening. He looked to left and right, but could see no sign of a goat. He proceeded cautiously around the side of the house, and found her at the back tied to a length of rope which enabled her to walk around in a wide semi-circle eating the grass or the thorns in the hedge according to her inclination. At the moment she was apparently not interested in either, but stood with her forelegs against the wall of the cabin eating the thatch off the roof. She had a roving eye, and when she saw Fursey coming around the corner on tiptoe with the pail, she paused in her meal to contemplate him. As he approached she took her forelegs from the wall and stood stockstill watching him. She had a pair of protuberant brown eyes and a long dun beard, so long that Fursey wondered whether she ever fell over it. She held a generous bundle of thatch sideways across her mouth, which created the illusion that she had a military moustache. They stood looking at one another in silence. Fursey did not like the look of her at all, but he approached, gently patting the milk-pail with his free hand to indicate what was expected of her.

" There's a good goat," he said. " Come and be milked."

The goat's moustache suddenly disappeared as she swallowed the thatch with no apparent effort. Fursey squatted on his hunkers and placed the pail in position to commence the operation. The goat immediately took a step sideways, presenting her hindquarters to Fursey. Again and again he placed the pail, but each time she repeated the manœuvre. He was squatting there contemplating her tufted stern despairingly, when all at once the pail fell from his fingers. He had suddenly remembered the grisly stories that were whispered in Clonmacnoise, of witches and covens, and of the Horned God whom the witches worshipped. What if this were the Horned God in person exacting from him the homage of the posterior kiss ? He remained in a squatting position grown languid with horror, until the increasing consciousness that he was being watched made him turn his head.

There was a man on the far side of the hedge looking in at him, a tall man with sloping shoulders and a wipe of black hair hanging down over his forehead. He was dressed in rusty black, and there was a knowing grin on his face. He turned away at once and made off with a queer sloping stride in the direction of a distant clump of trees. Fursey rose to his feet and ran around the house into the kitchen.

The Gray Mare had a broomstick up on the table and was anointing it with a white ointment.

" What's wrong ? " she said sharply, as Fursey stumbled into the kitchen.

" A queer-looking man," began Fursey, " with a fringe of hair along his forehead, and a big black lock falling over it—"

" That's Cuthbert," interrupted The Gray Mare. " He must know I'm back. There's not a moment to lose. Come on and help me."

She led the way out through the door, and with the handle of the broom on the ground ran around the cottage making a wide circle. Fursey ran behind her, not knowing the moment he might be called upon to assist. When they came around to the door again, the circle completed, she began carefully to trace a pentagram around the house, muttering an incantation as she went. It was borne in powerfully on Fursey that this was witchcraft beyond all question. Any doubts he may have retained were dispelled a few moments later when they returned to the kitchen. He saw her reaching up and taking down a box from the shelf. She took out a handful of newts' eyes and human knuckle-bones, and cast them into the brew. The cauldron moaned hideously.

" Where are you going ? " she asked sharply.

" I'm getting out of this while there's still time," answered Fursey. " Goodbye, and thank you very much for your hospitality."

" You're too late," replied the witch. " Listen."

Fursey's blood grew chill as he became aware of a low drumming, growing louder and louder as it approached. He heard a yelping and baying coming nearer and nearer, until before his horrified eyes a score of monstrous hounds with flaming eyes and lolling tongues came bounding over the hedge. He watched from the doorway as the ghastly pack began coursing in a circle around and around the house. When he tried to move, his knees gave away ; and The Gray Mare had to help him across the room and on to a stool, where he sat filled with dismal foreboding.

" It was a good thing we made that circle and pentagram," said the witch, " we were just in time."

Fursey was too depressed to take more than a gloomy interest in her further preparations. Above the howling and clamour of the hell-pack that circled the house, he was conscious of a scrambling sound on the roof, where the goat had taken refuge. A few moments later he saw her bearded visage looking down at him through the smoke hole.

" It's too late to make a wax image of him," muttered the old woman. " I should have thought of that before. I'll have to trust to the lightning and the enchanted fleas."

Fursey had just come to the conclusion that it was time for him to address himself to prayer and so provide for his own safety, when he observed a severed hand holding a knife come floating through the wall. As it drifted across the room towards The Gray Mare, Fursey bounded to his feet and shouted a warning. She turned in a flash and seizing the broom, struck at the horrid apparition. She missed, but the sweep of the broom deflected its course. The broom struck Fursey on the side of the head and sent him sprawling. From the floor he watched the hand and the knife floating out through the far wall.

" Are you hurt, love ? " asked The Gray Mare as she helped him to his feet. Before he could answer a wild scrambling was heard on the roof. The goat seemed to have lost her head, and the reason became apparent a moment later when a skeleton threw its legs over the smoke hole with the evident intention of descending into the kitchen. Fursey seized a box of moles' feet which lay to hand, and flung it, striking the skeleton somewhere about the middle. It immediately fell to pieces, and its constituent bones descended with a clatter on to the kitchen floor. It recovered at once, formed itself into a skeleton again, and threw itself into a fighting attitude facing Fursey. The Gray Mare came quickly to the rescue. She drew a hasty circle with her broom on the floor around the skeleton, and uttered a word unknown to Fursey. The skeleton once more fell to pieces, this time for good and all; and by direction of the witch Fursey collected the constituent bones and threw them into the fire.

" Counter-offensive ! " shouted The Gray Mare. " Open the door wide ! "

Fursey flung open the door and ran back into a corner. The witch struck the cauldron three times with the thigh bone, each time uttering a shrill cry. Immediately a swarm of fleas as big as mice sprang out. In two hops they were across the kitchen and had flung themselves on the coursing hellhounds. At first the giant dogs merely stopped occasionally in their career to scratch themselves, but when the fleas had warmed to their work, the hounds retreated precipitately, many attempting the pitiable impossibility of scratching and running at the same time.

" Further counter-offensive action ! " roared the witch. " Stand back ! "

Fursey crawled under the table as she beat on the cauldron. She shrieked a jumble of words.   There was a blinding flash as a stream of forked lightning streaked across the kitchen and precipitated itself into the sky in the direction of the sexton's house. The quaking Fursey could see through the doorway a similar bar of lightning arising from the house among the trees. The two streaks of lightning forked around one another for a moment as if manœuvering for position, then they met, wound into a corkscrew, and disappeared in a deafening explosion.

" They've negatived one another," commented the witch bitterly.

In the unearthly silence that followed, nothing was to be heard but a slight stirring overhead as the goat, thinking it was all over, began peacefully to crop her way through the roof.

The Gray Mare threw an angry glance at the ceiling.

" That one will fall in on us yet," she said.   " Drat her ! "

" Do you know," said Fursey, " if you don't mind, I think it was time I was going."

" You can't go," said the witch savagely.   " You're my husband. You can't leave me, a bride, on my wedding night."

" I think all the same," said Fursey feebly, " I'll take a little walk.   A breath of fresh air would be welcome before I turn in."

" Are you mad ? " screamed the witch.   " If you as much as put your nose outside the pentagram, Cuthbert will shrivel you."

Fursey ignored her and staggered towards the doorway ; but the sight of a bloody head dancing up and down in the air a couple of paces beyond the door made him change his mind, and he turned back.

" Maybe if we said a prayer—" he suggested in a weak whisper.

" What's wrong with you ? " barked the witch. " Are you losing your courage ? "

" I never had any," said Fursey as he went down on his knees.

The witch kicked him on to his feet again.

" If you're not going to help me, at least get out of the way. Along with you into the far room, you half-man, you."

Fursey crept into the other room and on to the bed, where he lay for a long time with his face turned to the wall. Everything was very still except for the tearing and champing of the goat on the roof. Several times The Gray Mare came into the room searching for the ingredients for new infusions and distillations ; one time it was the entrails of a sacrificed cock she was looking for, and she turned Fursey out of the bed to see if they were under the pillow : then she was in enquiring whether he had seen a box of dead men's fingernails which she particularly prized. It was eerie lying alone in the darkened room. He fancied that he could hear a muttering and a moaning about the house, and his imagination pictured hideous beings of dreadful aspect and fantastic shape hovering overhead, grinning and gnashing at him horribly. He could stand it no longer : even The Gray Mare's company was preferable to his own, so he crawled off the bed and noiselessly made his way back into the outer room. She was standing at the table muttering The Lord's Prayer backwards as she extracted the venom from a pair of toads. All around her was the horrid paraphernalia of her art, baneful herbs and cauldrons of hell-broth.

" How are things going ? " he enquired with an attempt at friendliness. She looked at him not unkindly.

" So you got lonely in there by yourself," she said.

" Yes," he answered shyly. " Do you hear something ? "

She paused in her work and listened.

" Yes," she said, " the rain."

Fursey listened too. It was pleasant to hear the friendly, familiar rain. He listened until he could distinguish the patter of the individual raindrops softly falling on the roof and around the house.

" I'm preparing to send out a spell," she said, " that will glue Cuthbert to his chair ; but before I send it, I want you to do something for me."

Fursey's heart sank.

" What is it ? " he quavered.

" I'll turn you into a hare," she said, " and you can course around and spy out Cuthbert's dispositions."

Fursey made a move as if he contemplated returning to his bed.

" Well," said the witch shortly, " at least you can creep up to the churchyard and bring me back some clay from a freshly-dug grave. That will help me to twist Cuthbert's magic backwards."

Before Fursey could answer he became sensible of a dreadful sound high up in the air above his head. It was an evil sound, as if the sky was humming with the approach of unholy legions. A look of maniacal menace and fury suddenly distorted The Gray Mare's face. She sprang to her feet.

" The rain ! " she screeched. " He sent the shower of rain to wash out the circle and pentagram."

She ran to the door, but it was too late. The roof was suddenly swept from the house, and as Fursey threw a terrified glance upwards, he saw a cyclopean claw that seemed to fill the whole sky. It paused for a moment, then it struck. The Gray Mare uttered a hoarse wail as the claw seized her, lifted her high above the house, and flung her back, mangled and broken, into a corner of the kitchen.

Fursey cowered in a corner. It was a long time before he ventured out, to pick his way over the debris of the kitchen to where the old woman lay in a crumpled heap. She was all but dead. Her eyes were still open and showed signs of recognising him, but she could move neither hand nor foot. He put his arm around her bony shoulders and raised her. Her breath came out in a whisper, which he bent his head to hear.

" Oh, the pain ! " she whispered. " I can't die. I wish I could die."

The generous tears flooded into Fursey's eyes.

" Kiss me once," came the feeble, throaty voice. " You've never kissed me. Kiss me once, please."

Fursey was embarrassed, but he knew his duty in the presence of death. He bent and placed his lips gently upon hers. The Gray Mare, with a superhuman effort, wrapped her skinny arm around his neck, and pressing her mouth to his, blew violently down his throat. A ball of fire seemed to roll through Fursey's veins, he gasped and shuddered. The Gray Mare fell backwards and lay, an old sack of bones, dead upon the floor. For a few moments Fursey crouched beside her while the fire in his body abated, his apprehension that something further had happened to him mingling disagreeably with his regret for the wretched old woman. At last he arose with a sign and leaning against the table, contemplated the ruin of the kitchen. He had no further fear of the sexton-sorcerer of Kilcock Churchyard : somehow he knew that Cuthbert had been intent on The Gray Mare's destruction, and not on his ; but he knew that he had nowhere to go, that no one wanted him, and that the sooner he too was dead, the better it would be for himself and for everyone else.

From these gloomy reflections he was awakened by something that was happening beside the fireplace. A large dark mass was slowly taking shape. Fursey watched aghast, and then he gave vent to a loud groan. There was no doubt about it : an animal like a large dog was sitting on the hearth. It had paws like a bear and was covered all over with rusty black hair. There was a red foggy light in its eyes ; and it was apparently a creature unknown to natural history. It did not show its teeth nor exhibit any sign of irritation ; but on the contrary gazed at Fursey with benevolence.

" Hello," said the apparition. " I'm Albert."

Fursey averted his eyes, but when he looked back again, it was still there.

" I better explain myself," continued the shaggy stranger, " I was The Gray Mare's familiar. Every witch, as you know, has a familiar ; and it's a strange fact that a witch cannot die until she has bequeathed her powers and her familiar to someone else. That's why the poor old lady was tossing about in such agony until she contrived to breathe her spirit into you. My lord Fursey, you have succeeded to her powers and incidentally to me."

Fursey made an attempt to speak, but no words came.

" I beg your pardon," said Albert.

After a struggle Fursey managed to gasp out the words. " Do you mean to say that I have become a sorcerer ? "

" I do," said Albert. " You are now a wizard and I'm your familiar, always at your service whenever you call upon me."

" But I don't want to be a wizard," protested Fursey.

" I'm afraid you can't help yourself," said Albert. " You have inherited the old lady's powers whether you like it or not. Of course you'll require a good deal of practice before you acquire in the exercises of those powers a proficiency similar to hers."

" What am I to do ? " moaned the hapless Fursey.

" If you take my advice," said Albert, " the first thing you'll do is make friends with Cuthbert. It's better to have him as a friend than as an enemy. The Gray Mare fell out with him, and you've seen what happened to her. Besides, he's a man from whom you can learn a great deal, and if I may say so without offence, you have a great deal to learn. It's not much use having the powers of a sorcerer unless you know how to use them."

" And do I have to have you following me around everywhere ? "

A look of surprise came into Albert's red foggy eyes.

" Not at all," he answered. " I'll take shape when you call on me for advice or for the performance of some task. You have only to utter one word of dismissal, and I automatically disappear. While I am bound to carry out your commands to the best of my ability, I would, however, point out the advisability of your deferring, at least at first, to my judgment in matters affecting the exercise of your craft. After all, I am a familiar of considerable experience."

Fursey passed his tongue over his parched lips and regarded his bestial companion with strong distaste.

" Furthermore," continued the shaggy creature, " if you desire efficient service from me, it's of the highest importance that you keep me well-fed and in good condition. I shall require, at least every second day, a feed of your blood."

" What ! " said Fursey, considerably startled.

" Somewhere about your person," continued Albert smoothly, " you will find that you have acquired a supernumerary nipple. It may look like a wart or excrescence of some sort. That is the point at which you must suckle me with your blood."

" I'll do nothing of the sort," asserted Fursey.

" You will perhaps change your mind," said Albert huffily, " when you discover the extent to which niggardliness in the matter affects my usefulness and efficiency. Lastly, it is my duty to inform you that if you have the misfortune to fall foul of the law, you will, while you're in custody, be automatically bereft of my assistance and the solace of my companionship."

" Why ? " asked Fursey dully.

Albert looked surprised.

" I don't know," he said. " That's the nature of familiars. That's just the way things are."

Deep in Fursey's consciousness thoughts tumbled and elbowed one another, trying vainly to sort themselves out ; but he was too tired, and he felt too broken and helpless to grapple with the situation. He realised that he was in a proper quagmire, but he had neither the heart nor the will to think about the matter further. He leaned against the table gazing dully before him.

" You ought to go down and make the sexton's acquaintance," suggested Albert.

"All right," muttered Fursey, rousing himself.

Albert glanced around the kitchen.

"Bring the broom," he said, "it may turn in useful. She anointed it and prepared it just before the end."

Fursey put the broom under his arm and stood in a half-stupor while Albert's red eye ran critically around the remaining poor possessions of the cottage.

"Nothing else of value," he said. "Oh yes, put this in your pocket, if you have a pocket in that long skirt you're wearing."

"What is it?" asked Fursey, looking down at the small box which Albert had placed in his hand.

"It's the ointment she prepared for anointing the broom," replied the familiar. "Brooms need anointing from time to time or they lose their virtue. I won't tell you what the ingredients are, as you seem as yet somewhat squeamish about these matters."

As they left the cottage and walked slowly down the road towards the clump of trees where the sexton's house stood buried in shadow, Fursey cast up his eyes to the wide star-shattered sky. The huge night was all about him. Houseless, friendless he knew himself to be; and nature, seen through the peculiar opalescent atmosphere of night, appeared not only indifferent, but harsh and estranged. Even the shred of moon that leaned drunkenly overhead seemed to him to be curved in a sneer. Was there anyone in the whole wide world who cared what became of Brother Fursey, late monk at Clonmacnoise? He told himself bitterly that there was not. He glanced at the ungainly monster shambling along by his side, grunting and belching in appreciation of the fine night air. There was no doubt about it, thought Fursey miserably, he was deeply in it: he had plumbed the lowest depths, and nothing worse could happen to him. He didn't care, his heart was dead: let come what would.

As they passed along by the wall of the churchyard, Fursey glanced indifferently at the headstones among the weeds. If all the dead who had ever been buried there, were out in the moonlight playing leapfrog over the tombstones, Fursey felt that he wouldn't have experienced either interest or alarm. He was past caring about anything.

They went on to where the shadows of the trees were deepest, and Fursey suddenly found that they were standing before a low thatched cottage. Albert rose on to his hindlegs and knocked discreetly at the door. Shuffling steps became audible within, and the door was opened by the lanky man in rusty black whom Fursey had seen gazing at him over the hedge earlier in the evening.

The sexton bowed, and with a graceful wave of his hand invited them to enter.

" Welcome to my house," he said courteously as Fursey stepped into the kitchen. The sexton nodded familiarly to Albert as to an old acquaintance, and politely relieving Fursey of the broom, he propped it carefully in a corner.

" Pray, be seated," he said.

Fursey sat down by the table and took a good look at the sexton. He was a lank, weedy man with sloping shoulders. His mouth was puckered, accentuating the general resemblance his countenance bore to that of a rabbit. A wipe of moist black hair hung down over his forehead. He wore rusty black clothes that had seen better days. He stood opposite Fursey cracking each of his fingers in turn, and regarding his visitor with a scarcely perceptible smile stirring the corners of his rabbit's mouth. Fursey with an effort withdrew his eyes from those of his host and looked around the room. Hanging in a neat row from the wall were wheelbarrows, spades, lengths of rope and the varied paraphernalia of the sexton's profession. There were shelves containing food and cooking utensils. A cheery fire blazed in one corner, and the smoke slithered gracefully up the wall and made its exit through an efficient smoke-hole in the roof. Everywhere was neatness and prosperity. The only evidence that the occupant was other than a highly respectable sexton was a manuscript with cabalistic signs which lay on the table between two rushlights, and a huge brindled cat sitting on the hearth who, when Fursey caught her eye, grinned at him furiously.

The sexton pulled a stool up to the table and seated himself opposite Fursey. He folded the manuscript carefully and put it aside.

" Very fine weather we're having for this time of the year," he remarked affably.

Fursey agreed that it was.

" Forgive me," said the sexton, " I have neglected to make the usual introductions. This is Tibbikins, my familiar."

" I'm pleased to make your acquaintance," muttered Fursey hoarsely.

The cat nodded cheerily and favoured Fursey with another grin. Albert lumbered over to the hearth, and the two familiars began a conversation in low tones.

" I judge from the fact that you have Albert attached to you, that you are now of the profession," continued the sexton, " but I am unaware of the name by which you are called."

" My name is Fursey."

" You are a monk ? "

" No. A widower."

" Ah yes," the sexton nodded sympathetically. " I watched the marriage ceremony on the road below this afternoon. Very unfortunate business, your wife's demise ; but, if I may say so, she had become a little high in herself recently. There was a goat also who, not content with eating a gatepost and a wire fence, consumed several of my trees and half the produce of my garden. I never knew an animal with such a prodigious appetite. No sooner had I some rare and valuable herbs planted, than they disappeared into her stomach. I'm fond of animals myself, but I do think that if one keeps livestock, one should keep them under control. Don't you agree with me ? "

Fursey nodded bleakly.

"Oh Tibbikins," said the sexton turning towards the hearth, "perhaps you would like to take Albert into the other room and offer him a bowl of blood."

Albert had no tail, but he wagged his hindquarters to show his appreciation as he shuffled out of the room in the wake of the brindled cat. Cuthbert leaned over towards Fursey and tapped him confidentially on the sleeve.

"You mustn't think I'm a snob," he said, "but I do believe in maintaining the distinctions of class. They are, after all, the chief bulwark of the social order. In any case, I should deem it a grave discourtesy to a fellow-human to discuss his private affairs in the presence of servants."

He arose and put the manuscript carefully away on a shelf. Then he stood for a moment warming his back before the fire.

"The Gray Mare," he said, "was a foolish woman. She had acquired a certain, I might even say, a considerable proficiency in the darker arts, but her over-weening confidence in herself betrayed her into the belief that she could match her powers with those of a master."

His eyes glittered as he brushed back the long lock of hair from his forehead. It immediately fell down over his other eye. He came to the table and again seated himself opposite Fursey.

"I hope you bear me no ill-feeling," he said anxiously. "I don't know what you did to the old lady; but somehow, this afternoon I got the impression that it was what is called 'a forced marriage'."

"It was," agreed Fursey. "I'm not conscious of personal loss."

"Good," said Cuthbert, rubbing his thin hands. "Then we can be friends. You now belong to the brotherhood, the oldest priesthood in the world, older than Christianity, druidism or any religion that man has ever thought up for himself."

Fursey felt that he should contradict these sentiments; but deeming it wise to be discreet, he continued to stare emptily at the smiling sexton.

"But, my dear Fursey, why are you so enveloped in gloom on what should be the happiest day of your life? Think of it, think of the vast inheritance into which you have entered."

"I'm rather tired," said Fursey apologetically. "I have only had one night's rest in several weeks; and I've had a rather trying time to-day."

"Insomnia!" said the sexton. "And here I am chattering away and keeping you from your bed. We'll have plenty of time to talk to-morrow. Come, my poor friend."

The sexton picked up one of the rushlights from the table and led Fursey into the other room. The two familiars were sitting on the floor engaged in desultory conversation.

"That will be all for to-night, Tibbikins," said the sorcerer. "You may disappear."

The brindled cat slowly vanished, beginning with her ears and continuing the process until it reached the tip of her tail.

"I think you might do the same for Albert," suggested the sexton. "You won't require him again to-night."

Albert looked up at Fursey, the light of expectancy in his smoky red eyes. As Fursey gazed at the rusty black coat and the bear's paws, the creature seemed to him to typify all that had made his life a misery in the foregoing weeks.

"Go away," he said with distaste.

Albert melted gracefully into the air with a final friendly waggle of his hindquarters.

"Now, lie down, my friend," said the sexton.

Fursey took off his sandals and stretched himself on the bed. He drew his tattered monk's robe about him and pulled up the blanket to his chin. He was conscious of the sexton's hands making weird passes in the air above him as he felt himself drawn into a blissful sleep.

CHAPTER V

THE cock is a sacred bird: no doubt that is why sorcerers seldom keep poultry. Cuthbert shared the prejudices of his class in this respect: his backyard was devoid of bird-life except for four sinister-looking ducks, who spent their day ambling back and forward from the withered hedge to a pool of the blackest and most revolting mud imaginable, where they disported themselves quacking hoarsely. So it came about that in the absence of a brazen-throated cock to awaken him, Fursey lay hour after hour in deep, hypnotic slumber long into the afternoon. When at last he awoke in the grey half-light of the inner room, he was reluctant to leave his bed, so appalled was he at the thought of having to face another day in the strange and terrible world beyond the blankets. His long sleep had rid him not only of bodily fatigue, but of the dumb, hopeless misery of the previous night, when indifferent to anything that might befall, he had allowed himself to be led into the house of a frantic and atrocious murderer, apparently competent in every kind of sorcery and enchantment. Fursey's mental agony became acute as he let pass before his mind the happenings of the previous day. He did not doubt but that his immortal soul was lost: he could not believe that a wizard would ever be allowed to enter Heaven ; and that he had become a wizard seemed beyond doubt. And, he reflected bitterly, even in this life he was fated to be dogged everywhere he went by a hideous creature with long, black, rusty hair, bear's paws and smoky red eyes, clamouring for his blood and pestering him with offers of services of doubtful value in return. It was a black look-out.

Thought after thought turned painfully in Fursey's head. The most urgent need, he told himself, was to escape from this house, which was a hotbed of magic and necromancy. Once away he would be beyond the power of Cuthbert ; and could worry about his other troubles in his own good time. But as long as he was within Cuthbert's reach anything might happen ; and anything that did happen was sure to be unpleasant and deplorable. If only there was someone to advise him ! A sudden thought struck him. There was one creature bound to his service, the hideous Albert. He shrunk from the thought of summoning the familiar, for to do so would be a positive exercise of the damnable powers with which he was vested, and he hoped that by neglecting to use those powers he might the more readily obtain divine forgiveness for possessing them. He even cherished a hope that it might be within the competence of skilful leeches and surgeons to cure him of being a wizard, though he had an uneasy feeling that the only way to cure a wizard is to burn him. He saw himself once more on his knees at the Abbot's feet blurting out the whole pitiful story, and the Abbot Marcus, who had never been unkind to him, raising him up gently and telling him not to worry, that all would be well.

A sob shook him as he realised his predicament, and he buried his face in the pillow. He was convinced that his only chance of avoiding utter destruction at the hands of the sexton was to summon Albert to help him ; yet by summoning Albert he would be accepting The Gray Mare's hateful legacy and admitting himself a practising sorcerer. He tossed on his bed in a sweat of indecision, but the issue was not long in doubt, for his fear of Cuthbert outweighed all other considerations. " The end justifies the means," he told himself. " Anyway, I can seek forgiveness afterwards." Besides, in the back of his mind swayed the vague hope that some, at least, of yesterday's happenings were just a bad dream or attributable to a heated and prepossessed imagination. Perhaps he wasn't a sorcerer at all. If Albert failed to appear when summoned, that would prove it.

Fursey sat up in bed and peered into the half-darkness. "Albert!" he called in a hoarse whisper, "Albert!"

For a moment nothing happened. Then Fursey discerned on the floor near the bed what appeared to be a small area of black mist. As he stared at it with peculiar foreboding, it quickly resolved itself into a shaggy hindquarters. Fursey groaned aloud as a pair of bear's paws came into view, followed by the rest of Albert's anatomy. The familiar fixed his red eyes on Fursey expectantly.

"Breakfast?" he asked hopefully. A broad pink tongue emerged from the creature's mouth, made a circuit of his snout, and disappeared again from view.

"No," replied Fursey with distaste. "Not yet."

"I see," said Albert, his voice betraying his disappointment.

"Tell me," queried Fursey, "are you bound absolutely to my service?"

"Of course I am," replied Albert. "That is the nature of familiars."

"Even if what I command you to do seems to you absurd and unreasonable?"

"Even so," answered Albert. "Your will is my will. Of course you would be wise to defer to my judgment, at least at first——"

"I know all that," interrupted Fursey. "Tell me, is it possible for you to betray me to someone whom I deem an enemy, to Cuthbert, the sexton, for instance?"

Albert looked surprised. "It's not possible," he responded. "I'm bound by my nature to your service, save only if you fall into the hands of the law. But with regard to Cuthbert, I assure you that you're mistaken in thinking him an enemy——"

"Stop talking," commanded Fursey.

Albert immediately ceased to speak. Fursey was conscious of a pleasant sense of power. For the first time in his life he had given an order, and he had been obeyed. He regarded the shaggy creature benevolently and noticed the hurt in its eyes.

" Come here," he said kindly.

Albert shambled over to the edge of the bed. Fursey put out his hand and patted him on the head. Albert wagged his hindquarters delightedly, and his smoky red eyes lit up with expectancy.

" Breakfast ? " he repeated hopefully.

" No," reiterated Fursey.

Albert looked aggrieved. " If you expect nimble and courteous service from me," he asserted plaintively, " you'll have to keep me fed. I'm that thirsty, the tongue is fair hanging out of my mouth for a drop of blood."

" That's enough of that," rejoined Fursey.

" You'll find that you have acquired a supplementary nipple," pleaded Albert.

" I have not," replied Fursey.

" At least have a look," begged Albert coaxingly.

Fursey ignored the creature's request. " Where's Cuthbert?" he asked.

" I don't know," answered Albert.

" Well, put your head around the door and see if he's in sight."

Albert did as he was told. " He's not in the kitchen," he said over his shoulder.

" Well, look outside."

Albert disappeared from view into the outer room. In a few moments he was back.

" Cuthbert's up at the end of the garden," he reported. " He has a stick in his hand and a sort of skipping rope. He's putting a gargoyle through its tricks."

Fursey concluded that the sexton was at a safe distance, so he slipped out of bed and pulled on his sandals.

" Listen, Albert," he said, " I want to get out of this place as quickly as possible. Can't you take me on your back and fly out through the far door and across the hills without Cuthbert knowing anything about it ? "

" I cannot," retorted Albert shortly. " What do you think I am, a bloody bird ? "

Fursey gazed at his familiar with exceeding distaste.

" Well, how am I to get away ? " he asked at last.

" There are only two ways," replied Albert, "either by walking or by flying on your broom."

" If I walk, Cuthbert will see me."

" He most certainly will," agreed Albert.

" And he probably doesn't want me to leave."

" You can rest assured that he does not. For one thing, you know too much about the demise of my late mistress, The Gray Mare. What's to prevent you going to the authorities and denouncing him as a sorcerer ? "

" What would he do if he caught me trying to escape ? "

" That's hard to say," replied Albert judiciously. " He might turn you into a toad and keep you indefinitely in a jar in a half-pickled state, or he might compound your ingredients with the white juice of a sea-lettuce and keep you for making love philtres. On the other hand, your bones, if ground to powder and mixed with pulverised flints——"

" Stop it," commanded Fursey as he seated himself on the edge of the bed and wiped the sweat from his face with the ragged sleeve of his habit. " It'll have to be the broom. You had better start teaching me how to fly on a broom."

" I can't," rejoined Albert. " I don't know how. You don't seem to have quite grasped our relationship. You're the master-brain, I'm only your servant."

" It seems to me," said Fursey shrilly, " that as a familiar you're pretty well useless. Here, in the first crisis in my affairs since I became a sorcerer, you're not able to afford me the slightest assistance."

" I'm doing my best," replied Albert sulkily. " What exactly do you want ? "

" I want to get away from here without Cuthbert knowing it."

" Well, get Cuthbert himself to teach you how to ride on a broom, and then when he's not looking, you can make your getaway."

" Do you think it would work ? " asked Fursey hopefully.

" It'll probably end by him turning you into an asp or a hyaena ; but if you exercise enough guile, you may manage it."

" Guile ? " repeated Fursey.

" Yes," said Albert shortly. " Doesn't your own Christian teaching urge you to be not only as innocent as a dove, but as wise as a serpent ? "

" So it does," confessed Fursey, astonished at the possibility of the practical application of Christian principles to the matter in hand. He sat for a long time in thought, wondering whether he could squeeze up enough guile to deceive the wily sexton. Albert's voice broke in on his reflections.

" I hope I'm not being unreasonable," said the familiar. " About a quarter-pint of blood would do for to-day, just enough to keep my coat in condition."

" Disappear," ordered Fursey.

Albert opened his mouth to protest, but he melted away before he had time to express his resentment. Still seated on the bed Fursey calculated with a coolness of mind that astonished himself. He must win the sexton's confidence ; he must convince Cuthbert that he was a genuine apprentice sorcerer eager to learn the craft and excel in wickedness. He must impress the sexton and gain his admiration and respect by pretending to be a character of more than ordinary depravity. The events that had led up to his expulsion from Clonmacnoise would be a great help. Cuthbert was sure to enquire as to his history, and a little alteration here and there in the Clonmacnoise story would make him appear a very evil fellow indeed. No need, for instance, to mention the one-time impediment in his speech ; he would pretend that he had willingly harboured the demons in his cell because they were friends of his. That was sure to impress the sexton.

Fursey rose to his feet marvelling at his own ingenuity. Before leaving the room he practised a couple of evil laughs, which were so effective that he found himself shuddering at the hideous sounds which he was able to produce. Then he tiptoed out into the kitchen. There was a pleasant smell of cooking from a cauldron which was suspended over the peat fire. He observed with gratification that the broom which he had brought from The Gray Mare's cottage, was still propped in its place in the corner ; and he remembered that he had a box of ointment in his pocket for use, should it be necessary to anoint it further. He hesitated for a moment in the doorway ; then with a beating heart he stepped out into the open air and went round the corner of the house to meet the sexton.

It was a day of shifting sunshine and shadow. Fursey was surprised to observe that the sun had long passed its zenith and was leaning down towards the west. It was therefore late in the afternoon ; no wonder he felt hungry. At the back of the house was a yard across which four ducks waddled determinedly in single file on their way to a small quagmire of filth and ooze. They crossed his path, making no attempt to get out of his way. In fact, as he approached, they quacked alarmingly and cast malevolent eyes in his direction. Fursey gave them a wide berth : you never knew in a place like this what was going to happen next—in one moment one of those ducks might have him by the throat.

At the other side of the yard was a blasted oak. Fursey carefully avoided its shadow and found himself at the edge of a small orchard. He shuddered and hesitated, for he remembered that orchards were peculiarly connected with sorcery due to the Devil's well-known interest in apples. Before he had summoned up courage to enter and walk down the avenue of fatal trees, he observed Cuthbert at the far end. The sexton waved to him cheerily and began at once to approach, not seeming to walk, but to glide with a curious smooth motion about a foot off the ground. As he alighted beside Fursey the latter put down his hand in an attempt to stay the knocking of his knees beneath his habit. To the sexton's polite enquiry as to how he had slept, Fursey replied hoarsely that he had slept very well indeed. The ex-monk had by now fallen into so languid a state that when Cuthbert

invited him to walk through the orchard with him and view
his domain, Fursey experienced considerable difficulty in
putting one foot before the other without falling on the
ground. As they slowly paced the patterned sunlight and
shadow beneath the trees, Cuthbert emitted a deep, long-
drawn, unearthly sigh.

" How I envy you," he said. " There's something beautiful
about a man at the threshold of his career. And what a
career ! By magic felicity can be conferred on one's friends
and destruction wrought on one's enemies. The skies will
be yours to command, you will ride the winds and the hurricane. It will be in your power to bring madness, and to
countenance or thwart fertility. You will pass through the
gates of midnight to the caverns of the dead, there to learn
the awful secrets of existence. Ah, Fursey, my friend,
forgive me if I repeat myself ; but my heart is full of joy for
you. I cannot understand why, with this immense heritage
in your grasp, you still remain languid and apparently reluctant. Is it that you are a man with a natural super-
abundance of melancholy ? "

Fursey's reply came from his throat in a husky whistle :
" I think I have not yet fully realised my good fortune."

Cuthbert nodded understandingly, and when he spoke
again his voice was heightened with enthusiasm.

" You will have intercourse with sylphs and salamanders,"
he declared. " You will learn the virtue of herb, wood and
stone. You will learn to raise spirits by conjured circles.
Circles, you must understand, are made round, triangular,
quadrangular, single, double, or treble according to the form
of apparition that you crave. Much you will learn by studying
the entrails of beasts, by the singing of fowls and by their
actions in the air."

" It sounds very interesting," quavered Fursey.

" Interesting ! " shouted Cuthbert. " Do you realise the
fierce joy of hidden knowledge and secret power ? To the
magician nothing is impossible. He knows the language of
the stars and directs the planetary courses. The elements

obey him. When he speaks, the moon falls blood-red from heaven, the dead arise in their shrouds and mutter ominous words as the night wind whistles through their skulls. The wizard at his pleasure can dispense joy or misery to mankind. He is the master of past, present and future. And this you speak of as ' interesting ' ! ''

Fursey passed his tongue over his parched lips.

" Is it not the case," he enquired feebly, " that sorcerers usually end their lives in a violent and dishonourable manner?"

" No," thundered Cuthbert. " Given ordinary guile and cunning, the sorcerer is master of his own safety. With the exercise of reasonable care he can be neither surprised by misfortune nor overwhelmed by disaster."

" I see," said Fursey.

" Well," asked Cuthbert more affably. " What kind of a sorcerer do you think you'll make ? "

" I'm afraid I'll need a good deal of practice and instruction," replied Fursey. " I must get you to teach me how to fly on a broom to begin with."

" All in good time," answered Cuthbert. " You will certainly need practice and careful instruction, but what you require most of all is courage. Neither skill nor courage must fail you ; if they do, there will be disaster. A sorcerer who is afraid of water, will never command the Undines ; one who is timid of fire, will never impress his will on salamanders. If one is liable to giddiness, one must leave the sylphs alone and forbear from irritating gnomes ; for you must know that inferior spirits will only obey a power that has overcome them in their own element."

" Have no fear that you will find me lacking in courage," squeaked Fursey.

Cuthbert threw a quick look at him, but did not reply. Fursey's heart began to hammer beneath his habit, and he plunged into a halting account of his adventures in Clonmacnoise. They had reached the further end of the orchard and stood at the fence gazing out over the sexton's garden, which stretched from where they stood to the hedge that bounded

The Gray Mare's property.   There were a few hazel trees and
chestnuts and neat rows of deadly nightshade, wild parsley
and sage.   Fursey observed peaches and bitter almonds, and
against the graveyard wall fungi noted for their deadly and
narcotic properties.   As he related the dark and mysterious
tale of the invasion of Clonmacnoise, he noted with gratification that the sexton seemed impressed.   Fursey's courage
grew with his narration, and he talked glibly of his acquaintance with incubi, hydras and gryphons ;   and boasted that
when the legions of Hell had been all but defeated, he was the
one who had saved them from expulsion from the monastery.

" You acted very well," said Cuthbert at last.   " It's true
that demons are inferior spiritual intelligences, with whom I
have little to do.   They are a creation of Christianity, while
I am the servant on a more venerable religion ;   still, demons
are all right in their own place.   I have more liking for them.
than for monks and religious jugglers.   You tell me that you
are acquainted with Satan himself ? "

" Acquainted ! " echoed Fursey indignantly.   " He's a very
dear friend of mine."

" Good," said Cuthbert with a tinge of respect in his voice.

Fursey realised that now was the moment to win the master
sorcerer's full confidence.   He emitted an evil laugh and
leered wickedly at the sexton.

" Well, what's doing to-day ? " he asked throatily.

Cuthbert's eyes expressed well-bred surprise.

" I beg your pardon," he replied.

" What's doing in the way of iniquity ? " demanded Fursey,
rubbing his hands in his best sinister fashion.

" Oh," responded Cuthbert.   " Perhaps to-night we'll
sacrifice a live cock at the crossroads by way of initiating you."

Fursey's eyes expressed his disappointment.   He stuck out
his underlip.

" Aren't there any women around ? " he asked harshly.
" I'd like to make the acquaintance of a lively and engaging
female vampire.   Couldn't you conjure up one for me ? "

Cuthbert became very grave. Fursey's heart missed a beat as he thought for a moment that his request was going to be granted. The sexton took him by the arm.

" My dear Fursey," he said, " you must learn to walk before you can fly. I must warn you that the activities of vampires are very destructive of the health of their acquaintances. In fact, visits from the tribe are fraught with danger."

" Ah, who minds danger ? " retorted Fursey lustily. " We must have courage."

Cuthbert shook his head gravely.

" If you take my advice," he said, " you'll lay off the vampires. I had one staying with me here once for the week-end, a rather cadaverous gentleman. I distinctly recollect that when he took his departure on the Monday morning, he left me somewhat debilitated as a result of his attentions. I never invited one since. After all, that was no way to repay hospitality."

" I suppose you're right," admitted Fursey.

They moved away from the fence and started to walk slowly back along a path that bordered the orchard.

" Strange thing," said Cuthbert. " When you were telling me just now of the demons in the shape of fabulous beasts with whom you are acquainted, your story recalled to my mind an incident that happened to me when I was a young man. I had forgotten it these many years."

" Yes," said Fursey politely.

" I suppose you've never met a basilisk ? " asked Cuthbert.

Fursey thought rapidly and decided that it was safer to say " no."

" Just as well for you," observed Cuthbert. " You'd scarcely be here if you had. Instead there would be a fine stone statue to you in Clonmacnoise. This story of mine has a moral, so you might as well hear it. The moral is : ' Keep your wits about you and always act with expedition in a crisis '."

" Act with expedition in a crisis," repeated Fursey. " I'll make a note of it."

" When I was quite a young man," began Cuthbert, " I was out walking one evening along a country road, when on turning a corner I came suddenly on a basilisk rambling along by himself enjoying, I suppose, the mild evening air. Fortunately I recognised him at once for what he was, and knowing that the gaze of a basilisk turns one to stone if one is so foolish as to meet it, I immediately dropped my eyes and fixed them on a spot on the road midway between his front two hooves. At the same time I bent rapidly and picked up from the ground a piece of straight stick which was lying to hand."

" And did you feel no ill-effect from his gaze ? " asked Fursey breathlessly.

" I felt a certain chill," conceded Cuthbert, " and I cannot say but that an occasional twinge of rheumatism which I get to the present day is not the result of his survey. However, my whole being told me that I must act with the utmost despatch ; so, holding the piece of stick vertically at arm's length, I advanced it rapidly to the tip of his nose. I did not dare look up, but I judged accurately where the tip of his nose must be, by keeping my eyes directed on a spot on the road midway between his front hooves. As you know, the instinct of both animal and human is to keep the eyes fixed on any object that is rapidly approaching. A basilisk's eyes are protuberant, so that by the time the vertical stick had reached his nose, his two protuberant eyes were looking inward at one another, and he effectively turned himself into stone. When I ventured to look up, there was a very fine specimen of a young bull basilisk in stone with his eyes crossed."

" Dear me," ejaculated Fursey.

" He remained there for many years, much admired by the besotted peasantry, and an object of great interest to visitors. Finally he was discovered by an archaeologist who had lost his way one night. A learned paper was written, and a whole school of archaeologists descended on the neighbourhood from the monastery of Cong. They took measurements and drew pictures of him, and wrote several shelves of learned volumes.

I understand that they argued his presence proved the early
inhabitants of this island to have come from the land of
Egypt, where such monuments abound. The fact that his
eyes were looking into one another interested them greatly;
and they deduced from that fact that the religion of our
Egyptian forefathers laid great stress on the virtues of intro-
spection."

" Is he there still ? " asked Fursey.

" Unfortunately," replied Cuthbert, " some years later the
local authority broke him up for road metal. As you are no
doubt aware, material considerations in this country always
outweigh considerations of antiquarian interest. I thought
it was a pity myself. He was an interesting and unusual
monument of our past and was of considerable importance to
the local tourist industry."

" Well," averred Fursey, " I'll know what to do if I ever
meet a basilisk."

Their path had brought them to a small grotto in the shade
of an oak tree that seemed to Fursey to have a particularly
haunted look. Cuthbert paused.

" I want to show you my latest acquisition," he remarked,
" a young gargoyle which I purchased from a seafaring man
from the country of the Franks."

He whistled sharply, and an ungainly creature lurched into
view from the dark interior of the grotto. It was swarthy in
hue and had two sharply pointed ears. Its mouth hung open
in a permanent grin, and from the tip of its tongue there
was a steady drip of yellowish liquid. Fursey, who felt
himself afraid of nothing as long as he had Cuthbert on his
side, cautiously ventured out his hand to pet the creature.

" Be careful," warned the sexton. " That drip from its
tongue is venom. Every drop wounds."

Fursey hastily withdrew his hand and stepped back a pace.

" It's nearly an obsolete form," explained Cuthbert,
" although the creatures were at one time common in the
country of the Franks. Of late the people in those territories
have been making images of them in stone and affixing them

to the exterior of their churches. There's a perverse strain in the master builders of that country, which finds expression from time to time in such freakish behaviour."

" What are you going to do with him ? " asked Fursey.

" Well," said Cuthbert, " it's a little experiment of mine. I'm trying to make him half-human. I hope to pass him off as a minor man of letters. He has many of the qualities. Observe the cute narrowly-spaced eyes and the steady dribble of venom from the tongue. He will make a very passable man of letters, or rather one who imagines himself to be a man of letters."

" He doesn't look very human to me," observed Fursey.

" He's not supposed to be very human," rejoined Cuthbert. " Didn't I tell you he's to be a minor literary man ? Wait."

Cuthbert put his hand into his pocket and took out a handful of horse's teeth, which he spaced carefully across the gargoyle's mouth, beneath the upper lip. " How's that ? " he asked.

" I suppose it's an improvement," muttered Fursey, without much conviction.

Cuthbert nodded to the gargoyle, which shambled back into the depths of its cave. The sexton glanced up at the sun, which was very round and red, and just above the horizon. " Time for something to eat," he remarked, and started to lead the way back to the cottage. As the two sorcerers crossed the orchard, the shadows of the trees lay like long grasping arms across the grass. With the advent of evening Fursey felt that something more than eerie had begun to pervade the neighbourhood of the sexton's house. As they left the orchard and passed the blasted oak at the end of the yard, something in its woody depths sighed heartbrokenly.

" What was that ? " enquired Fursey with a tremor of fear in his voice.

Cuthbert smiled slightly. " A tax-collector whom I embedded there many years ago," he replied. " A very forward fellow."

As they made their way across the yard, the four ducks buried their heads in their inky pool, so that as Fursey and Cuthbert passed, only four sinister sterns were visible pointing heavenwards. Whether they were eating mud off the bottom or whether it was an act of homage to their master, Fursey was unable to say. Cuthbert pushed in the door of the cottage, and Fursey, with growing apprehension, followed him into the kitchen. The sexton took the lid off the cauldron, which was simmering over fire, and smelt its contents.

"Done to a turn," he remarked brightly. He removed the meat with a pair of tongs and placing it on the table, deftly hacked it into two portions with a hatchet. He pushed one portion in front of Fursey.

"I think I can produce food too," announced Fursey, who thought it was time to give a further demonstration of his wickedness. "You haven't got a rope, have you."

Cuthbert pointed to a coil of rope on the wall, and watched approvingly while Fursey took the rope down and with trembling hands cast one end of it over the crossbeam that supported the roof.

"What will we require?" asked Fursey.

"Butter, bread, ale and condiments," replied Cuthbert, beaming at his pupil.

Fursey fixed his mind on butter and pulled the rope gently. A lump of choice butter slid half-way down the rope, stopped, and travelled back into the rafters again, where it disappeared.

"You must pull harder," said Cuthbert encouragingly.

Fursey flung all his weight on the rope and was immediately deluged in a shower of foodstuffs. Rather breathlessly he retrieved them from the floor and placed them in a neat pile on the table.

"My soul is lost," he told himself; but he didn't allow his mind to dwell on such a painful subject. As he seated himself at the table he found himself wishing that he knew how to imprison Cuthbert in a tin canister, so that he might make his escape. The two ate in silence, Fursey tearing greedily at the meat, for he was very hungry. At length they sat back and contemplated with satisfaction the heap of bones that lay piled between them.

" Do you know," began Cuthbert, " I never saw a goodlier man than yourself, nor one so well of eating. It's hard to believe that you're a monk at large."

" I'm no longer a monk," responded Fursey. " They relieved me of my vows. That was good meat," he added by way of changing the subject.

" Very succulent," agreed the sexton. " I'm very addicted to goat's flesh myself."

A sudden feeling of nausea clutched at Fursey's stomach.

" Was that a goat ? " he asked faintly.

" Yes," replied Cuthbert, his eyes glinting viciously, " that was The Gray Mare's goat. She died last night in the course of certain operations of a magical character which I was forced to conduct in self-defence. I think you were present at the time."

Generous tears came into Fursey's eyes as he gazed down at the neat heap of bones which represented the last mortal remains of his late acquaintance. " I'm not only a sorcerer," he told himself, " I'm a cannibal."

The sexton noticed his distress.

" Come now," he said soothingly, " a mug of ale."

He filled two beakers, and a long draught of the heady brew served to clear Fursey's depression of spirit.

" To give that goat her due," said Cuthbert, " she was a most remarkable animal. One afternoon in the course of one of her incursions into my garden she ate a row and a half of belladonna—enough poison to lay every man, woman and child in the territory on their backs frothing at the mouth, but did she show any sign of it ? Not a bit, except for a gamey light in her eye. She finished off with a dessert of mandrakes, hemlock and hazelnuts, and walked back to The Gray Mare's cottage without a stagger."

Fursey contemplated the heap of bones and shook his head sadly.

"You know," continued Cuthbert reminiscently, "The Gray Mare was a bit of a snob—she liked to show off, and she always rode that goat to a sabbath instead of coming on a broom like the other warlocks and witches of the countryside. I remember once as she was flying by the steeple of Kilpuggin Church, nothing would do the goat but to turn aside to eat the weather vane and some of the lead off the spire. It was a most comical sight—the other witches careering by on their brooms enjoying to the full The Gray Mare's embarrassment ; while the poor old lady, red in the face and half mad with chagrin, belaboured the goat and tried to drag her away from the weather vane, and all the while the goat held on to the lead of the spire with her teeth."

Cuthbert was silent as memory after memory chased across his forehead. At length Fursey ventured to speak.

"I don't wish to interrupt your contemplations," he said, "but I have resolved to let no day pass without learning something of value to me in my new profession. I should deem it a great favour if you would instruct me as to how to ride on a broom. I have my late wife's besom with me, and it wants still a couple of hours to darkness. I could do a couple of practice flights up and down the orchard."

"Certainly," replied Cuthbert, "but first I must show you my store-room."

Fursey chafed at the prolongation of his stay in the cottage, but he was careful to avoid arousing the sexton's suspicions. It was evident that Cuthbert was rather vain of his possessions. The sexton led the way across the room to what seemed to Fursey to be a blank wall.

"You see," remarked Cuthbert, "the magician also controls visibility."

He clapped his hands and uttered a string of evil-sounding jargon. Immediately there appeared in the wall a green door engraved with the mystical number seven. Cuthbert opened it, and they went in.

The store-room was not large, but its contents were so neatly packed on shelving which reached from floor to ceiling, that advantage had been taken of every inch of available space. Fursey realised with horror that he was in a veritable arsenal of witchcraft. There was a shelf of witches' poisons : aconite, deadly nightshade and hemlock. Neat trays contained the ingredients for vicious brews and enchantments : hazelnuts, chestnuts, mandrakes, mallows, metals, poplar leaves, salt, wild parsley and vervain. There was a plentiful supply of mandragora, which is potent in death spells. In a corner was a keg of powder suitable for the manufacture of love philtres. There were cages containing snakes, toads, frogs, beetles, hornets, ferrets, owls, vipers and asps ; and a neat row of bats hung upside down from a rack on the wall. In carefully labelled boxes there were moles' feet, murderers' knucklebones, hogs' bristles, sage, powdered flints and loadstone. Nothing was wanting that might be required in the black ceremonies of the night. Fursey realised with horror how well Cuthbert was supplied so as promptly to execute whatever iniquity his mind might suggest.

" It's fascinating," he muttered as he followed Cuthbert out again into the kitchen, and the green door effaced itself from the wall behind them.

" Fascinating," said Cuthbert, " but rather frightening. Isn't that what you really mean ? "

" Yes," agreed Fursey.

Cuthbert seemed pleased at this attitude of mind in his pupil, and as they made their way once more to the orchard, he chatted wickedly, giving Fursey many abominable counsels. Fursey scarcely heard him, his mind was too taken up with the necessity of making his departure with the utmost despatch. He kept a tight grip on the broom, which he had taken from its corner behind the door. When they reached the orchard, they took their stand on the grass between the trees.

" You'll have a clear run," remarked Cuthbert, " down the avenue between the trees, and then you can fly back. Don't try for altitude at first. Keep about a yard and half off the ground."

" What do I do ? " asked Fursey.

" Throw your leg across, and sit on it," replied Cuthbert. " It's only a matter of balance."

" But how do I make it go ? " enquired Fursey.

" Just wish it to go," answered Cuthbert. " You can give your directions aloud if you like."

" But is it not the case," queried Fursey anxiously, " that once unknown forces have been unloosed, not even the sorcerer himself can always control them ? "

" Nonsense," retorted Cuthbert. " I don't know where you got these odd scraps of information. They're certainly not applicable in the circumstances. Try it now."

Fursey gripped the broom frantically with his hands and knees. He closed his eyes.

" Fly," he lisped in a thin, quavering voice.

He was conscious of being suddenly yanked into the air and found himself a moment later in a tree. Cuthbert was standing underneath with set lips contemplating the broken branches and the pink apple blossom which was still fluttering to the ground.

" What did you do that for ? " asked the sexton crossly. " Come down."

" How did I get here ? " asked Fursey in amazement.

" You flew straight into it," replied Cuthbert shortly. " Come down before you do any more damage."

Fursey descended amid a further shower of apple blossom.

" Now be careful," admonished Cuthbert. " Look where you're going."

Fursey threw his leg over the broom once more. " Fly," he repeated desperately.

The broom shot over the hedge, across the yard and made straight for the wall of the cottage.

" Stop ! " howled Fursey.

The broom reared in mid-air, and fell, together with Fursey, into the ducks' pool.

" You appear to have an impetuous and fatal tendency to do the wrong thing," asserted Cuthbert a moment later, as he helped Fursey out of the quagmire. " You're very black ; you better come in and wash yourself. I wonder where my ducks are."

" I'll try it once more," declared Fursey desperately. He pointed the handle of the broom at the gap between the cottage and the clump of neighbouring trees.

" Fly," he shouted, " as quick as you can."

The broom sprang forward. It just missed the gable of the cottage, and in a moment was careering down the road borne at a height of about two yards above the ground.

" Come back ! " he heard the sexton shouting, but he bent his head over the handle of the broom and whispered agonisingly " Quicker ! "

His habit flapped madly in the breeze as he careered around the bend of the road and over a bridge. It was difficult to steer the broom around the many corners of the road without disaster, but Fursey clung on grimly, a great feeling of exultation in his heart. " I'm away," he kept telling himself. " I've escaped."

A mongrel dog came tearing out of a farmhouse and followed the broom for half a mile barking furiously, but the pace was too much for him, and he had to give up the chase exhausted. A band of pilgrims which was coming along the road intoning a doleful hymn, dropped their staves when they saw Fursey approaching, and precipitated themselves over the hedges. One foolish fellow who kept running back and forward, unable to make up his mind as to whether the left- or right-hand ditch promised the greater safety, had reason to repent his indecision, for he was struck on the forehead by Fursey's sandal and stretched senseless as the broom careered past. Fursey held on like grim death, not presuming to move a muscle for fear he would fall off. The cattle in the fields stared at him with unbelieving eyes before turning to scamper in all directions. A hen who seemed to imagine that he was chasing her, ran in front of him for at least a mile before flinging herself in desperation through a hole in the hedge.

Fursey had been so intent on escaping from Cuthbert's cottage that he had given no thought at all to the question of where he was to go. This problem began now to insinuate itself into his mind. The only place he could think of was the monastery. It was the only home he knew, and the Abbot Marcus was the only person who had ever been really kind to him. So he bent towards the broom handle and whispered : " Take me to Clonmacnoise."

No sooner were the words uttered than the broom forsook the road and made across country towards the line of mountains. Most alarming of all, it started to rise steadily, and the terrified Fursey observed the fields beneath him shrinking in size and the roads becoming thin wavering threads. It seemed to him that his plight was desperate, alone in the upper air, with only a slippery shaft of wood between him and destruction. Suppose he ran into a cloud and was suffocated !

" Albert ! " he called hoarsely. " Albert ! "

Slowly the familiar took shape, seated on the broom handle facing Fursey. His fur was all blown backwards by the wind, and he clung desperately to the slippery handle with his bears' paws. He glared at Fursey with angry resentment.

" Nice time to summon me," he snarled. " Do you want to break my neck as well as your own ? "

" Albert," whimpered Fursey, " stop it from going so high. Bring it down nearer the earth."

" Why did you get on to the bloody yoke," screamed Albert, " when you didn't know how to manage it ? "

" Albert, please. How will I get it to go down ? "

" You've only to tell it to stop," shouted Albert above the screaming of the wind. " Not now, you nincompoop ! We're flying over a lake."

Fursey ventured to look down and saw a stretch of water far below. He shuddered and closed his eyes.

" Albert, don't go away."

" Open your eyes and look where you're going," howled Albert. " Do you want us to crash into a mountain at this speed ? "

" Albert, I'm sorry if I was ever unkind to you—"

Albert bared his teeth in a hideous grin.

" Order me to disappear," he screeched. " I'm only upsetting the balance of the broom."

" Don't go, Albert. I like your company."

Albert glared at his master with his eyes full of bale.

" We're crossing the mountain ridge," gasped Fursey.

Albert made an effort and swallowed his ire. " Tell the broom to go down to within a few yards of the ground and not to hit anything," he said huskily.

Fursey managed to enunciate the command and added the injunction that speed should be slackened. The broom descended and swooped gracefully over a mountain top. Fursey drew his breath and looked around him. They were descending a green, swampy glen that cut deep into the hills. Lower in the valley were scattered cottages and in the distance a glittering river winding through the plain. He recognised the curve of the River Shannon.

" It won't be far now," he announced joyfully.

" If you're making for Clonmacnoise, as I judge from the look of the countryside," responded Albert, " I'd advise you to dismiss me. I don't imagine I'll be popular with the monks."

" That's true," admitted Fursey. " You may vanish."

Albert thoughtlessly permitted his paws to disappear first, with the result that he fell off the broom before the process was complete. Fursey looked over his shoulder and saw the familiar rolling among the rocks and vanishing as he rolled. But Fursey had no time to feel concern for Albert's safety. The broom had crossed a small stream on the floor of the valley and was ascending a low ridge of grassy hill. As it topped the rise Fursey saw the broad, sluggish Shannon before him meandering between its lines of golden reeds. Between him and the river was the Pilgrims' Way and a mile away on his left the two round towers and the cluttered huts of Clonmacnoise. As he came sailing down the hillside and turned into the Pilgrims' Way he saw monks who had been working in scattered groups in the fields, suddenly dropping

their spades and running hell-for-leather for the monastery.
As he approached flying at a height of six feet above the
roadway, he saw the great gates being slammed, and a moment
later a discordant clamour of bells smote the air.   The broom
reared sharply and flung Fursey on to the road, where he
rolled over and over in the dust.

When he scrambled to his feet he found he was only twenty
paces from the gates.   A sea of horrified white faces stared
out at him from between the wickerwork.   The din of the
bells was deafening, for the monks were ringing everything
that they had got.   As they watched the ragged, entirely
black figure picking itself up off the road and come staggering
towards the gates, they retreated precipitately, ringing their
handbells like so many maniacs.   Brother Patrick's horror
was such that he lost the use of his legs, and on the approach
of the ooze- and slime-covered stranger, he pitched forward
senseless.   Father Crustaceous began a hymn in a thin,
cracked treble ; and those of the monks who were able to
produce a sound from their throats, followed him in shrill
falsettos.   Quavering, the hymn rose and fell.

Fursey reached the gates and gripping the wickerwork
desperately with his hands, he stared in, half-blinded with
tears at the wide semi-circle of retreating monks and the
prone body of Brother Patrick in the foreground.

" Let me in," he cried.   " I'm Fursey.   Brother Fursey."
The hymn stopped dead on a high note, but was immediately
taken up with renewed vigour.   If anything, the clangour of
the handbells increased, and it was swollen by the pealing of
the great bell of the monastery which Father Sampson had
reached and was dragging at, as if he wanted to pull down the
steeple.   Again and again Fursey cried aloud for admittance,
but on the semi-circle of white faces he could see only horror
and hatred.   Still holding fast to the wickerwork, he sank
in a heap on the ground and buried his head, sobbing bitterly.

The singing and the rattling of the bells ceased suddenly as
the Abbot Marcus strode out of the great church and forced
his way through the crowd of monks.

" What's the matter ? " he demanded sternly.

" Fursey ! " shouted a dozen voices.

The Abbot looked towards the gate ; then his eyes fell on Brother Patrick, who had recovered consciousness, but had not enough strength in his arms to raise himself from the ground. In his efforts to rise the wretched lay-brother was scratching at the ground like a dog digging a hole.

" What's wrong with Brother Patrick ? " demanded the Abbot.

" Fright," replied Father Leo.

" Some of you go and help him," commanded the Abbot.

The monks looked at one another uncertainly, but under the Abbot's fixed gaze two of the fathers stepped forward and advanced gingerly towards the gate. They lifted the prostrate lay-brother under the armpits and ran back quickly with him to the others, his feet trailing along the ground behind him. Father Sampson was with difficulty detached from the monastery bell-rope and instructed to practice his first aid on Brother Patrick.

The Abbot stood motionless gazing across the short intervening space to where Fursey lay slumped before the gate. A few of the older monks had crowded around the Abbot and were talking to him in urgent whispers.

" We all saw him ! He flew over the hill and down the road on a broom. There it is, about twenty paces down the road, can't you see it ? "

For a long time the Abbot Marcus stood silent and like a statue, while the semi-circle of monks watched breathlessly. Then the Abbot moved. Brother Cook immediately burst from the crowd and flung himself at the Abbot's feet.

" Don't let him back," he wailed. " Father Abbot, don't let him back. If you let him back, there'll be demons grinning at me from every corner of the kitchen."

The Abbot paid no heed, but advancing slowly towards the gate, he began to pull back the wooden bolts. A murmur of

horror arose from the monks. Marcus dragged the gate
open and stepped out into the road. Fursey turned up a
grimy, tear-stained face.

"Get up, Fursey," commanded the Abbot.

Fursey struggled uncertainly to his feet.

"Come with me," said the Abbot, and he led the way down
the road to a grassy bank, on which he seated himself.

"You may sit down too, Fursey," he said.

Fursey seated himself on a stone. Within the gates the
horrified monks had fallen on their knees, and Father Crustaceous was leading the prayers 'for the safety of our beloved
father, the Abbot'.

"Now tell me everything," commanded the Abbot. "Why
have you left your wife?"

Fursey's story took a long time. The shadow of approaching
night deepened on The Pilgrims' Way; a chill breeze moved
among the rushes at the river's edge and came stirring the
long grasses by the roadside. From within the monastery
gates the murmur of prayer arose and fell, and all the time
the Abbot sat motionless looking into Fursey's face as the
story was slowly unfolded. Occasionally his eyes widened
with surprise, but he spoke no word until Fursey had finished.
Then he sighed.

"So it's true," he said, "that you flew over the hill on a
broom. You admit that you're a sorcerer?"

"Yes," agreed Fursey. "I'm a sorcerer."

For a long time nothing more was said. A rabbit emerged
on the far side of the track, and stared hard at the two motionless figures before bolting again into its burrow.

At length the Abbot arose. He seemed stiff and tired.

"I can't let you into the monastery," he said, "but there's
a swineherd's hut beside the river. You can sleep there for
the night. In the morning we'll talk further."

Fursey thanked him profusely, and together they walked
down to the hut by the river. When the swineherd was
informed that Fursey was to pass the night in his hut, he
manifested a marked disinclination to remain there himself.

He volunteered to sleep out on the mountain if the monastery could not accommodate him, but the Abbot promised him a pallet within the gates, and assisted with his own hands in spreading the straw for Fursey's bed. As he and the swineherd made ready to depart, Fursey from his couch in the straw suddenly seized the Abbot's hand and kissed it. When the door closed behind them, he stretched himself on his warm, rustling bed, his face wet with happy tears.

CHAPTER VI

IN the chill, unfriendly morning when the sky was yellowing in the east, the monk whom the Abbot had despatched to Cashel on his fleetest horse, arrived back at Clonmacnoise, jaded and travel-stained, at the head of a troop of armed men. The door of the swineherd's hut was flung open, and Fursey was dragged out. He was thrown on his face, and his hands fastened behind his back with stout thongs. Fursey whimpered as he was pulled on to his feet and bundled into a high cart. The Abbot stood in the roadway, his face as if carved out of stone. Trembling, Fursey ventured to look at him.

" I must do my duty like every other man," said the Abbot. " You have admitted that you are a sorcerer. Goodbye, Fursey."

He turned and walked slowly back to the monastery while Fursey stood making little whimpering sounds as he watched the retreating figure. A soldier raised the butt of his spear and pushed Fursey on to the floor of the cart, where he lay in abject misery. The soldiers were more diffident about handling the broom. Four of them took it gingerly and quickly tied it to a second cart which had been provided for the purpose. Then the procession moved off rapidly, armed men riding before and behind.

It was a dreary journey, the cart jolting along the rocky road, mile after mile, while the sun arose, became enmeshed in patches of grey cloud and was finally lost in the overcast sky. The thin rain fell, wetting Fursey through and through. He lay prostrate on the floor of the cart, more a suffering

animal than a man, more a dumb, lifeless thing than an animal.
They paused about mid-day beneath some overhanging trees,
the soldiers crouching for shelter from the rain while they ate
ravenously their small ration of bread and stopped to drink
at a wayside well.   No one came to feed Fursey.   They
moved off again through the thin mist, the horses steaming,
their riders cursing and yanking at the bits every time they
stumbled.   Mile after weary mile was left behind, and it
was late in the evening when the exhausted cavalcade arrived
at the northern gate of Cashel.

The torchlight shone on the ruddy faces of the guards as
the wicker gates were dragged open, and the troop moved
slowly between the cabins to draw rein finally before the
cluster of monastic huts which occupied a quarter of the area
of the city.   Fursey was hoisted from the cart ; and as he
was too stiff to walk, he was carried within the enclosure,
down a flight of steps, and into a cave-like cell which had been
excavated deep in the earth.   He was flung on a crude pallet,
where he lay motionless.   His captors untied his limbs, and
closing the door behind them, left him in darkness.   Hour
after hour he lay in his wet clothes shivering with cold and
misery, until at last sleep came, and he slumbered fitfully.

On the following morning Bishop Flanagan breakfasted
heartily on eels' meat and stirabout, washed down by a
flagon of black ale.   Father Furiosus was early in attendance,
and when he had kissed the Bishop's ring, he wryly sipped
the dregs of ale which the hospitable prelate poured into a
cup for him.   A slave was despatched to the Royal House
with a message that the Bishop desired the presence of the
King.   Cormac lost no time, but came galloping in his chariot
down the hill from his own house and up the hill to the
Bishop's Palace.   Stable boys ran to hold the restive steeds
and assist the monarch to alight.   Cormac entered the Palace
and the Bishop's presence with all the dignity possible to a
man only five feet in height.   After the usual courtesies the
three seated themselves, and the Bishop broached the matter
in hand.

" I have given the affair much thought," began the prelate,
" and I have no doubt whatever but that we have in custody
a wizard of the most subtle character imaginable. Father
Furiosus and I have met this man before, and his seeming
innocence is in the highest degree deceptive. For twenty
years he has succeeded in deceiving the worthy monks at
Clonmacnoise and in convincing them that he is a man of
exemplary virtue. When I presided at his nuptials a few
days ago, having a quick capacity I did vehemently suspect
him, for I felt that such innocence and simplicity as he manifested were altogether out of the course of nature ; but I
allowed myself to be persuaded by the Abbot Marcus, whom
this odious sorcerer appears to have thoroughly befooled.
We have had ample evidence that the countryside is abounding
fearfully in witches and wizards. They will have us all
properly bedevilled unless we take immediate steps to thwart
their direful and insupportable activities. I believe this man,
Fursey, to be the Master and Prince of the satanic coven
which operates in this neighbourhood. The good God has
delivered him into our hands. Nothing remains but to
torment him as grievously as can be devised, prior to burning
him alive and scattering his ashes to the wind."

King Cormac nodded sagaciously, but deemed it wise to say
nothing until a question was addressed to him. Father
Furiosus shifted his great bulk on his stool.

" Of course," he said heavily, " the wretched man is
entitled to a fair trial."

" He'll get it," snapped the Bishop. " A fair trial and a
quick burning, but first we must sift him as wheat : he must
undergo the question, ordinary and extraordinary."

" The matter of torture hardly arises," observed the friar,
" if he admits his guilt, as I understand he does."

The Bishop's underlip began to vibrate with a curious
jerking motion as he sensed opposition.

" What about his accomplices in the monstrous and detestable art ? " he asked with acrimony. " Only by the most
prolonged and excruciating torments can we hope to wring

from him the names of the members of his coven, so that we may utterly destroy the infernal regiment and prevent thousands of innocent people being carried away to their final confusion. Don't you agree with me ? " he asked, turning sharply to the King.

" Of course, my lord," answered Cormac hurriedly.

" It needs thought," retorted Furiosus obstinately, " but first of all one of us should visit him in his cell to ascertain from his own lips whether or not he is pleading guilty to the dire charges that are laid against him. Procedure in these matters has been fixed by centuries of traditional practice, and it would ill behove us to depart from what is usual. I know that your lordship would not wish to break with the established tradition of the Church."

" Of course not," said the Bishop hastily. " God forbid ! "

" Then no doubt your lordship will wish to undertake the examination personally ? "

The Bishop stirred uncomfortably. " Is it not the case," he asked hesitantly, " that sorcerers, even when they are in custody, are sometimes dangerous to those that approach them ? "

" Sorcerers are always dangerous," replied Furiosus smoothly.

The Bishop's eyes shifted nervously from the placid face of the friar to that of King Cormac.

" I imagine," he said, " that the King, as representative of the civil arm, should undertake the holy duty of interviewing and questioning the prisoner."

" I plead to be excused," exclaimed the King. " I know nothing of witchcraft, or of how these people should be examined. Father Furiosus is experienced in these matters. He is licensed by the Synod of Kells to search for necromancers and conjurors. Surely it is but commonsense to let him conduct the proceedings, seeing that he has conducted many such examinations without hurt to himself."

" Well, Furiosus ? " said the Bishop.

" I will conduct the preliminary examination if your lordship wishes it," replied the friar, " but only on one condition."

" You presume to make conditions with me," asked the Bishop hotly.

" I do," rejoined Furiosus, pushing out his red, stubbly jowl determinedly. " I beg respectfully to remind you that I am licensed for this work by a Synod of the Church, and that I'm merely a visitor in your lordship's diocese, and as such not subject to your lordship's jurisdiction. If your lordship does not wish to make use of my services, I shall betake myself to another diocese where perhaps my work will be accorded greater appreciation."

The Bishop bent a sour gaze on the sturdy friar.

" What is the condition on which you insist ? " he enquired at last.

" I'm a man," said Furiosus, " who is not accustomed to do things by halves. If I'm to conduct the preliminary examination of this man, I must have charge of the entire proceedings—his trial, torture and execution."

For some moments the Bishop hesitated.

" Very well," he agreed grudgingly.

" Order the prisoner to be conveyed here," said Furiosus, " I'll examine him in your presence and in the presence of the King."

" But is not the proximity of a sorcerer dangerous in the extreme ? " began the Bishop.

" Not when one knows how to handle him," retorted the friar. " He should be led here with his hands tied and with an adequate armed guard."

When Fursey was dragged out of his dank cell, he stood at first blinking in the light of day while the soldiers pinioned his hands behind his back. As they led him between the huts and up the incline to the Bishop's Palace, he began to notice the motley groups of people in the streets and the unusual hubbub. A many-coloured stream of life was pouring into the settlement, for it had been noised far abroad that a

master-sorcerer had been taken. As Fursey was led past, the
crowds withdrew hastily into the shadows between the cabins,
from which they watched him with livid faces. With sick
apprehension he observed a file of men sedulously toiling up
the incline bowed beneath bundles of brushwood, which they
cast on a great pyre in the open space in front of the Bishop's
dwelling.

In the audience chamber King Cormac had taken a seat in
that corner of the room furthest from the door through
which the odious sorcerer was to be led, while Furiosus stood
boldly in the centre with his hands on his hips. The Bishop
sat on his gilded throne and fixed on Fursey a penetrating
and animated eye. Cramp seized both of Fursey's legs as he
encountered the Bishop's gaze, and he had to be supported
by a soldier on either side.

" We have a repertoire of the most exquisite tortures,"
began the Bishop in a hard metallic voice. " If you fail to
answer our questions to our satisfaction, I'll have you most
strangely tormented until your blood and marrow spout
forth in great abundance."

The hinges of Fursey's knees gave away, and he fell on the
floor. The two soldiers dragged him to his feet and held
him in an upright position facing his lordship.

" Have you ever heard of the torture of the Pilliwinckes
upon the fingers," asked the prelate, " or the binding and
wrenching of the head with cord ? "

" My lord bishop," remonstrated Father Furiosus. The
Bishop was silent as the friar stepped up to the quaking
Fursey.

" Wretched man," thundered Furiosus, " you are accused
of being one of a swarm of wizards and witches that infest
this territory and hover abroad at night in the foul and murky
air. You are accused of being a man of wonderfully evil
and pernicious example, guilty of deeds foul, unheard of, and
productive of ill. What have you to say to these accusations?"

Fursey returned the gaze of his questioner, but was unable
to speak. He was experiencing an intense weakness in all

his limbs, and a swooning sensation came over him. Father
Furiosus retired a few paces to consult with the Bishop.

" It's remarkable that he attempts no answer to these
grave charges," he said. " Most sorcerers are hot in denial.
I do remember that the Abbot Marcus told us that this man
was afflicted at one time with an impediment in his speech.
Could that be the reason for this strange silence ? "

" No," replied the Bishop. " It's perversity, or a ruse to
defeat the ends of justice."

King Cormac, who was becoming frightened in his corner
of the room, crept forward to the foot of the Bishop's throne
so as to be near the others.

" Did you ever see such a grim and ill-favoured fellow ? "
whispered the King in awestricken tones, as he gazed at the
unfortunate Fursey's moonlike face. " He has a fierce and
horrid visage. I can smell the brimstone off him."

" Indeed, he is ill-looking, dark and hideous," answered
the Bishop, " but I wouldn't expect anything else. Please
continue your examination, Father Furiosus."

The friar turned to confront Fursey once more, but it was
obvious that the latter had lost consciousness. The friar
seemed puzzled, and he contemplated the sorcerer for some
time without speaking while the two soldiers, with beads of
sweat on their foreheads, supported Fursey by the armpits.
His head hung forward on his chest, and his legs were stretched
out left and right with the heels resting on the floor.

" Has he had food since he was brought to Cashel ? " asked
Furiosus suddenly.

" No," replied one of the soldiers.

" Return him to his cell," commanded the friar, " and
keep him fed until he's wanted again."

The two soldiers dragged Fursey out, his heels rattling
across the floor. When the door had been closed, the Bishop
could no longer contain his exasperation.

" Is he not to be tortured ? " he burst out. " Not even a
taste of the *Peine Forte et Dure* ? "

" No," answered the friar shortly.

"Why not?" snarled the Bishop.

"Because I'm in charge," replied Furiosus fiercely.

The Bishop from his high throne watched venomously as the friar strode thoughtfully up and down the floor. At length the prelate spoke again, this time mildly and in carefully modulated tones.

"But is there to be no torture at all, not even a turn on the wheel? After all, we have to find his accomplices."

Father Furiosus stopped in his walk.

"My lord bishop," he said, "forgive me if I have been short in my answers, but this is a case of considerable complexity and one that requires judicious consideration. I suspect that the trial will show Fursey's sorcery to have been of a very subtle quality. I admit that I don't yet quite understand his style of villainy. We cannot proceed with the trial until the arrival from Clonmacnoise of the Abbot Marcus and of any other witnesses who may wish to testify. When Fursey has been found guilty, then will be the time for the application of the best available tortures with the object of securing the names of his confederates. If he pleads guilty and penitently names his accomplices in the Black Art, there will be no need for torture at all: we may proceed straight to the burning. If, however, he should obstinately insist on his innocence, torture will of course be necessary until he admits himself guilty of those crimes with which he is charged. So contain yourself in patience; and please trust my experience in these matters, which is considerable."

Bishop Flanagan made no answer, but gathering his robes about him, left the room.

Meanwhile Fursey had been revived by the action of the fresh air and by a bucket of water emptied over him by the soldiers, who had grown tired of carrying him; and he was proceeding feebly back to his cell. His guards untied his hands, and leaving him a pitcher of water and a crust they withdrew, fastening the door behind them. Fursey groped in the darkness until he found the pitcher. He raised it shakily and took a long draught. Then, cupping the crust in his hand he succeeded in smashing it against the stone that served him as bolster, and for some time the cell echoed to the grinding of the pieces between his teeth. When he had finished his meal he rolled himself on to his pallet and lay with his face pressed against the wall, listening dolefully to the scampering of the rats across the floor.

A few days later a distinguished stranger arrived at the southern gate of Cashel. He was dark in complexion and was dressed in an expensive sable robe, which proclaimed him a person to whom every consideration was due. When asked his name and condition, he replied that he was Apollyon, a prince of the Byzantine Empire, and that as a traveller in these parts he had been commissioned by the Emperor at Constantinople to convey the Emperor's greetings to his noble brothers, the King and Bishop of Cashel, together with sundry gifts. The dark stranger was attended by a numerous retinue, all heavily veiled, as was apparently the custom in the distant country from which they had come. The stranger's courtliness and affability won for him the good opinion of all, and this was by no means diminished when it was learned that the ox-cart in his train was loaded with boxes of gold and precious stones, the gifts of the Emperor to his good friends in Cashel. What a pity, everyone said, that such a noble and gracious gentleman should have that slight limp.

Father Furiosus watched with disapproval as two lines of porters carried the boxes of gold into the houses of the beaming King and the delighted Bishop, but a moment later the courtly stranger approached him leading on a leash a high-stepping dog of very superior pedigree.

" The special gift of the Emperor to Father Furiosus," said Apollyon with a courtly bow. " The Emperor is very well acquainted with the noble work you are doing in suppressing the hateful passion of love in this land, and he bade me present you with this sagacious animal to assist you in your labours. He is called a ' pointer ' and is trained by huntsmen to spot game. With a little further direction from you he will be an invaluable ally to you in your rambles along the roads of

Ireland. He will ' point ' the lovers in the ditches and doorways from a distance of thirty paces, and enable you to deal
with many whom you would otherwise have missed. No, do
not thank me. The Emperor graciously added that when
you have cleaned up the holy land of Ireland, he would be
pleased to welcome you to the Byzantine Empire, where the
relations between the sexes are not all that His Imperial
Majesty would wish."

The friar's ill-humour immediately vanished and, having
thanked the stranger profusely, he led the graceful hound
around to the back of the palace, where he secured for it a
comfortable habitation and a bed of clean straw. After a
sumptuous dinner in the stranger's honour the Bishop conducted his guests to the sun-room, where reclining gracefully
in intricately carved chairs, they engaged in genteel conversation. It was not long until the capture of the notorious
sorcerer, Fursey, came to be mentioned.

" The trial is fixed for tomorrow," said Bishop Flanagan,
" and will be conducted before the Canons of the Chapter,
who will be his judges."

The Prince of the Byzantine Empire immediately smote
his forehead and apologised for his forgetfulness. The
Emperor had especially charged him with the duty of conveying valuable gifts to the Canons of the Chapter of Cashel, who,
the Emperor had been informed, were the finest and stoutest
body of ecclesiastics in Christendom. Further boxes of gold
were unloaded from the ox-cart and carried to the apartments
of the joyful churchmen. Meanwhile in the sun-room of the
Bishop's Palace the mead and ale flowed freely. Furiosus
regaled the company with story after story of mighty tussles
with the forces of evil, of shifty demons battered into sub-
mission, and of noonday devils encountered by the roadside
sitting on stiles, and wrestled with during an entire afternoon.

The Bishop made from the corner of his mouth subtle
ecclesiastical jokes with a strong dogmatic flavour. King
Cormac plunged into a rambling account of one of his cam-
paigns, but fell asleep in his chair before he had it finished,

his head drooping forward on his chest and his beard covering his knees like a white apron. But the Byzantine prince outshone everyone with the brilliance of his wit and the charm of his conversation, so that at times his hearers were filled with a dazed delight. It was when the joyousness and goodfeeling of the company were at their height, that the dark stranger made his strange request.

" When I was a younger man," he said, " I practised law, and I have appeared in cases which resulted in the happy burning of as many as twenty sorcerers at a time on the banks of the Bosphorus. It would intrigue me greatly if you would allow me to enter this case and conduct the defence of this wretched man Fursey. It can do no harm : from what you tell me he is as good as ashes and cinders already ; but the clash of two legal systems and methods of procedure, that of your mighty Kingdom of Cashel and that of the Byzantine Empire, cannot but be in the highest degree instructive to us both."

The Bishop put down his ale mug suddenly and regarded Apollyon with narrowing eyes.

" The man is capable of conducting his own defence," he asserted suspiciously. " He is the slyest sorcerer imaginable."

" I don't for a moment presume to think," replied Apollyon, " that I shall be able to influence the verdict of your court. The Canons of your Chapter are obviously estimable men who are determined to see justice done, but a legal tussle with the famous Father Furiosus would afford me the greatest intellectual pleasure, as well as providing me with something of which I can boast at some future date to my children's children. What do you say, Father ? "

The friar met the stranger's eye gladly.

" I think it's an excellent idea," he said. " There's nothing I like better than a fight, mental or physical. And I have every confidence in my ability to bend back the sophistries practised in Byzantine argument and tie them into knots."

" I must withhold my approval—" began the Bishop.

" I don't care who approves," roared the friar, banging his ale-mug on the arm of his chair. "I'm in charge of this case. I appoint Prince Apollyon counsel for the defence."

The Bishop did not reply, but sat vulpine in his great chair. He drank no more that night.

On the following morning Apollyon craved permission to pay a visit to his client before the trial began. Permission was courteously accorded, and the guards conducted him to the cell, and rolled Fursey off his pallet on to the floor, so that the foreign gentleman could see him with convenience. At Apollyon's request they closed the door and left lawyer and client alone.

" Don't you know me ? " queried the Prince eagerly.

Fursey had been so many days in darkness that he could see as well as a cat. He took one look at the stranger's face and emitted a hollow groan.

" So you've come for me," he said. " Aren't you a little premature ? I'm not burnt yet."

" Come now, Fursey," answered the Devil, " get up off the floor before the rats eat you."

Fursey struggled up and sat on the edge of his pallet, sunk in the profoundest melancholy. He thought of the flames of Hell and of the flames of the pyre that was shortly to consume him, and he couldn't make up his mind which he disliked most. The Devil took his limp hand and shook it warmly.

" How are you, my dear friend ? " he asked.

" You find me in a deep despair," answered Fursey.

" Come now, where's your courage ? "

" Please don't make jokes," replied Fursey. " I'm shortly to be incinerated, and I cannot truthfully say that I regard the prospect with equanimity."

" But while there's life there's hope," urged the Devil.

" I'm glad you think so," replied Fursey gloomily. " Will you please go away and leave me to be burnt in peace."

The Devil appeared to be deeply moved. He seated himself on the pallet and took Fursey's arm impulsively.

" Have confidence in me," he said earnestly. " I will never desert you."

Fursey glanced up at him, and seemed to become even more depressed.

" It looks as if that's the way it's going to be," he answered huskily.

The Devil shook his head reprovingly. " I don't know how a man of your intelligence allowed himself to be caught," he said. " Why didn't you order your familiar to thicken and obscure the air about you ? By his familiar's workmanship upon the atmosphere a wizard may remain unespied."

" It's a long story," answered Fursey. " Anyway, my familiar is no good. He's always thinking of himself. He suffers from a raging thirst."

" Hm ! " said the Devil. He was silent for a while ; then he cocked a sympathetic eye at Fursey's honest visage. " I suppose you know," he said, " that your trial is due to commence at noon."

" What ! " ejaculated Fursey, " as soon as that ! "

" They have assembled an imposing battery of witnesses," continued the Prince of Darkness, " not that it makes much difference. I never knew a man or a woman tried for sorcery who didn't end by going up in smoke."

" You needn't keep harping on it," replied Fursey irritably.

" Trust me," said the Devil, " I have been commissioned with your defence."

" Oh my God ! " said Fursey, and he spoke no more.

" You may wonder," continued Satan, " why I concern myself on your behalf at all. Well, firstly, I feel myself in your debt for the hospitality, unwilling though it was, which you extended to myself and the boys in your cell at Clonmacnoise. Secondly, I have a strong personal affection for yourself. Thirdly, I have every hope that now that you have become a wizard, you will view in a more favourable light that little business proposition of mine relative to the sale of your soul. Fourthly and lastly, I'm determined to get the better of these clerical jugglers. I'm particularly down on his lordship the Bishop Flanagan. I'm going to harry that man exceedingly before I leave this city. Mark my words," added the Devil darkly, " when that man finishes his career in this world and gets to Hell, the first thing he'll do is found a Vigilance Society. He'll have us all properly pestered with complaints about the nudity of the damned and the like, as if anyone could expect clothing to survive in that temperature. He'll still be trying to alter the machinery of creation, like he does in this world."

The Devil brooded darkly for a few moments. " As if Hell wasn't bad enough already," he muttered. " As it is, I'm bored stiff most of the time. But come, Fursey, why are you so sunk in gloom ? Be not moved to fear. The hour of battle is at hand ; and the victory is not to the strong, but to the crafty."

Fursey did not answer, so the Devil arose with a sigh, patted him kindly on the shoulder and took his leave.

It was high noon. In the Chapter House the Canons had assembled, rotund men with placid, proud faces. The Civil Service sat on their two little stools, their filing cabinets of wax tablets piled about them, the younger Civil Service looking demure and shabby, the older pompous and self-important. King Cormac sat in his chair, his beard freshly brushed and powdered, and his chubby face screwed up into an expression of extreme sagacity. To one side stood Prince Apollyon, unassuming, courtly and civilised ; while over against him the stalwart Furiosus had taken his stand, clutching his blackthorn stick as if he suspected that someone present might presume to contradict him. On a bench against the wall amongst those who were to testify, sat the Abbot Marcus, his face gentle and meditative. Beside him sat Cuthbert, the sexton of Kilcock Churchyard, his eyes turned up to Heaven and his lips moving in silent prayer to the great edification of all. Three monks were present from Clonmacnoise, Father Crustaceous, Father Placidus and Father Sampson, their folded arms expressing their determination to do their duty. The broom on which Fursey had made his ill-fated journey was clamped to a table in the centre of the hall. Beside it lay a goat's horns and a long dun beard, while at the other end of the table was a board on which were stretched the bedraggled corpses of four ducks. At the far end of the room there was an interesting display of wheels, thumbscrews, charcoal braziers and other instruments which might be required by the counsel for the prosecution ; and alongside was a comfortable couch for the convenience of the prisoner and his questioners. Two sallow gentlemen in holy orders presided over that part of the arrangements. Bishop Flanagan sat remote from everyone, high up on his great mauve, gold and purple throne, his chin resting on his hand, his gaunt, ascetic face intent.

A shudder of expectancy passed through the assembly as the doors were thrown open, and the entire armed forces of Cashel in a solid phalanx marched into the room. In obedience to a ringing command four soldiers stepped smartly to one side, and it was seen that Fursey was in the midst loaded down to the ground with chains. Two blacksmiths came forward and riveted the hanging pieces of chain to the floor with iron spikes. Although it was generally believed that a sorcerer was bereft of his powers while in the hands of lawful authority, it was thought wise in the present instance, in view of the fearsome reputation of the prisoner, to forestall any attempt on his part to escape by flying through the smoke-hole in the roof.

The moment he entered the hall Fursey's eyes fastened themselves on the array of peculiar instruments at the far end of the room. The two hard-featured clerics who presided there, returned his gaze impassively.

" How do you feel ? " whispered the Prince of the Byzantine Empire.

" I wish I was elsewhere," muttered Fursey, without turning his head.

The reading of the indictment passed unheard by Fursey, and it was only when he was ordered to plead guilty or not guilty that he managed to tear away his eyes from the array of instruments and look at his questioner. His gaze wandered from the full-blooded face of the friar across to the smug faces of the Canons, then up to the lean visage of the Bishop. He shuddered ; then his eye fell on the row of witnesses, and he recognised Abbot Marcus. The Abbot had his face averted and was looking at the floor.

" Guilty," said Fursey.

Father Furiosus shot out a huge fist covered with ginger down. His forefinger snapped out and pointed straight at Fursey.

" You admit that you are a sorcerer ? "

" Yes. I'm a sorcerer."

" I object," interjected the Byzantine Prince.

" Sit down," said the friar, " you can't object at this stage."

" Why not ? " queried Apollyon determinedly.

" Because the prosecution does not accept the prisoner's plea," replied the friar. " His guilt must be proved. Witnesses have come here at great trouble and expense, and they can't be sent home again after a trial lasting only six minutes. Anyway, the accused is entitled to a fair trial."

Apollyon appeared to meditate for some moments, then he sat down without a word.

" If the accused should be found not guilty after the evidence has been considered," conceded the friar, " we will start again at the beginning and accept his plea of guilty. First witness."

The first witness proved to be a shepherd clad inadequately in a yard-and-a-half of sacking. He testified to happenings of a diabolical character in the neighbourhood of The Gray Mare's cabin, sundry lightnings, and barbarous and discordant screams. He was followed by Cuthbert, who left his coat open so that the court might appreciate the fact that he was wearing a hair-shirt. Cuthbert, it appeared, had been startled from his prayers by the hubbub at the old woman's cottage, and on coming out into his yard to investigate, he had been nearly knocked down by the sudden descent of Fursey on a broom. When he had sought refuge in his cottage and bolted the door, the baffled Fursey had cast a malignant spell and slain everything within its ambit. The sexton burst into tears as he contemplated the four stricken ducks. A murmur of sympathy ran around the hall.

"How precious to him are a poor man's possessions," muttered Canon Pomponius.

Other witnesses testified to finding the murdered body of The Gray Mare. The three monks from Clonmacnoise swore to having seen Fursey capering and ambling through the air on a broomstick up to the very gates of the settlement. Lastly, the Abbot Marcus arose and in dry, colourless words answered the questions that were put to him by Father Furiosus. Yes, the prisoner had told him a long, rambling story, in the course of which he had freely admitted that he was a sorcerer and had practised sorcery. The Abbot's voice sounded through the room like a dull bell, cold and toneless. Not once did he glance at Fursey. At the other end of the hall the two grim-visaged clerics, who had been listening intently to all that was said, began to lay out additional instruments and to test their machinery, watched by Fursey with a disturbed and unquiet eye. Suddenly Bishop Flanagan's voice inserted itself between the friar's questions and the Abbot's mechanical answers.

"We have heard enough," he announced, his words falling like metallic drops. "The wretched man is a very synthesis of deformities. Let us proceed at once to break him on the wheel and tear his flesh from his bones with hooks of iron."

A murmur of approval passed along the benches. When Fursey recovered his breath, he glanced agonisingly at his lawyer. Apollyon shook his head dolefully.

"You're in a tight corner," he whispered, "but I have a card up my sleeve yet."

Abbot Marcus did not resume his seat. "My lord bishop," he said, " I have not finished. It is but proper that I should relate to you the story that this poor man, your prisoner, told me when he admitted his sorcery."

Cuthbert stirred uneasily on his seat and threw a covert look at Apollyon who immediately glanced away. From the moment he had first espied the Byzantine Prince in the court, Cuthbert had manifested a slight uneasiness and the appearance of being puzzled. The two had glanced at one another frequently during the proceedings, but had not once met one another's eyes. It was as if two armed, but mutually neutral, powers had for the first time discovered that there was a point at which their interests clashed, and each seemed to feel embarrassment.

The court listened spellbound while the Abbot Marcus repeated Fursey's story in simple, telling words. Cuthbert's face expressed bewildered indignation as the tale of his sorceries was unfolded. Father Furiosus was the only one who manifested impatience. When the Abbot had finished he could contain himself no longer.

" Of all the absurd stories," he burst out. " It was clearly demonstrated at the water-trial which I myself conducted a week ago, that this much-maligned woman, The Gray Mare, was innocent of the charge of witchcraft. Anyone who doubts it, flies in the face of the whole body of canon law and sacred tradition, and is little better than a heretic."

The friar glanced fiercely from face to face as if to challenge anyone to contradict him, but no one seemed interested in The Gray Mare ; all eyes were bent on Cuthbert. The Bishop's nostrils had widened, and when he spoke, his voice was as smooth as silk.

" What has our honest friend Cuthbert to say to these charges which the prisoner has levelled against him ? "

The sexton fell upon his knees and, throwing his eyes to Heaven, called on all the saints in the calendar as witnesses of his innocence. He tore open his coat to show that he was the wearer of a hair-shirt ; and struggling to his feet, he raised his robe so that all might see the horniness of his knees from frequent praying. Never had such a wicked charge, he said, been preferred against a good man. Was further proof needed of the execrable Fursey's guilt ?

Not a muscle moved in the rows of white faces that were bent upon the sexton. At length Father Furiosus spoke.

" Was not this the man who laid the charge of witchcraft against the saintly Gray Mare ? "

There was a nodding of bald heads.

" And was not this the man against whom the saintly Gray Mare laid a countercharge of sorcery ? "

There was a further nodding of heads.

" And that charge is now corroborated by the story of the prisoner. My lord bishop," said the friar with finality, turning to the great gilt throne, " this matter requires further investigation."

" Why ? " asked the Bishop mildly. " Is it not an accepted principle in witchcraft proceedings that where doubt exists, one should convict. The Church's point of view is happily summed up in the well-known phrase : ' Burn all ; God will distinguish His own '."

" That is true," agreed the friar.

" There is an excellent pyre erected outside my palace," continued the Bishop. " It can easily accommodate two."

Cuthbert emitted a forlorn groan as if to express his opinion of human depravity, and once more cast up his eyes to Heaven ; but this time he was careful to note the exact position of the smoke-hole in the roof. Help came, however, from an unexpected quarter. The Byzantine Prince was once more on his feet.

" I object," he said.

" Sit down," commanded the friar.

" I won't sit down," replied Apollyon hotly. " I object."

" You can't object," retorted Furiosus.

" What about the defence ? " asked Apollyon shrilly.

" What defence ? Your client has been proved guilty."

Apollyon swung away from Furiosus and faced the Bishop and the assembled clergy.

" My lord and very reverend fathers," he cried, " my client is not a sorcerer. The unfortunate Fursey has had an experience which few of us would wish to undergo, he has become possessed by a devil. And this devil, intent on the innocent Fursey's destruction, speaks through his mouth and proclaims him a sorcerer, just as he pours forth hideous lies damaging to the character of this good man, the sexton Cuthbert."

A wavelet of excitement stirred in the hall. The Abbot Marcus rose to his feet and for the first time looked across at Fursey. Then he turned to the Bishop and spoke with agitation.

"This may well be," he said. "It would explain much. I can vouch that Fursey has been all his life an exemplary monk. A man does not all at once turn to wickedness."

Cuthbert was quick to see his advantage. "It's very likely true," he cried. "When Fursey came careering into my yard on the broomstick, he swayed uncertainly as if the control did not rest in his own will, but in some force hidden in the dark depths within. And this extraordinary fabrication of lies about me is surely not the invention of a simple monk, but of a demon of more than ordinary wickedness and wile."

Father Furiosus seemed momentarily thrown off his balance by the quick turn of events and by the change in mood of those present. While he hesitated, Apollyon addressed the assembly in ringing tones.

"During the recent haunting of Clonmacnoise," he cried, "when devils abounded in every hole and corner, my client had the misfortune to inhale a demon of a particularly mischievous and mendacious character, who now possesses him utterly. In Fursey himself there is no guile. He is deserving of your tears, not your reprobation."

"Have you known of such cases?" queried the Bishop, turning to Furiosus.

"They're quite common," replied the friar shortly. "I knew an Archdeacon once who swallowed a demon in a lettuce. But if this man is possessed, I'll soon rid him of his tormentor."

"What are they going to do to me now?" quavered Fursey, as he saw the friar rolling up his sleeves.

" It's all right," hissed Apollyon in his ear. " It'll hurt, but it's far better than being burnt."

The Bishop did not seem to like the turn of events, but he said nothing as the friar ordered the two blacksmiths to unloosen Fursey from the floor. Furiosus then took Fursey by the arm and led him gently but firmly to the end of the room where the two hard-featured clerics were sorting out their instruments.

" Don't worry," he said kindly, as he gripped Fursey firmly by the shoulders. " I'll have that noisome devil out in no time."

" You won't hurt me ? " whimpered Fursey.

" No," replied Furiosus, surprised. " I won't hurt *you*. I'll only hurt the devil that possesses you. Open your mouth wide, and keep it open."

The friar shouted a litany of prayers down Fursey's throat, and then three times adjured the devil to come forth. Nothing happened. All present had crowded around and gave sundry advice, which the friar shook off impatiently. He commanded that the doors be left wide open so that the devil might find a ready exit ; and he advised that all should keep their mouths tightly closed lest the demon discover a refuge, and he would have to go through the whole exorcism again. The onlookers needed no second warning, but stood with their lips tightly compressed. King Cormac made doubly certain by covering his mouth with both hands. Prince Apollyon followed the proceedings with the greatest interest. In fact, everyone was pleasantly thrilled except Fursey.

" The essence of the operation," explained Father Furiosus, " is to make the body of the possessed person such an uncomfortable habitation that even the most obstinate demon does not care to remain in it."

Fursey heard this speech with dismay, and he was further disquieted when he saw the two sallow clerics come forward and take their places on either side of the friar.

" I want to give warning," continued Furiosus, " that there will be much fracas when I draw forth the foul and unclean spirit. He will be in the highest degree evil-smelling and may box the ears of some of those present, but no matter what buffets you must endure, stand your ground and do not withdraw. The strength of the possessed person may well exceed the strength of the weightiest Canons of the Chapter, so you must all be ready to fling yourselves on this unfortunate man and hold him down while I draw forth the confused demon. The first method I shall attempt is that of fumigation."

One of the lantern-jawed assistants handed the friar a salver of white powder. Furiosus applied a taper and held the burning material under Fursey's nose. Fursey sneezed several times, and the tears ran down his cheeks while the friar with much muttering and murmuring attempted to draw the demon from his nostrils. This method proved unsuccessful, and on the friar's instructions a tub was filled with water. Fursey showed exemplary patience as he was deftly stripped and immersed.

" We may get the demon out by the fear of drowning," explained Furiosus, " but the subject must be held completely under the surface lest the demon seek refuge in his hair."

Several of the bystanders ventured to open their lips to mutter from the corners of their mouths that it was all most interesting, and that there could be no doubt but that Father Furiosus was a most well-informed and experienced man. When a few minutes later Fursey was lifted from the tub and laid on the couch in a half-drowned condition, they crowded around, anxious to miss nothing. Furiosus expanded his chest and addressed his audience once more.

" Indeed, this is a most stubborn demon," he said. " We must apply fire to the subject's feet."

When a moment later Fursey emitted a bloodcurdling, sub-human howl, a thrill of excitement passed through the onlookers.

" At last," said the friar with satisfaction, " we have made contact with the demon, and it is evident that he does not

like our attentions," and he distributed cudgels to six of the
sturdiest present. Between them they gave Fursey many
sore strokes, but in spite of his screams and harrowing con-
tortions, the demon would not come forth. They ceased their
good work at last through pure weariness, and Fursey's cries
died away in a whine of despair.

" Indeed, he is troubling you sorely," said the friar, bending
over Fursey sympathetically. Fursey returned his gaze with
eyes dull and glazed.

" Carry him to his cell," commanded the friar. " It is
grown late in the afternoon. Let his wounds be searched in
the best manner. Tomorrow we will try breaking him on
the wheel."

Fursey was carried out by four soldiers, and the company
broke up, congratulating each other on their interesting and
informative day.

CHAPTER VII

IT is usual to complete a day of arduous religious duties with a solemn banquet. When the foods and wines had been transferred from the sweating tables to the capacious ecclesiastical stomachs, and the guests were reclining on the rush-strewn floor about the great fire in the Bishop's dining hall, Apollyon announced that it was incumbent on him to leave Cashel on the morrow and continue his journey. The other guests were too replete to argue with him, so they contented themselves with murmuring their regrets and continued dreamily cracking walnuts between their teeth. Apollyon obtained permission to pay a last visit to his client, and left the fire-lit room alone. When he reached the street, he summoned one of his veiled attendants, who was on duty at the ox-cart.

"Be prepared to vanish, ox-cart and all," he told the rest of his entourage, "immediately on my return."

He then made his way between the huts closely attended by his cloaked and veiled companion. When he reached the flight of steps that led underground to Fursey's cell, the soldiers on guard, who had already experienced the foreign gentleman's generosity, hurried forward to open the gates. Apollyon paused to congratulate them on the care they were taking of their prisoner, and distributed a few chunks of gold which he withdrew from the depths of his pocket. When he reached the noisome cell in which Fursey was confined, he found the demoniac sitting on the edge of his pallet dolefully examining the blackened skin and blisters on the soles of his feet. He greeted Fursey heartily.

"Well," he said, "we can congratulate ourselves on our resounding victory."

"Ay," replied Fursey colourlessly.

"Why are you so morose?" asked the Devil warmly. "You're alive, aren't you, unburnt?"

"Yes," replied Fursey, "but I think that most of my bones are broken."

"Tut, tut," said the Devil. "I never knew such a complaining fellow. It's nothing to what they propose to do to you to-morrow."

Fursey looked at him, but said nothing.

"They're determined to get that devil out of you. They're going to break you on the wheel to begin with, and then they'll proceed to tear you in all parts of your body with red-hot pincers. If the demon still obstinately refuses to quit your body in spite of the dire tortures to which he is subjected, they will have to dig for him."

"What do you mean, 'dig for him'?"

"Disembowelling," replied the Devil.

"But can't you explain to them," suggested Fursey anxiously, "that all this vast expenditure of labour will avail them nought, as I haven't got a devil."

"If they can't find a devil after thoroughly searching you, they'll conclude that their first diagnosis must have been correct, and they'll burn you as a wizard."

"I see," said Fursey.

"I'm told," remarked the Devil, "that a sorcerer in the fire feels only the calm ecstacy of purification and deliverance as the flames devour his body."

"I hope you're right," responded Fursey, without much conviction.

"Don't worry," declared the Devil. "I have a plan."

"No, thank you," rejoined Fursey. "I'd rather be disembowelled. I don't think you're a man whose judgment can be trusted."

"Don't be silly," replied Satan, "I can effect your escape."

" That's all very well," replied Fursey, " but will I survive the project ? "

" Of course," asserted the Devil, stepping aside. " Look."

" Who's that behind you ? " asked Fursey suspiciously, as he peered at the cloaked figure in the shadows.

" One of my faithful servants, who will now exchange clothes with you and so enable you, in the guise of my attendant, to effect your departure from this melancholy abode."

" It's very nice of your faithful servant," replied Fursey, " but what happens when they find him in the morning ? Has he no objection to being disembowelled in my stead ? "

" Your substitute, who by the way is a lady, will vanish shortly after you and I gain the street, and in the morning when they come to look for you, the cell will be empty."

" Oh, so she's a demon," observed Fursey with distaste.

A shrill feminine voice came from behind the veil.

" I'm not a demon," it said testily. " I'm an elemental."

" That's all right, Gertie," said the Devil soothingly. " He didn't mean any offence."

Satan seated himself beside Fursey and rubbed his hands with satisfaction.

" I'd better explain," he said. " Take off your cloak and veil, Gertie, and let the gentleman see you."

Gertie did as she was bid and disclosed an attractive young woman of considerable embonpoint, daintily clad in the prevailing fashion.

" The stench in this place is something awful," she remarked acidly.

" To the best of my recollection," said the Devil, turning to Fursey, " I've already informed you that certain of the ecclesiastics known to us both fill me with a strong distaste. In particular I don't relish that vulpine bishop at all. I think he's about due for a very thorough harrowing, and I'm going to set the matter in train to-night. Now, it's not easy for a demon to harrow an ecclesiastic who is quick with the holy water and the Latin adjurations. Many of my nimblest demons have been worsted in such an encounter and bear the marks of the struggle to the present day.   So I've borrowed four frisky elementals, who, as they are many thousand years older than Christianity, are quite unaffected by holy water, adjuration or exorcism ; and I've instructed them carefully in the principles of infestation and temptation.   Gertie here is a specimen.   Isn't she lovely ? "

" Don't judge all sylphs by me," interjected Gertie bitterly. " I had a figure once, but what he's done to the four of us in the way of exaggerating our curves passes all belief.   I always said the Devil had no taste."

" Now Gertie, don't start complaining again," retorted the Prince of Darkness.   " You'll all get your figures back when the job is done.   I've explained to you till I'm worn out that the clergy's conception of women, both physically and mentally, is a conception of something which doesn't exist in this world.   To tempt them properly and efficiently you must appear to them as they conceive women to be.   The moment the operation is complete I'll restore your figures to the four of you, and you can wander off to your woods and streams, the sweet, slender creatures that you always were."

" I hope there'll be no mistakes when you're turning us back," was Gertie's acid retort as she looked down in disgust at her plump hips.

" Come on," said the Devil, " we've wasted enough time already.   Strip off, Fursey, and exchange clothes with the lady.   You can turn your face to the wall and throw your clothes over your shoulder if you're bothered by the virtue of modesty."

" I don't think I like the plan," said Fursey.

" So you'd prefer to be disembowelled and burnt ? "

" No," responded Fursey glumly, and he turned his face to the wall.   As he took off his habit he felt in the pocket the little box of ointment which he had taken from The Gray Mare's cabin.   Reflecting that it was his only possession, he pulled it out and laid it on the bed.

" Here," said the Devil, " put these on."

" I don't know how women's clothes go on."

" I'll help you," said Satan impatiently.

In a few moments Fursey was dressed, the Devil hooking him dexterously down the back and helping him into the sylph's cloak and veil.   Fursey picked up the box of ointment and after some struggling with the unaccustomed clothes, found a small pocket into which it fitted nicely.   Meanwhile, Gertie, wearing his tattered habit and sandals, had stretched herslf on the pallet.   The Devil shouted for the guard, and when the door was opened, the two conspirators passed out and up the narrow steps into the open air.

" What are you walking like that for ? " hissed the Devil. " Do you want to attract everyone's attention ? "

" I can't help limping," replied Fursey indignantly, " with the soles nearly burnt off my feet."

" There's no need for you to limp with both feet at the same time," retorted the Archfiend.   " It looks awful.   I never saw anything like it.   It looks as if both your knees were broken."

" I'll try walking on my toes," replied Fursey miserably.

It was dark in the street at first, but a round, jolly-faced moon came sailing from behind a cloud, flooding the open space with mellow light.

" Come into the shadow," whispered the Devil.

Fursey stood shivering against the gable of a cottage while the Devil gave him his final directions.

" Go up the hill past the King's House.   You'll meet less people that way.   Keep in the shadow of the houses.   The palisade of the city runs along by the King's House.   You must get over it somehow."

" How ? " interjected Fursey.

" By ingenuity," answered the Fiend impatiently.   " Once you're across it, you're out of the city.   If you turn to the left, you will come to the northern road ; if you turn to the right, you will soon reach the road that leads to the south."

" Which way will I go ? " asked Fursey.

" How do I know which way you'll go ? " replied the Devil irritably.   " That's your affair.   Go now, and go quickly ;

for you've one thing to remember. The moment Gertie decides to vanish from your cell, her clothes which you're wearing will vanish too. And let me tell you, it'll be no joke for you if they catch you in a Christian city like this scampering around in your pelt. You'll have to face a charge of indecent exposure as well as charges of murder and witchcraft, and I don't know that the authorities don't look on it as worse. Goodbye now, and go quickly."

As the Devil vanished in a delicate thread of smoke, Fursey glanced around fearfully. The moonlight lay on the roofs of the huts and the cabins, giving the entire settlement a ghostly character. The shadows of the houses lay squat and square across the silvery road. Fursey gulped and set off, hobbling rapidly in the direction that the Devil had indicated, pausing hesitantly before he ventured to cross each patch of moonlit street. He stopped once to crouch in a doorway as a drunken townsman passed him singing heartbrokenly about the beauty of love. Otherwise the streets seemed deserted : the hour was late ; good people, no doubt, were at home and in bed. As the moon drifted coyly behind a downy cloud, Fursey uttered a sigh of thankfulness and limped quickly up the incline towards the King's House. He was skirting the King's backyard when the sound of someone humming a gay, little air made him press himself back against the wall, where he stood, not daring to breathe. He heard footsteps slowly approaching, and a moment later a small figure turned the corner. It was King Cormac, back from the Bishop's banquet, full to the gills with wine, out for a saunter up and down his yard before going to bed. Fursey uttered a prayer that he would not be seen, but it must be that a wizard's prayers are obnoxious to Heaven, for at that moment the moon began to come out again smilingly from behind her cloud, as if she and Fursey were playing a game. As the shadows crept back before the light, Fursey glanced around him desperately. In a moment the moonlight would reach him. He made out the outline of a doorway behind him, and quickly lifting the latch, he disappeared into the interior, closing the door gently behind him. Breathlessly he watched through a crevice as Cormac sauntered unsteadily up and down the yard in the best of good humour, stroking his beard and telling himself jokes, but a moment later Fursey was startled by a rustling of wings in his rear. He threw a frightened glance in the direction from which the sound had come, and realised with a sinking heart that he was in the Royal poultry house. A monotonous clucking began in the darkness, and in a moment every hen and fowl had awakened and was clucking and cackling indignantly at the intruder. Fursey pressed his face against the door and gazed out in terror through the crevice to see whether the King had heard. Yes, Cormac had heard, and evidently believing that some dishonourable fellow was stealing his hens, had drawn his sword and was creeping towards the poultry house on tiptoe.

The door was flung open, and Cormac stood with his sword at the ready, the fire of battle in his eyes.

" Come out," he commanded.

Fursey emerged without a word.

" Ha ! " said the King. " A wench. Exactly what was needed to finish a perfect day."

He returned his sword to its sheath and stood beaming at Fursey. Then he laid his hand on Fursey's arm. " Come around the corner of the house," he whispered, " there's a seat there."

" What for ? " asked Fursey.

The King nudged him playfully. " As if you didn't know," he said.

Fursey followed the King apprehensively around the corner of the house and seated himself on the edge of the bench.

" You seem to be bad on the feet," remarked Cormac as he sat down in close proximity. " Have you been drinking too ? "

He went off into a fit of convulsive laughter at this jest, and Fursey managed to conjure up a feeble grin with the object of keeping the King in good humour. Then Cormac

plunged into a rambling account of the evening's festivities,
every sentence borne on a wave of wine fumes, which he
exhaled as a dragon does its fiery breath ; but Fursey scarcely
listened. He was too worried at the possibility of being
seduced. At last the King was silent, and Fursey cautiously
turning his head, observed that Cormac was watching him
roguishly. A moment later the monarch had slipped an arm
around his waist. Fursey withdrew as far as it was possible
to do so, without falling off the bench.

" A high-born gentleman like you wouldn't take advantage
of a poor girl," pleaded Fursey, pitching his voice to a shrill
falsetto in keeping with his character as a lady.

" Wouldn't I now ? " rejoined Cormac, stroking his moustaches in a very dashing fashion. " You don't know the sort
of fellow I am."

" If you don't behave yourself, I'll scream," declared
Fursey in a cracked treble.

" What are you afraid of ? " asked the King. " There are
none of the clergy around."

" I'm a decent girl," asserted Fursey.

" That's what they all say," grinned the King, " but I
know better."

Fursey's brain simmered as he laboured to find a solution
to his present predicament, but almost before he realised it,
the situation resolved itself.

" You've a lovely face," murmured the King, bending
forward, a tremor of emotion in his voice. He raised a be-
jewelled hand and gently drew back Fursey's hood, advancing
at the same time his white bewhiskered visage with the
evident intention of planting on Fursey's cheek a chaste kiss,
but at the sight of Fursey's close-cropped head of white,
stubbly hair he stopped petrified. The arm encircling
Fursey's waist stiffened with terror. For a moment he
stared at Fursey, then his voice came out of his throat in a
horrified hiccough.

" The sorcerer ! The demoniac ! Maybe both ! "

It was borne in powerfully on Fursey that it was time to betake himself elsewhere. He arose quickly and ran around the corner of the building, pulling his hood over his ears as he ran. The fascinated King came staggering after him. In front was the palisade, but against it leaned a man-at-arms, idly sharpening the head of his spear. He glanced up quickly as Fursey approached ; then his eyes fell on the King, who had reached the corner, but whose legs would take him no further. For once Fursey's little share of wit stood by him. He walked coolly up to the soldier.

"Here, fellow," he pronounced in ringing, feminine tones. "Help me over the stockade."

The surprised soldier glanced from Fursey to the frozen figure of King Cormac in the shadow of the building. Fursey turned and waved his plump hand daintily in the King's direction.

"Goodbye, my love," he shrilled.

Cormac staggered and leaned unsteadily against the wall, still incapable of speech ; but the guard appeared to notice nothing untoward. A sly smile spread slowly over his honest visage.

"I understand, my lady," he said knowingly. "You don't want to be seen leaving by the front."

The soldier bent his shoulder and in a moment had hoisted Fursey on to the top of the palisade. Fursey squirmed uncomfortably on the tips of the sharpened stakes, but the solder lent a willing hand to disentangle his dress, which was caught in the thorns and spikes. It was at this moment that Fursey's clothing suddenly vanished, leaving him struggling on the top of the stockade completely naked. The sudden disappearance of a charming, well-dressed lady and the unaccountable substitution of a small, plump, white-headed man in the buff was too much for the soldier. He immediately took to his heels, and King Cormac, who saw no reason for remaining, joined him in his flight. The two of them ran hell-for-leather around the building, and Fursey, who had fallen on the far side of the palisade, only paused to pick up his box of ointment before making off as fast as his legs could carry him in the opposite direction. He had run down the incline and half-way up the opposite hill before he paused to consider in which direction he should go. He stood trying to recover his breath as he stared at the settlement below him and at the two white roads that led north and south. The northern road led to Clonmacnoise. For a long time he stood uncertain. He thought of the peace which he had once known in the cloister, and he remembered the gates closed in his face. Still he hesitated. Then he remembered the Abbot Marcus as he had stood in the roadway in the cold, early-morning light when Fursey had been pinioned by the soldiers and thrown into the high cart. He saw the Abbot's face again, hard, as if carved out of stone ; and a cold flood of water seemed to flow over Fursey's heart. He turned his back to Clonmacnoise and slowly made his way to the moonlit road that crept away over the hills towards the south.

* * *

It was late in the night when the Bishop's serving men helped the last guest into his cloak and persuaded him to go home. Bishop Flanagan stood in the doorway of his dining hall and eyed with distaste the overturned goblets and the scattered remnants of food that lay on the tables and floor. Father Furiosus who was in residence at the Palace, was the only one left. He sat crouched over the fire, his wine-flushed face reflecting the leaping flames, whistling meditatively the notes of one of the more popular hymns.

" The worst of these banquets," declared the Bishop, " is that there are always some few of the fathers who manifest a marked disinclination to go home. I thought I'd never get rid of Canon Pomponius. He attempted to sing his way through the entire Seven Penitential Psalms in the hall. I had to send two of my houseboys home with him lest he be an occasion of scandal to the neighbourhood."

The friar interrupted his whistling for a moment.

"I never saw a man with a goodlier appetite for wine," he averred.

"I am not myself a wine-bibber, as you have no doubt observed," remarked the Bishop frigidly. "It disagrees with my stomach."

"You might be a better man if you were," replied the friar mildly, and he re-commenced his whistling.

"I think it's time for bed," said the Bishop, lifting a torch from its bracket. Father Furiosus arose and stretched his huge frame until the joints cracked.

"It was a massive feast," he remarked regretfully as he followed the prelate to the door, the nutshells that littered the floor cracking pleasantly beneath their feet. They made their way along the dim corridor to the sleeping apartments. The Bishop's room adjoined, but was beyond that which Father Furiosus occupied. In fact, the only entrance to the prelate's chamber was through the room in which the friar slept. When they entered the first room, Father Furiosus wandered across to his bed and stretching himself again, opened his mouth to emit a yawn like the roar of a young lion. When Bishop Flanagan had lit the rushlight by the friar's bed from the torch which he carried, he paused at his own door and stood watching the friar's tonsils vibrating in the torchlight. When the yawn was finished, and the friar had closed his mouth, the Bishop addressed him.

"Do you remember during the trial this afternoon," he asked, "it was asserted that a witch could only die if she succeeded in breathing her unholy powers into someone else? Can that be altogether true? After all, a witch is successfully disposed of at the stake."

"Cases vary," replied the friar, "but it has been proved to be true in many instances. Witches, however, may always be destroyed by fire or by drowning. That's why the Church and the secular authority always insist on execution by fire, so as to make certain of the witch's destruction."

"Yes, of course," agreed the Bishop. "The assertion of the demoniac Fursey, that detestable powers were breathed

into him by the old woman so that she might find relief from
her pains in death has been exercising my mind ever since.
That's why I asked you."

Father Furiosus had drawn his habit over his head preparatory to retiring, and his voice came out muffled by its
folds.

" The story told by the devil who possesses Fursey, was
logical and correct," he answered, " but fortunately we know
that The Gray Mare was not a witch."

The Bishop remembered that The Gray Mare's innocence
was a point on which Father Furiosus felt strongly, so he did
not pursue the matter further.

" Good night," he said.

" Good night, my lord," replied the friar, hanging his habit
on the back of the door.

In his own room Bishop Flanagan lit the rushlight on the
table beside his bed and extinguished the torch by pressing it
against the earthen floor.   Then he knelt to say his prayers,
which were tedious and protracted.   He had not been praying
for very long before he heard the friar's snores reverberating
in the neighbouring room.   He shook his head disapprovingly.
The fact that Father Furiosus was already asleep meant that
the friar's prayers had been brief, even if fervent. Bishop
Flanagan continued on his knees for an hour, ending with a
stern petition for a recall to their duty of those of his flock
who were in arrears with their contributions to their pastors.
At length he arose and turning down the bedclothes, drew
back the undersheet.   He took from the table by his bedside
a small shovel, and from a corner of the room he shovelled up
a heap of smooth stones that were neatly piled there.   These
he distributed judiciously beneath the sheet on which he was
to lie.   Such was the nightly practice of this godly man so as
to mortify the flesh, lest unawares he should fall into the sin
of luxury.   When this pious operation was completed, he
undressed himself and assumed a long nightshirt composed
of crude linen and horsehair, which modestly covered his
person from his ears to his heels.   Then he clambered gingerly

on to his hard couch and drawing the blankets over him, composed himself for sleep.

With his long, lank neck stretched on the pillow the Bishop had passed into the happy, dreamy state between waking and sleeping, when from ever so far away the sound of soft music came seeping into his consciousness. The music was sweet, and the Bishop's thin lips jerked with sleepy satisfaction and appreciation. The soft, insidious air increased in volume, the melody swaying from something that was very near to heartbreak, back through tones that came falling prettily, little golden notes that dropped one by one. The prelate moved his head restlessly on the pillow, and the corners of his mouth came apart in a happy grin as the memory of Prince Apollyon's gift of gold now in his cellar came creeping in upon his mind. The music swelled in a voluptuous curve, and fell ; and from nowhere there crept in on the harp notes a woman's singing voice, laden with sweetness.

Bishop Flanagan sat up in bed suddenly, his heart pounding with terror. There could be no doubt about it : the music and the cloying voice filled the room. Could it be that there was a woman in his palace ? He stretched out his arm and taking the flint from the table by his bedside, struck it and lit the rushlight with a shaky hand. The flame threw grotesque shadows on the walls as he moved the taper to left and right, and peered around the room and up at the ceiling. The music had ceased. He listened for a long time, but he could hear nothing other than the surge and ebb of the friar's snoring in the neighbouring room.

" Most remarkable," he said aloud, as he extinguished the rushlight and laid his head back on the pillow, but he had no sooner decided that his experience belonged to the deceptive borderland of dreams, than he was once more startled in to a sitting position by a sound which he immediately identified as the insidious rustling of a comb. His ears followed in horror the sensuous sweep and the little crackling sounds of a comb moving through hair that was long and luxurious. There could be no doubt about it, there *was* a woman in his room. Before the affrighted prelate could decide what action to take in this unprecedented situation, a sweet, winning voice spoke close to his ear.

" What a lovely man ! "

Surrendering himself to the wild impulse of the moment the Bishop precipitated himself on to the floor. He scrambled hastily to his feet and retained enough presence of mind to seize the rushlight and flint before dashing into the friar's room. He closed the door behind him and, after several attempts, succeeded in lighting the taper. He glanced fearfully at the wavering shadows on the walls, and then hurried over to the friar's bed. Father Furiosus was slumbering fitfully, but when Bishop Flanagan shook him, a tousled red head rose suddenly from the pillow.

" There's an evil and sportful female in my room," whispered the Bishop urgently, " She's trying to entice me to licentiousness ! "

" What's that ? " exclaimed Furiosus, sitting bolt upright in bed and disclosing a chest covered with matted ginger hair.

The Bishop repeated his alarming intelligence. Father Furiosus stared at him incredulously, but the prelate's estranged face and his eyes, fiery and hollow, carried conviction.

" Did you see her ? " demanded the friar.

" No," replied the Bishop, " but I heard her combing her hair, and I heard her voice when she tried to entice me, a voice sweet and evil like the sound of flutes."

" I'll soon fix her," exclaimed the friar, stretching a muscular arm under the bed for his blackthorn stick. " Do not let the matter flurry or excite you. I can see that your nerves are all unstrung."

" Be careful," begged the Bishop as Furiosus clambered out of bed. " She can sing. Take heed lest she lewdly excite you by trolling filthy songs."

" I can withstand the most alluring nymphs," affirmed the friar, brushing him aside. " Before I've done with the trollop," he added fiercely as he tightened his grip on the blackthorn, " I'll give her many sad strokes."

He snatched the rushlight from Bishop Flanagan and striding across the floor, flung open the door of the other room.

" There's no one here," he exclaimed.

Bishop Flanagan peered nervously over the friar's shoulder.

" She was here," he asserted.   " Look under the bed."

There was no one under the bed.   Father Furiosus held up the rushlight and examined the ceiling, then he turned and eyed Bishop Flanagan suspiciously.

" Are you quite certain that you didn't consume more wine this evening than you admit ? " he asked roughly.

All the Bishop's dignity and habits of command came back to him as he heard this insult.

" Certainly not," he retorted frigidly, and he drew himself up to his full height, an imposing figure in his horsehair night-shirt.   " I tell you I was not mistaken.   If there is no one here of flesh and blood, then what I heard was by the con-trivance of a demon."

Furiosus expanded his nostrils judiciously.

" It may be," he said at last.   " I myself have been much troubled this night by persistent dreams of a very lewd character.   The Devil may be attempting to excite us to bad thoughts.   But it's cold here, so I'm going back to bed ; and I advise you to do the same.   Address yourself to prayer, and if there's a further manifestation, call me."

The friar strode out of the room banging the door behind him, and the Bishop heard the bed in the far room creaking painfully as Furiosus climbed into it.   Bishop Flanagan crept back into his own bed too, more chagrined at the ease with which the friar had taken charge of the situation than fearful for his own safety.   He left the taper lighting on the table so that he might be the better able to grapple with any situation that might present itself, and he saw to it that his bowl of holy water and his book of exorcisms were close to hand. What an overbearing fellow Furiosus was, always ready to push himself forward and take charge, making everyone feel like a small boy in his presence !   Bishop Flanagan made up his mind firmly to deal himself with any further lascivious sleight-of-hand on the part of visiting sprites or imps, and on no account to summon the help of the masterful friar. He was sitting in bed propped up by the pillows, meditating thus when he became aware of a well-shaped damsel slowly assuming shape in the far corner of the room. In spite of his determination to remain cool, sweat broke out on the Bishop's forehead and, trickling down his face, disappeared drop by drop inside the collar of his nightshirt. Still he refrained from stretching out his hand for the holy water. He told himself that he must wait until the impudent vision had taken full shape ; the target would be bigger and there would be less chance of missing with the holy water.

At last she was entirely there in all her evil comeliness, an enchanting vision, her form elastic and light, with flexible limbs and a juvenile grace in her every movement. As she moved towards the alarmed prelate, her expressive features and eloquent action harmonised blandly with each other. A sound indicative of his anguish burst from Bishop Flanagan's throat, and seizing the bowl of holy water he flung it desperately at the approaching vision. To his horror it passed right through her and was shivered in atoms against the wall. As she continued to approach he sprang out the far side of the bed and, clutching the book of exorcisms, he swamped her in a deluge from the Vulgate. He did not dare raise his eyes from the page until he was out of breath. When he glanced up fearfully she was still there, scarcely three paces from him, evidently experiencing the greatest difficulty in restraining her merriment.

" Begone ! " quavered the Bishop. " I know you to be nought but a vain impression in the air."

She regarded him for a moment roguishly ; and when she spoke, her voice modulated itself with natural and winning ease.

" I'm thousands of years old," she said in dulcet tones. " You'll never get rid of me with that modern Christian stuff."

Bishop Flanagan's mouth fell open, but no sound came forth. He cowered against the wall as she opened her lips again, and sweet, amatory words came out.

" Why are you so difficult ? " she asked.   " You will never find a woman so passionate, so loving or so submissive."

It is likely that the Bishop would have lost his life through sheer horror at these plausible words, only that he was suddenly recalled to the consciousness that the friar was in the neighbouring room by a series of bull-like roars which proceeded therefrom. Bishop Flanagan was immediately galvanised into action, and seizing the rushlight, he tore open the door and dashed into Furiosus' bedroom. Great as was the Bishop's alarm, he stopped petrified at the sight that met his eyes. The friar was tumbling around on the floor fighting madly to escape from the obscene advances and abandoned caresses of three females of the most luscious character imaginable. But Bishop Flanagan did not forget his own peril for long. He ran to the struggling mass on the floor.

" Nice time," he snarled, " to be slaking your lusts, when I'm half-slaughtered by the most hideous apparition that was ever seen ! "

With a mighty heave Father Furiosus was on his feet, flinging the three sportful damsels against the far wall. He seized Bishop Flanagan by the throat and pressed him back against the bed-post.

" Let me go," gasped the Bishop, " or you will incur the penalty of excommunication."

" What do you mean by that accusation," howled the friar, " and I locked in deadly combat with the forces of Hell ? Take it back before I tear the skinny throat out of you."

" I'm sorry," panted the Bishop, " I take it back. I didn't know they were demons too. There's one in my room, the most terrible vision that eye has ever seen."

Father Furiosus released the Bishop and stood looking around the room breathing heavily. The three high-stepping females had disappeared. The friar tiptoed over to the door and looked into the Bishop's room. It was likewise empty.

Then he returned to Bishop Flanagan, and the two of them conversed in whispers.

" She had a singularly evil countenance," said Bishop Flanagan," his voice still trembling with fear. " There was a hot, unholy fire in her eye. Neither holy water nor exorcism availed ought against her."

" That's bad," replied Furiosus, shaking his head gravely. " It would appear from what you tell me that these painful phenomena are female elementals, probably sylphides—most difficult to get rid of. However, I will sprinkle my stoup of holy water on the walls and ceiling. While I am so engaged, do you turn up your most powerful exorcism, and we will read it aloud together."

" What will we do if all four renew the assault in unison ? " asked the Bishop shakily.

" It will be a triste and ominous affair," replied the friar gloomily, " and may well spell damnation for us both."

" Not if we continue heroically to resist their unhallowed designs," asserted the Bishop hysterically.

" The flesh is weak," muttered the friar darkly. " I will thoroughly besprinkle the walls. Then we will pray."

When the last drop of sanctified water was exhausted, and the pair had read in tremulous tones the most powerful exorcisms available, they took their seats back to back in the doorway between the two rooms, so that between them they had the whole field of battle under surveillance.

" I fear me," said the Bishop in a tremulous voice, " that if they renew the onset, they will have some new artifices and stratagems at their command."

" Whatever they contrive or whatever manœuvres they indulge in, we will give them a good fight," responded Father Furiosus.

" What avails a good fight, if one loses it ? " said the despondent Bishop.

Father Furiosus did not answer. Though he did not care to admit it even to himself, he was considerably shaken by the night's happenings. It was the first time in his career as

a thwarter and scarifier of demons that he was faced with the
probability of the usual spiritual weapons breaking in his
hands.   Moreover, he was a man who never before had failed
in such work, and the possibility of being this time unsuccessful
was galling to his spirit in the extreme.   He had never before
been faced by forces as old as the world itself, and he did not
like the new experience.   Further, he was a man of simple
mind, who became annoyed when confronted with something
which he did not understand.   And he could not understand
what had got into the elementals to make them behave as
they did.   He understood them to be ordinarily a people who
amused themselves playing hide-and-seek in forests and rivers,
or disporting themselves in flame or in the upper air— a more
or less useless people who had at least the virtue that they left
human beings alone.   But if what Bishop Flanagan asserted
was true, if both holy water and exorcism had failed, then
things looked black indeed.   He hardly cared to think what
might be the outcome of the affair.

He was sunk in gloomy contemplation when the Bishop's
sharp elbow stabbed him in the ribs.

" Listen," squealed the Bishop hoarsely.

Furiosus listened.   He heard music, at first faint, then
swelling in volume and coming nearer, soft, sensual cadences,
with little runs of semiquavers of a particularly suggestive
character.   The friar raised the sleeve of his nightshirt and
wiped his eye into which the sweat was running, half-blinding
him.   He could feel the Bishop's bony back pressed against
his own, stiff as a board with fright.   In a few moments the
air about them was throbbing with curious songs and music.
The friar turned, and putting out his hand, took his companion by the arm.   The Bishop immediately fell on the
floor.

" What did you do that for ? " demanded the friar in a
testy whisper.

Bishop Flanagan seemed incapable of movement, but his
eyes held a world of pathos.

" Don't leave me," he managed to gasp.

Father Furiosus helped him to his feet.

" The holy water has let us down," said the friar hoarsely. " It must indeed be elementals. Be prepared for a manifestation any moment."

It had begun. In the wavering glimmer cast by the rushlight, gossamer shapes swayed and slowly took on the form of four highly agreeable females. They lounged gracefully in a corner of the room, smiling engagingly at the paralysed ecclesiastics. Father Furiosus essayed an exorcism in a cracked voice, but his heart was not in it, for he felt a certain premonition that his efforts would be unavailing. His voice trailed off and stopped. Just as he had feared, the four sylphs, far from disappearing in a sulphur flash and a foul smoke, started putting the finishing touches to their coiffures and adding a last dab of rouge to their lips and cheeks.

" Hurry up, Gertie," said one of them. " Let's get them."

" It's my considered opinion," muttered the friar, " that it's high time for both of us to take evasive action. The best moral theologians have only one recommendation to make in cases of acute temptation—*Fuga*, which is translated 'Flight '."

" But suppose," quavered the Bishop, " that they surround us ? "

" I wish you wouldn't keep clinging to me," exclaimed Father Furiosus irritably. " Please let go my nightshirt. Now, listen. By ' Flight ' the Fathers do not mean merely that one should remove oneself physically from the location and occasion of the temptation : that would avail us little, as I doubt not but that these harpies can run as fast as we ; but it is implied also that one should forcibly occupy one's mind with other things, and on no account venture to reason or argue the temptation out of existence. That way lies failure, the death of the soul and the pit of Hell. Nothing is so salubrious in temptation as the mortification of the flesh which is tempted, so let us betake ourselves with all speed to some refuge where we can proceed at once to the practice of the counsels of the Fathers in the matter."

" There's a fine bed of nettles against the wall of my stock-yard," said the Bishop eagerly.

" Come on," said the friar, and the two of them made off through the far door. The Bishop, who was lithe and nimble, soon outdistanced the friar, and he had the backdoor of the Palace unbolted before Furiosus caught up with him.   They raced across the yard barefoot, the Bishop pattering far ahead.   The prelate, who felt that the situation was critical, did not hesitate to pull his nightshirt over his head as he ran, so that he was stark naked when he reached the nettles, of which there was a particularly luxurious bed.   Father Furiosus saw him stretch his skinny frame at the head of the slight incline where the nettles grew, and roll himself over and over down through the nettles until he reached the bottom.   Then he picked himself up, scampered up again over the broken stems and repeated the operation.

" There'll be a nice scandal," muttered the friar, " if any of the parishioners see his lordship running around in the buff."

But Father Furiosus did not delay in following the Bishop's example.   He stripped off his nightshirt and with tightset lips selected a corner where the nettles were five feet high. The ground shook as his brawny frame tumbled over and over down the incline.

Some time later the moon which had modestly hidden her head, emerged sailing from behind a cloud.   She saw two naked men squatting uncomfortably in the centre of a completely flattened nettlebed, watched from beyond its fringes by four pensive sylphs.

" I fear we have ground all the venom out of the nettles," whispered Furiosus, " and the bad women are still there.   I fear that unholy desires may yet arise in me."

" Sh ! " said the Bishop, " lest they hear.   There's a small pond beyond the stockade.   Let's make a run for it."

All the long night through, the sylphs, once more in their native element, danced beneath the trees by the side of the pond, while from the centre, immersed to their necks in freezing water, the Bishop and the friar watched them glumly.

CHAPTER VIII

THE road that goes south from Cashel winds crazily ; taking little runs over ridges, and curving so as to skirt the irregular boundaries of the farmlands. It is an absurd, switchbacking Irish road, never straight for more than a hundred paces, encouraging the wayfarer with the hope that there may be something unusual and peculiar around the bend or over the brow of the hill. The roadway is hemmed in on either side by hedges of blackthorn, brambles, gorse and sallies. Through gaps, ineffectively blocked by old buckets and pieces of bedsteads, the traveller catches glimpses of the endless green fields and the contented cattle scattered over the plain. From behind a gate an occasional cow, having nothing better to do, will stare with gloomy insolence at the passer-by ; or on turning a corner you may suddenly come upon a donkey who to all appearances has been standing in the middle of the roadway for weeks sunk in inutterable boredom. There are not many human habitations, and such few as there are, are built in the wrong places—on low ground, so that the rainwater gathers on the surrounding hillocks and flows with ease in through the front door. When evening comes and the beginning of twilight, the road and countryside become charged with a peculiar opalescent atmosphere as if a faery world had been superimposed upon our own, so that one almost doubts the reality of tree and field ; and, according as temperament dictates, either hurries on in terror of what one may meet, or else lingers filled with a sense of wonder and a content that seems to belong to another existence.

But as the traveller by daylight winds his way further, he will come nearer and nearer to the great mountain wall that bounds the Tipperary plain on the south. When he has passed through a brief stretch of woodland and stream, he will find to his astonishment that the road, instead of going around the mountains in a civilised manner, is intent on running straight at them and trying to jump. More amazing still is the road's success. It is true that its progress up the precipitous hillside is drunken in the extreme, but a thousand feet up it finds a great cleft which local people call " The Gap " ; and in there, a little out of breath, the road knowingly worms its way.

At this point, twenty miles south of Cashel and a thousand feet above the Tipperary plain, on a grassy bank by the road-side sat Fursey thinking of his sins. Below him lay the rich plain, an astonishing checkerboard of green and golden fields in neat squares, the opulent domain of the men of affairs and of the priests. Above him arose the cliffs and shoulders of the Knockmealdown Mountains, windswept and torn by storms. Over on his left he could see among the bogs and the rocks the shimmer of a small mountain lake, and near it a white dot which was a cottage.

" I seem to be a desperate character," was Fursey's sad summing-up of the situation. " To begin with, I'm a genuine sorcerer. It would be useless to deny that I've meddled with very dark powers and practised the blacker forms of magic. Then, in one afternoon I told Cuthbert more lies than most men tell in a lifetime. I'm a notorious hobnobber with demons, and I encouraged King Cormac to lechery, at least I did not repel his advances as a decent girl should. I have probably been an occasion of sin to the innocent in that for a day and a half I roamed about the countryside undraped (someone is sure to have seen me), and lastly I'm a thief. I had no moral right to rob that scarecrow of his rags—he was possibly the property of a poor man, and now the birds will eat all the seed so laboriously sown. There's no doubt about it but that I'm a most abandoned ruffian," he concluded gloomily. " Probably my like for villainy has never been seen in the world before."

Fursey sighed and grew tired of thinking of his iniquities. Instead he began to remember that he was very hungry. If only he had a rope——! Even the tiniest bit of cord would do. If he had a little bit of cord, he would throw it over a thorn bush, and by pulling hard enough he could probably produce at least a couple of hard-boiled eggs. He sighed a second time and told himself that the practice of sorcery was a sin ; still he wished he had a small piece of cord. His soul was by now so deformed and hideous that one extra little sin wouldn't make much difference.

However, sitting still wasn't going to produce food, so he got wearily to his feet and continued his way along the rocky road. From time to time he glanced across at the distant white-washed cottage beside the mountain tarn. There would be food there, but would they give him any ? Would they even lend him a rope for a few minutes if he promised to bring it back ? They'd probably conclude, he reflected gloomily, that he wanted to hang himself, and indignantly refuse.

He came to a point where a pathway joined his road. He paused and looked down the crooked track. That would be the path that led to the cottage. He felt that if he went down the track and approached the dwelling, the owner would probably set the dogs on him. Hospitality would scarcely be extended to a man of the tramp class so inadequately clad in a scarecrow's cloak and kilt, as to be almost an offence against decency. Yet he hated to continue further on his way : the mountain road looked as if it led only to menacing and barren lands, and he was sick and tired of nature anyway. He longed to hear human voices and feel the warmth of a peat fire against his knees. Then he remembered again how hungry he was, and he sat down on a stone. He sat there for a long time with his head between his hands thinking of nothing, and then he began to think of Albert. He hesitated for a while, but at last he raised his head.

" Albert ! " he called softly. " Albert ! "

There was a movement in the dust of the road, and Albert's bear's paws slowly took shape, and soon the whole of Albert was there, but an Albert jaded and sulky-looking and very much emaciated. His red, foggy eyes observed Fursey steadily.

" Nice mess you got yourself into with the clergy," he said. " I thought they'd burn you to a cinder."

" Well, they didn't," replied Fursey.

" I suppose you'll tell me that it was your superior intelligence that got you out of it," remarked Albert sarcastically.

" Please don't nag," answered Fursey. " I'm hungry. I want something to eat."

" *You* want something to eat ! " replied Albert shrilly. " What about me ? Look at the state I'm in, with the skin of my belly clinging to my spine. For once and for all, are you, or are you not, going to part with some of your blood ? Answer yes or no."

Fursey looked at his familiar with heavy eyes. Right enough, the creature had shrunk away to mere skin and bone. Fursey felt sorry for him, but he did not see that he could do anything about it. He sighed again.

" I want you to scout around, Albert," he said, " and see if you can find me a bit of rope."

Albert faced him determinedly. " Once," he said with a tremor of indignation in his voice, " I was as frisky a familiar as you'd meet in a day's walk, but your confounded meanness—"

" Don't argue," commanded Fursey. " Do as you're told. Scout around and find me a rope."

Albert threw a venomous look at his master and began a half-hearted sniffing and snuffling up and down the ditch. It was just then that an old man of the farmer class came around the bend of the track. He was carrying a long stick of ashwood to which was tied a piece of cord and a worm. He stopped opposite Fursey.

" That's a queer class of a dog you have, mister," he said, blinking short-sightedly at Albert. " What breed would he be, now ? "

" Vanish," commanded Fursey.

" What's that ? " asked the old man.

" Nothing," answered Fursey. " I haven't got a dog. You're making a mistake."

The old man peered where Albert had been.

" Dear me," he said, " the old eyes are going on me. I would have sworn I saw a dog."

" Not a dog for miles around," responded Fursey blithely. " Are you going fishing, sir ? "

" Yes," replied the old man. " I'm going down to the lake."

" Then you're going in the wrong direction," said Fursey. " The lake is behind you."

The old farmer looked bewildered.

" So it is," he replied at last, and turned back the way he had come. Fursey arose from the stone and fell into step beside him.

" May I ask if you live in the cottage beyond ? " he queried.

" Yes," responded the ancient. " That's my house."

" Very convenient having the fishing right at your front door."

The old man looked surprised.

" The lake is at the back of the house," he said.

For a few minutes they walked side by side in silence. Then the old man stopped and peered sharply at Fursey.

" What are you accompanying me for ? " he asked.

" So that you won't lose your way to the lake."

" How could I lose my way to the lake ? " retorted the old man. " Don't I live beside it, and haven't I fished it these forty years."

He continued on his way, and Fursey fell into step with him once more. When they were within a few hundred yards of the cottage, the old man stopped again and turned to Fursey.

" You're still following me," he asserted. " You're up to something. If you don't go away, I'll call my daughter."

Fursey's voice broke. "It's some days since I've had anything to eat," he said. "Maybe you have a slice of bread in the house that's not wanted, and a cup of milk?"

"What are you?" asked the old man, looking down suspiciously at the scarecrow rags that covered Fursey. "A travelling man?"

"Yes," lied Fursey.

The ancient regarded him closely for a few moments, then he answered gruffly.

"All right. I'll see what the daughter can do for you."

Fursey stepped out joyfully beside him.

"Do you do much fishing, sir?" he asked politely.

"Forty years," responded his companion, "and I haven't caught one of the little devils yet. I'm beginning to suspect that there aren't any fish in the lake."

Fursey, who had fished once or twice with a bent nail and the cord of his habit in the Shannon at Clonmacnoise, plunged into a discussion on the relative merits of the lugworm and the lobworm as bait. The old man listened with interest until they came to the fence of the cottage.

"We'll have to find the daughter first," he said. "She's probably feeding the hens at the back of the house."

As they made their way into the yard, the old man sighed and turned to Fursey.

"I'm in a bad way here," he confided, "what with the advancing years and the fishing, I don't be able to do much work about the farm. I had a good farmboy, but off he went yesterday to fight in the war."

Fursey muttered sympathetically. He did not enquire which war, as he knew that among the one hundred and eighty kingdoms of Ireland there were always several wars in progress, and they were usually very confusing. Moreover, he had never understood geography. But he quickly saw his opportunity.

"What about taking on a new boy?" he asked eagerly. "I'm a willing and hardy worker."

The old man turned his head and inspected Fursey closely.

" You're a queer-looking boy," he replied at last, " with your hair snow-white. How old are you ? "

" I'm forty."

" You look about a hundred."

" You'd do well to take me," rejoined Fursey. " I understand everything about a farm, from paring edible roots to milking a goat. I'm a great hand at feeding hens. To say nothing of my knowledge of fishing."

The old man seemed impressed.

" I'll have to talk to the daughter," he replied.

They found her at the back of the house spreading out clothes on the hedge to dry, a fine, wide-eyed girl of about thirty-two, with a large, full-lipped mouth and two sets of the whitest teeth Fursey had ever seen. She watched Fursey curiously while the old man explained the immediate need for a slice of bread and a cup of milk. Under her friendly gaze Fursey stood grinning bashfully, his cheeks and his ears pink with his blushes. When the old man had finished, she immediately led the way into the kitchen and put Fursey on a stool by the fire. She loaded the table with bread, butter, cheese and cold vegetables, and drew a beaker of ale from a cask in the corner. Fursey ate with difficulty, partly because he was embarrassed by such hospitality, and partly because the old man had emptied three canisters of lugworms on to a corner of the table and was earnestly soliciting Fursey's opinion as to their quality and striking power. He was too shortsighted to observe Fursey's efforts to be polite and at the same time to prevent the bait from crawling into his food and up his sleeves. The girl stood leaning against the wall by the hearth smiling at them both.

When the meal was finished and the lugworms had been returned with difficulty into the three canisters, the old man and the girl went into the far corner of the room and conducted a long conversation in whispers, while Fursey sat with his knees to the fire anxiously awaiting the outcome. At length the girl came forward and seated herself at the table.

" My father tells me," she said, " that you'd like to be taken on here as farmboy."

" Yes," replied Fursey eagerly.

" There's not a great deal of work to be done," she explained. " Just to keep the yard and outhouses clean and dry, bring water from the well and milk the cow. We'll give you your food and your bed here by the fire, and an old suit of my father's as well. He thinks it's hardly decent to have you going around the way you are, with a young woman in the house."

Fursey could find no words to express his thanks, but the tears welled up into his eyes and crept down his face. When the old man observed Fursey's emotion he was powerfully affected himself, and it was with difficulty that his daughter succeeded in shepherding the two of them through the door out into the yard, where she put the ash rod and line into her father's hand. She instructed Fursey that his first duty was to see the old man down to the shore of the lake and into his coracle. Then Fursey was to return and sweep the yard.

Day after day crept by, days of scudding cloud, of rustling showers and defiant sunshine. Never had Fursey been so happy. In the mornings he accompanied Old Declan to the lake and saw him safely into the coracle. The old man browsed around the little tarn all day, and it was one of Fursey's duties to summon him to his meals, otherwise he would have forgotten to come home at all. Fursey swept the house and the yard, milked the cow and carried water from the well. He flapped around in a suit of the old man's clothes, which were far too big for him, chatting amiably to the cow and the hens, amusing Declan and his daughter with his antics, and all the time he felt an elevation of heart that he had never known before. He could scarcely credit his happiness and good fortune. Sometimes in the cool of the day he sat on a rock at the edge of the lake, and as he watched the water come wrinkling in towards his feet, he brooded on his happiness and wondered uneasily how long it would last. He would close his eyes and tell himself that there was no reason why his present blissful state should not continue always. Then he would hug his knees and lose himself listening to the hollow slapping of the water among the stones and the metallic notes of the birds, the long drawn-out twitter of some individual songster that seemed to have an impediment in its speech, mingling with the curling chirps and the tuneful tootings of the others.

Fursey thought it was a most beautiful lake. Its threatening cliffs awed and delighted him. When the sun was high overhead he would stand dazzled by the sparkle of its waters, and many an afternoon he sat hour after hour wondering how it was that the water seemed all the time to be moving in towards him, although there was no breeze and the fringes of the water did no more than rustle among the reeds. When he arose and moved back towards the cottage, it often seemed to him that the whole hollow in the hills where lake and cottage lay was filled with a music of which he was aware but which he could not hear. He would look up at the heights where mountain was piled upon mountain, and his heart would be flooded with humility. As he approached the cottage he would, as often as not, hear the sound of Maeve's singing as she went about her work. " It's a good thing to hear a woman singing in a house," Old Declan confided to him. " It means that the house is a happy one." Fursey would creep noiselessly into the kitchen, returning diffidently her ready smile ; and seated on his stool by the hearth, he would watch her surreptitiously as she kneaded the dough or turned the handle of the churn.

Occasionally he accompanied Declan on his fishing excursions, but the old man had to fish from the shore when Fursey was with him, for nothing would persuade Fursey to trust himself to the frail coracle. Declan did not mind very much where he fished from : he never caught anything anyway. Sitting on a boulder he would explain the philosophy of fishing to Fursey.

" It's not necessary to catch fish," he would say. " Men fish because it brings them back to their boyhood. They like scrambling over rocks and crossing streams and endangering their lives on lakes, just as they did when they were children. Moreover, it brings them to pleasant, interesting places which they wouldn't ordinarily have a chance of seeing. All the same," the old man would add grimly, " I wish I could catch one of the little devils."

But it was when the door of the cottage was closed against the freshness of the night, and Declan and Maeve had drawn in about the glowing peat fire, that Fursey really came into his own. They quickly discovered that their unusual farm-boy, though he could neither read nor write, had a fund of peculiar information. He seemed to have a wide knowledge of demonology and the unprincipled behaviour of witches, and from his stool beside the fire he gravely gave them advice as to the correct procedure in certain unpleasant sets of circumstances ; for instance, if one had the misfortune to encounter a basilisk on the highway. He seemed to them a man with a considerable knowledge of the great world beyond " The Gap." He had visited Cashel and seen in the flesh the great men of the Kingdom, the Bishop, the King and the great lords and ecclesiastics ; he had even visited remote Clonmacnoise and seen the River Shannon. While Fursey told his halting tales, Maeve, from her place on the far side of the fire, kept her big eyes fixed on his face. Declan mut-tered to himself all during Fursey's recital, and occasionally gave vent to a mournful groan when some act of human or demoniacal depravity came to be told.

There was one thing that puzzled Fursey greatly. Often, on a warm, golden evening as he sat by the lakeside, he asked himself how it was that in his flight from Cashel he had not been pursued. He had been two days on the road, and in that time he could easily have been overtaken by horsemen or by fleet runners. It was true that he had spent most of the daylight hiding in the hedges and had travelled for the greater part by night ; still, there had been no evidence what-ever of a desire on the part of the authorities to recapture him. Was it that they were afraid to approach him and that they

thought they were well rid of him ? He could not bring himself
to believe it. Father Furiosus and the Bishop, he felt, were
not the kind of men to allow a suspected sorcerer to be at
large without making every effort to capture him. And even
if they were convinced that he was not a sorcerer, but a
demoniac, they would be just as inflamed with zeal to catch
him and rid him of his malignant guest. Fursey could not
understand it ; but as day after day passed and he found
himself unmolested, he began to think about the matter less,
being only too willing to believe himself secure. He took the
precaution, however, of surreptitiously anointing the cottage
broom with the ointment which he still carried, lest it should
be necessary to make a hurried escape ; and one evening
when Declan and Maeve were absent, he had a practice flight
up and down the yard to the considerable alarm of a large
body of hens. He had of course taken the further precaution
of not telling his name to the old cottager and his daughter.
On his first evening when they had asked him how he was
called, he had answered on the spur of the moment, giving his
dead father's name—Flinthead, and as Flinthead he was
known to Declan and Maeve.

Although it was still only July it was time to commence
bringing in the winter's supply of peat, and this onerous task
was willingly accepted by Fursey. Late one evening as he
came to the cottage sweating under the weight of the heavy
creel on his back, he saw three horses tethered in the yard.
He at once swung the creel to the ground, but before he could
properly grapple with his alarm, Declan came to the door
and beckoned him reassuringly.

" We have three old friends paying us a visit," said the old
man, taking Fursey by the arm and conducting him into the
kitchen. Maeve was clearing the table of the remnants of
a meal, and Fursey glanced fearfully at the three strangers.
One was a more than middle-aged woman with a gamey eye,
who was introduced as ' the Widow Dykes from beyond the
mountain.' The second was Phineas the Clerk, a rusty little
fellow of indeterminate age, clad in a shabby, black cloak.

From the inkhorn and bunch of quills which were slung from a cord over his shoulder, Fursey identified him at once as one of those men who could read and write and who made a living travelling around the country writing letters for people. But it was the third stranger who filled Fursey with instinctive dislike and dread. He was Magnus, a soldier, a big, lusty fellow, who rested his elbows on the table as if he owned it. He was sucking the last succulent morsel of marrow from a bone when Fursey entered, and he nodded contemptuously when the new farmboy, Flinthead, was introduced. The others smiled slightly as they glanced at Fursey's cloak, which was so big for him that it had to be wrapped around him twice, and at his kilt, which was so long that it covered the calves of his legs. Fursey threw a quick glance towards the door to assure himself that his broom was in its accustomed place, before seating himself in the darkest corner of the room. Maeve handed him his bowl of stirabout, for he had not yet had his evening meal.

"Go on with your story, Phineas," said Magnus, flinging the bone into the fire.

From his place beside the comfortable widow Declan bent towards Fursey.

"Phineas has been telling us," he explained, "about the extraordinary happenings at Cashel. It seems that they captured the prince of all sorcerers, a man called Fursey ; but he subsequently escaped."

"Indeed," replied Fursey, burying his head in the bowl of stirabout.

"There's nothing much more to tell," said Phineas. "As I have already related to you, he appeared in the guise of a woman in the Royal courtyard and tried to strangle good King Cormac. On the night on which he disappeared, he took with him by some magic art known only to himself, every bit of gold which the Byzantine prince had so generously bestowed on the clergy and citizens. Every gold bar vanished at the same instant as the monstrous Fursey himself. Chunks of gold disappeared from the soldiers' pockets. They were there one moment, and they were gone the next. Even a valuable dog of superior pedigree, presented by Apollyon to Father Furiosus, disappeared without leaving a trace."

" But was he not pursued ? " asked Declan. " A sorcerer in woman's clothing, loaded down with gold, and with a pedigree dog under his arm, should be easily identified."

" No," replied Phineas. " Those who were best qualified to direct the pursuit, the Bishop and Father Furiosus, were incapable of doing so. They were found in the early morning in a semi-frozen condition in a pond on the Bishop's estate, having apparently been enmeshed in the spells of this malignant wizard. They were in bed for some days half paralysed and with violent colds in the head and chest ; and when they became once more capable of movement, the scent had grown cold. Even yet, good Bishop Flanagan cannot be said to have fully recovered, for he is still much given to involuntary crying, shouting and barking, and other symptoms of hysteria."

" How terrible," murmured Maeve. " Did you see the wizard yourself ? "

" Yes," replied Phineas a trifle pompously. " I saw him."

" Oh ! " breathed Maeve. " How old was he ? What did he look like ? "

" I should say that he was very old," answered Phineas judiciously, " perhaps eighty. His hair was snow-white, and he was much bowed both by his years and by the heavy weight of his iniquities."

" I was told," interrupted Magnus, who seemed restless because Phineas was monopolising the conversation, " that the fellow was entirely black in appearance."

" I saw him myself," answered Phineas testily. " It's true that his face was black, as was appropriate considering that all his contrivings against mankind were of a black and deadly nature, but the rest of him was white, particularly his hair. It was snow-white like Flinthead's over there."

The company glanced involuntarily into the chimney corner from which Fursey's moon-round visage stared back at them from behind his bowl of stirabout.

" He must have been a fearsome sight," ejaculated Declan.

" He was," replied Phineas. " He was a man of singularly evil countenance. His mouth was twisted towards his ear, and from him there came a cadaverous smell which was well-nigh insupportable. When he spoke it was in a muffled voice. You had but to look at him to realise that never was there in any character a more complete concentration of every quality that distinguishes a man of evil and pernicious principles. They say that he was the seventh son of a seventh son, which means that the Devil had marked him as his own from the very day of his birth."

" He used preside .at cannibal feasts," said Magnus, " and he put on Cuthbert the Sexton such a malignant spell that after violent retching the unfortunate man brought up pieces of coal, bodkins, stones, brass, eggshells and a variety of other objects."

" I'll be afraid to go to bed to-night," shivered Maeve.

" But isn't it a terrible thing," interjected the widow, " that even godly men like Bishop Flanagan and Father Furiosus are not immune from his spells ? I heard that his parting gift to them was a murrain, which still afflicts them sorely."

" God save me and mine from all such legacies ! " ejaculated Declan piously.

" It may well be," replied Phineas. " It is certainly the case that he caused the unfortunate Cuthbert to vomit stones so big that it was incredible how they could come out of any Christian mouth."

" What do you think of it, Flinthead ? " asked Declan, turning to where Fursey sat quiet as a mouse in his corner. " Would you not be scared by such horrid manifestations ? "

Fursey grinned feebly, but before he could think of an answer Magnus let out a great horse laugh.

"Why do you ask him?" he demanded roughly. "I wouldn't set any great value on an opinion of his."

"Oh," rejoined the old man mildly, "Flinthead is very learned in the ways of witches and demons."

Magnus leaned back in his chair and shifted his soldier's belt as if to laugh more comfortably.

"My God!" he said, "you're not serious. Why, one has only to look at him to see that his brain is naturally moist."

For a moment the heart of Fursey burned within him at these contemptuous words, but the fire flickered and went out as Maeve leaned across and placed her hand comfortingly on his.

"Now, now," she said, "I won't have anyone making fun of Flinthead. He's a friend of mine, and we all like him very much."

The Widow and Phineas the Clerk smiled tolerantly. Old Declan seemed to be still worried about details of Phineas' story, and he did not appear to notice that the Widow had quietly taken his hand into her plump paw and was gently squeezing his gnarled fingers.

"What about The Gray Mare?" he asked anxiously. "Was she a witch or not?"

"There are two schools of thought in the matter," replied Phineas. "The Bishop and the King are believed to be of opinion that she was a witch; but Father Furiosus urges that she was undoubtedly innocent and was murdered by Fursey, whom he now believes to be possessed by a devil as well as being a sorcerer. Father Furiosus is a man of great force of character, and he has a considerable following among the clergy and the populace. He believes The Gray Mare to have been a martyr, and he has had her remains translated to an expensive tomb in Kilpuggin Church, which has become a place of pilgrimage. Sundry cures have already been reported, and only for the outbreak of war with Thomond, the cause for her canonisation would have been by now well advanced."

Fursey sat motionless in his corner, his countenance seemingly busied in unceasing converse with his heart. At first he had listened anxiously, but as he became convinced that there was little danger of being recognised, his attention wandered, and he reflected how little he knew of human nature and of the ways of the world. From time to time he gathered in his vagrant thoughts and told himself that he must listen because all this news was of the most immediate concern to him ; but his eyes invariably returned to rest on the line of Maeve's temple where the hair was brushed back, and he would feel for a moment as if he were falling into a lunacy, for ever since she had lain her comforting hand on his, his love was so hot that he wist not where he was. Once more he pulled himself together. They were talking of war. War had broken out between Cashel and Thomond. It was very difficult to grasp what it was all about, but it seemed that the King of Thomond was an idealist, who kept reiterating that " a principle is a principle." In answer to King Cormac's curt ultimatum, his reply had been : " Men and matters come and go, but a principle is eternal." Thereupon the hounds of war had been unleashed, and the whole fighting forces of Cashel had been flung into Thomond territory. No engagement had ensued, for the reason that the army of the King of Thomond was not yet ready—the season had been late, and the hay had not yet been saved. Accordingly, the only casualties that had resulted were two Thomond hermits who, betrayed by wanton curiosity, had put their heads out of their caves to find out what all the noise was about, and had immediately had their heads struck off.

Magnus had now got control of the conversation.

" Cormac is a master strategist," he said approvingly. " He is the only king in Ireland who maintains a standing army, and although the upkeep of those twenty-four men is a considerable burden on the State, they are well worth it. Other kings must wait until the agricultural work of the spring and early summer is over before their clansmen are free for warfare ; and again and again it has happened that a king has been left alone in the field of battle by reason of his army going home to their farms to gather in the harvest. Cormac's long-sighted policy has ensured that he is never wholly deserted in this fashion. Nine-tenths of his army may go home, but he has always the hard core of twenty-four men left to fight for him. His strategy consists then in this : that he keeps manœuvring his forces with consummate skill all during the summer ; and with the coming of the harvest when the fighting men must go home, the opposing king finds that he and his sons have to face alone the full onset of the standing army of Cashel. Many and many a war has Cormac won by these methods. He is admitted all over the world to be the finest general in the history of warfare."

" You won't have to go to the war yet awhile ? " asked Maeve.

" Well, I've been summoned," replied Magnus, " but my hay isn't quite in yet, and I've a cow with a swollen teat ; I'll have to fix that first. But in a week or so I expect to be in a position to answer the call."

" Maybe the war will be over before you're ready to go," said Declan hopefully.

" I don't think so," replied Magnus. " It will be a long and bitter conflict. I estimate that in another week agricultural operations will be completed throughout the territory, and provided the weather remains good Cormac should be able to gather a sufficiency of men to form an army large enough to manœuvre."

" It's time for us to go," announced Phineas, rising to his feet and moving his inkhorn and quills to a more comfortable position in the small of his back. " We've allowed the night to overtake us."

There was a moving back of chairs and a stirring of feet as the guests were assisted into their cloaks. Fursey was sent to the yard to untie the horses and lead them around to the door. He stood back in the shadow of the cottage listening to the muffled wailing of the wind through the mountain gap as Phineas, Magnus and the Widow from their saddles bade farewell to Declan and Maeve. Magnus sat astride his horse like a king, his great bulk silhouetted against the night sky, while Maeve stood at the horse's head talking to him. Fursey could hear his hearty laugh as he slapped his sword. Then in a chorus of farewells he rode off jingling, followed by the other two. None of them had remembered to say goodbye to Fursey.

On the following afternoon Fursey and Maeve sat by the edge of the lake breathing in the warm, sweet air. She was seated on a smooth rock while Fursey squatted on the ground facing her. There were clouds overhead and a breeze, and Fursey watched the shadows scampering across the flanks of the hills when he wasn't engaged in watching her face. She seemed to him pensive and sad, and to have lost a little of the freshness of her youth.

" Flinthead," she said suddenly, " I'm afraid my father is going to marry the Widow Dykes."

Fursey grunted to show his astonishment.

" He has formed an unfortunate attachment to her," continued Maeve sadly.

" But," remarked Fursey diffidently, " she is no longer young."

" Neither is my father," replied the girl. " She is a scheming woman, and she wants the house and the little bit of land. She knows how to flatter him, and men are so vain. I fear that he is sore assotted on her."

An image of Declan doddering around the house and the lake, came into Fursey's mind, and he marvelled exceedingly.

" Well," he answered at last. " After all, if your father is seriously and honourably attached to her—"

" Do you know anything about marriage," interrupted Maeve, " the kinship of soul that is necessary—? "

" Yes," replied Fursey with conviction. " I'm a widower myself."

" I didn't know you were ever married," replied Maeve, surprised.

" My wife predeceased me," explained Fursey.

"That's too bad," said Maeve, dropping her voice sympathetically. "How long were you married?"

"About six hours," replied Fursey gloomily, "but I know all about marriage. Compatibility of temperament is of the first importance."

A laugh bubbled up from Maeve's heart. Fursey glanced up at the two rows of pearly teeth and smiled himself. He knew that she was laughing at him, but he did not mind. She arose and began to lead the way back to the house.

"I don't think it will be a good thing," she said, and Fursey wondered at her gravity. He did not venture to speak for a few moments, and when he did speak, he spoke unevenly with a little break in his voice.

"It may be," he suggested, "that he loves her passing well. When I close my eyes, I can picture the two of them walking down the path from the house and around the borders of the lake, having goodly language and lovely behaviour together."

Maeve seemed annoyed. "I tell you," she said, "that she is after his house and land, and he is too blind and foolish and vain to realise it."

"Maybe," said Fursey miserably, "he so burns in love that he is past himself in his understanding."

They had reached the door of the cottage. Maeve turned and faced him. "What you don't appear to realise," she said with a sudden sob, "is that there's no room for two women in the one house," and she turned and hurried into the cottage.

Several times during the ensuing week Phineas the Clerk came and went. He spread his parchments and quills on the table in the kitchen and seemed always on the point of indicting something important. There were conferences between him and Declan and Maeve, but nothing seemed ever to come of them. He would sigh and rolling up his parchments, address himself to the evening meal which they spread before him. He brought news from the great world beyond The Gap. There had been a fierce and bloody encounter at

a ford in the Mulkeen River.   From sunrise until sunset the
conflicting armies had been in death grips.   The countryside
had echoed to the thunder of chariot wheels, and many a field
of promising corn had been trampled into the earth by the
manœuvring legions.   At sunset the King of Thomond had
withdrawn his defeated forces leaving two men dead on the
field.   Cashel's losses were a sergeant deprived of an eye by
a well-aimed stone.   " The battle was fiercely and evenly
contested," says the Annalist, " and to this day the place is
known in the Gaelic language as ' The Ford of Slaughter.' "

But later news was not so good.   King Cormac, elated by
his resounding victory, had withdrawn his army into the hills,
where he had commenced manœuvring with consummate
strategy.   In his absence the armies of Thomond, swollen now
by hundreds of troops released from their agricultural pursuits, had swept across the Tipperary plain, laying fire to the
houses of the rich.   A trail of flaming residences and billowing
white smoke marked their passage.   " Every gentleman's seat
in the country is aflame," said Phineas vehemently to Fursey,
who nodded sympathetically and continued for some hours to
ponder on the meaning of the strange phrase.   When news
of these happenings had been conveyed to King Cormac in
the hills, he was reported to have remarked philosophically,
" The King of Thomond doesn't understand the art of warfare," and to have moved his army into the mountains nearer
the Thomond border, where he recommenced manœuvring
on a larger scale.

One evening ten days later while Fursey was milking the
cow in the kitchen where he had brought her because of the
rain, he was startled by the sudden clatter of a horse's hooves
on the cobbles of the yard outside.   He went to the door and
saw Magnus astride his steaming war-horse, looking very
important and terrible with his sword and spear, and his
leathern shield upon his arm.   He dismounted and ignoring
Fursey's feeble welcome, pushed by him into the kitchen with
a curt " Out of my way, farmboy."   Inside he shook the rainwater from his martial cloak.

" Where's Maeve ? " he demanded of Fursey, who was trying to persuade the cow to leave the house.

" In the other room," answered Fursey.

" Tell her I'm here," commanded Magnus.

With a final heave of his shoulder, which he had placed against the cow's buttock, Fursey succeeded in expelling her through the front door. He turned and knocked at the door of the other room.

" Come in," came Maeve's voice.

Fursey opened the door and went in. Declan was sitting on the floor trying shortsightedly to disentangle a fishing line. There was a flush in Maeve's cheeks, and Fursey noticed with a sinking heart that she was tying a ribbon in her hair.

" Magnus is here," reported Fursey.

" Yes, I heard him," she replied. " Tell him I'll be out in a moment."

Fursey conveyed the message, and when he had lifted the pail of milk on to its shelf, he sat down despondently in his corner by the fire. Magnus strode up and down without deigning to speak to him. Maeve emerged a few moments later in a flutter of ribbon and girlish laughter. She gave Magnus her hand.

" So you're off to the wars," she said gayly.

" Yes," replied the soldier.

" I'm proud of you, my boy," said Declan, who had followed his daughter into the room.

Fursey dutifully drew a mug of beer and placed it before Magnus. Then he returned to his corner and, seating himself, fixed his eyes furtively on the soldier's broad, handsome face.

" The situation in which the Kingdom finds itself," began Magnus, " is in the highest degree critical. The cowardly King of Thomond, instead of leading his army into the hills and starting to manœuvre opposite King Cormac, has flung his entire forces into the Cashel plain, and the capital city itself is closely beleaguered."

" Dear me ! " exclaimed Declan. " And what is King Cormac doing to counter this outrageous behaviour ? "

" He is manoeuvring frantically in the hills, trying to attract the King of Thomond's attention and coax him to lead off his forces from the devoted city ; but seemingly to no avail.   The King of Thomond, who is as cowardly as he is ignorant of the principles of warfare, shows not the slightest inclination to face Cormac in the field.   Instead, four hundred of his slingsmen surround the city of Cashel and shower stones on it as big as your fist by day and by night.   The unceasing whistling of their artillery is something terrible, and already a most respected citizen of the town has had his brains dashed out as he ventured forth from the door of his dwelling to bring in the morning milk."

" But," asked Declan, " what of good Bishop Flanagan ? Can he do nought to abate the murderous rage of Thomond ? "

" The Bishop is playing a man's part," replied Magnus. " From the door of his palace on the hill he hurls anathemas and maledictions at the enemy.   He has pronounced the sentence of excommunication against the first man that damages ecclesiastical property."

" Is then Thomond so abandoned to wickedness as not to be moved by the representations of his lordship ? "

" Unfortunately," replied Magnus.   " Bishop Flanagan's efforts are largely negatived by the counter-maledictions and anathemas of the Bishop of Thomond, who is urging on his countrymen to raze every church and abbey in Cashel to the ground, having first sequestered the gold ornaments and valuables for the use of the Church in the Thomond diocese."

" I think war is terrible," said Maeve.

" It is a pursuit in the highest degree dangerous to the participants," declared Declan, shaking his head gravely. " I hope you come through it without any broken limbs, Magnus."

" I'll be all right," replied Magnus jovially, " but God help any man that stands against me ! "

" And what of the courageous garrison that defends Cashel ? " the old man asked.

" There is a sprinkling of soldiers," replied Magnus, " but it is the townspeople themselves, men, women and children, who are manning the palisade. Every stone that falls on the city is flung back in the faces of the encircling enemy."

" Bravo ! " exclaimed Declan enthusiastically.

" It shows fighting spirit," agreed Magnus, " but unfortunately it also serves to keep the enemy provided with an endless supply of ammunition. However, the forces of Thomond have been kept at a sufficient distance to prevent their setting fire to the thatch roofs of the city. In this regard the recent rain must also have been a help."

" The dirty ruffians ! " exclaimed the old man.   " I've a good mind to join Magnus and fight in the war myself."

" You'll do nothing of the sort," said Maeve. " Who'd guard the house if you were gone, with broken bands of soldiers roaming the countryside lusting for blood and plunder ? "

" That's true," muttered Declan, sitting back in his chair.

" The siege will be raised to-night," asserted Magnus with conviction.   " The hay is in, and there'll be a full five hundred of us gathered at the Cow's Head Tavern two hours before sunset. When we march, God help Thomond ! "

There was a few moments silence in the kitchen as the listeners pondered these ominous words. Fursey stirred uneasily and wondered why Magnus gazed so long and so steadfastly at Maeve. At last the soldier arose.

" It is time for me to go," he said gruffly.

" Run out to the yard, Flinthead," said Declan, " and lead Magnus' horse around to the door."

Fursey did as he was bid, and stood holding the halter until the soldier came and took it from him. Maeve had accompanied Magnus out into the thin rain, and as they came up to Fursey, he heard Magnus say to her, " It's definitely fixed for Saturday then."

Fursey retired to the shelter of the doorway with a strange, oppressive feeling in his heart. He stood beside the old man as Declan shouted good wishes and farewells to the soldier.

Magnus waved his hand to Declan, and putting his arms around Maeve, kissed her tenderly.   Then he sprang into the saddle, waved his hand in a final adieu, and slowly paced his horse out of the farmyard.   Maeve walked behind the horse until she came to the head of the track, where she stood waving her hand to the retreating horseman.

"Did you see that?" the question came from Fursey in a breathless gasp.   "He kissed her."

"Of course he did," grinned the old man.   "They're being married on Saturday in Kilpuggin Church.   It'll be a double wedding.   I'm marrying the Widow Dykes myself."

He doddered off into the far room, emitting little crackles of knowing laughter.   Fursey stood stock-still while moment after moment passed.   Then he walked across the kitchen to the fireplace and took down a coil of rope that hung there. As he moved back towards the door, Declan emerged from the far room.

"Where are you going?" he asked.

"To Cashel," replied Fursey.

"Not to fight in the war?" gasped the old man.

"No," replied Fursey.   "The war will be over by the time I arrive.   Didn't you hear the soldier say so?"

"What are you going for then?" asked the old man shrilly.

Fursey turned to him a face that was expressionless and dead.

"To give myself up to the authorities," he answered.   Then he turned and left the house, going round by the back and across the yard, for fear that he would meet Maeve.

CHAPTER IX

O NE hour after sunset all the dogs in the neighbourhood of Cashel awoke and began to bark. Battle had been joined in a field within sight of the city, and the irate farmer was running up and down the boundary dyke screaming to the opposing armies that they were ruining his spring wheat. Within half-an-hour the issue was decided. The Cashel legions had the advantage of surprise. The slingsmen of Thomond had been for two days hurling their ammunition at the city, which was a large target impossible to miss ; and they experienced considerable difficulty in suddenly shortening their range and hitting individual infantrymen who appeared out of nowhere and ran at them brandishing swords and shouting obscene and blasphemous language. The Thomond swordsmen, who should have taken the first shock of the assault, had been corrupted by two days' inactivity ; and they were carousing in a neighbouring ditch when the battle broke upon them. They were immediately overthrown and their ale-kegs seized by the patriot forces. The soldiers of Thomond were in no way lacking in courage and martial ardour, but the surprise was complete in that they understood from their generals that every Cashel fighting man was in the hills manœuvring with King Cormac ; and their once-proud army of five hundred men trailed back, broken and in disorder, towards the frontiers of Thomond, each man with a sense of grievance and feeling that somewhere or other there had been foul play. Forty-two of their generals and many other high officers fell into the hands of the victors, and were immediately put to death by immersion in a neighbouring pond. The gates of the city were flung open, and the excited populace vociferously welcomed the victors and the captured ale-kegs. Bishop Flanagan ordered a solemn *Te Deum* to be sung in the Cathedral, which was attended by those of the army who did not feel it incumbent on them to return to their farms. A fleet runner was despatched to the hills to inform King Cormac of the good news, and to suggest respectfully that the moment was now opportune for him to descend into the plains and wipe out Thomond for ever.

Fursey heard the news from individual soldiers who passed him on the road on their way back to their farms. He nodded indifferently and continued to plod fatalistically towards Cashel. Few thoughts passed through his head as he trod the road, for his mind was cold and dead. When it became dark, he crept into a dry corner of the hedge, but he did not sleep ; he lay instead all through the night gazing up at the indifferent stars. At sunrise and at midday he cast his rope over the branch of a tree and procured food ; but he ate little ; most of the time he squatted on his hunkers gazing dully at the bread and meat. He walked on towards Cashel as if impelled by some force outside himself, but the nearer he approached the settlement, the slower grew his gait, for somewhere inside himself he did not want to die, and least of all by fire. It was on the evening of the next day when he was still about ten miles from the city, that he sat down on a stone by the wayside and began to think. He remembered the trees as they had been in early spring, their skeleton branches sprinkled with green. He remembered the primroses, the dandelions and the wayward daffodils. All yellow, he said to himself dully, all yellow and green. That was before the demons had come to Clonmacnoise. He tried to conjure up a picture of himself as he had been then, a simple, innocent, stuttering lay-brother paring edible roots in a corner of the monastery kitchen, while Brother Cook stood by the fire humming grimly to himself as he stirred the soup. He remembered Father Crustaceous, who had only one tooth, and was always complaining that the meat was tough. He remembered Father Sampson, who had been a professional

wrestler before he entered the cloister, big Father Sampson
with his swinging stride, the only monk who had not been
afraid of the demons, but seemed rather to enjoy an encounter
with them as it gave him an opportunity of trying out once
more his wrestler's grips and holds. He recalled Father
Placidus, that testy, purse-lipped man ; and the suave, cool
Master of Novices, whom everyone feared. He remembered
with a lump in his throat little Brother Patrick, a lay-brother
like himself, and the fun they all had years before when a class
had been set up in a half-hearted attempt to teach the laybrothers to read and write. And he remembered the Abbot
Marcus—Abbot Marcus as he used to enter the refectory, his
robes rustling, to take his seat at the centre of the table on
the dais, his scholarly face shadowed by thought. " I
mustn't think of him," muttered Fursey through his clenched
teeth, " it'll only make me cry." But in spite of himself he
did think of Abbot Marcus, and he did not cry. Something
had entered into Fursey ; his heart felt like a chunk of the
moon, cold, dead and indifferent.

" How happy I was," he said, " though I didn't realise it."
But then the year had moved into late spring, the trees had
darkened to a deeper green, and the demons had come and the
beginning of his tribulations. With the first brazen flowers
of summer had come sin. He had practised sorcery, had
become an accomplished liar and even a thief.

" There's no going back," he meditated bitterly. " Clonmacnoise is closed to me for ever."

Then he thought sourly of what a weak, frightened creature
he himself was, when compared with a broad-shouldered,
daring fellow like Magnus. What a contrast ! Magnus des-
pised a mean, little fellow like him, a wearer of another man's
cast-off clothes. At best Magnus thought him funny and
looked at him, when he noticed him at all, with amused
contempt. And Magnus was right ! Fursey rested his forehead between his two clenched fists, his elbows on his knees,
and reflected how much he hated Magnus—a coarse and
boastful bully, who had only to put out his hand to get all

that he wanted in the world. Success went to the men of action, the men of affairs ; as for the dreamers and the gentle, it was enough for them that they were permitted to live.

" That's another sin," he said, sighing hopelessly. " Hatred is a great sin. We must hate no one on this earth." With a painful effort that was like a stone being turned over in his head, he put Magnus out of his mind. He remembered that he had one friend, or rather one creature bound by nature to his service, whatever that creature's real feelings might be— the lugubrious Albert. The moment he remembered Albert, he felt the pressing necessity of opening his heart to someone. He leaned forward and whispered the name gently. He waited for a few moments, his eyes fixed on the dust of the road, but he could note no movement.

" Albert ! " he said more loudly. There was still no sign of the bear's paws or the red, foggy eyes. Fursey looked over his shoulder to see whether the creature was behind him, but there was no trace of his familiar. Very astonished, he rose to his feet and taking his stand in the middle of the road-way he called a third time in a loud voice : " Albert ! "

Nothing happened. The full significance of his familiar's failure to appear came to Fursey in a rush. Could it be that he was no longer a sorcerer, or at least that his damnable powers were wearing off ? With a beating heart he hurried to the nearest tree. He uncoiled his rope with trembling fingers and flung it over a branch.

" Bread ! " he shouted exultingly, and gave the rope a mighty chuck. His hopes were immediately dashed by the descent of a huge loaf, which struck him on the forehead and knocked him into the ditch. As he strove to rise, the prey of bitter disappointment, he observed a pale man with very black eyes clambering over the fence on the far side of the road. When the stranger had successfully surmounted the obstruc-tion, he crossed the road, and coming across to where Fursey lay, he stood looking down at Fursey's floundering attempts to get out of the ditch.

"You ought to be ashamed of yourself," said the stranger.
"Drunk again."

Fursey gaped up at him in astonishment. He immediately
recognised the stranger as an anchorite, one of those holy men
who retire to remote caverns, and having turned out the wild
beasts dwelling therein, make such gloomy spots their
habitation where they pass the rest of their lives on a sparse
diet, praying for themselves and for mankind. The one who
gazed down disapprovingly at Fursey, was an uncouth hermit
covered with long, black, rusty hair. He was a living skeleton,
yellow, haggard and hatchet-faced, mere cuticle and cartilage.
In short, he was a hideous and dirty-looking apparition, clad
in an inadequate piece of sacking, and the odour of sanctity
that he shed around him was well-nigh insupportable.

"It's an ill wind that blows no one good," said the gaunt
stranger at last. "I hate drinking alone. Get up and come
with me."

The astonished Fursey struggled out of the ditch.

"They call me 'The Gentle Anchorite '," said the ascetic
by way of introducing himself. "Come along with me, but
bring your loaf of bread with you. It'll pay for a drink."

The two of them walked down the road together. Fursey
wondered why he was accompanying the anchorite, but he
told himself that he might as well go where the stranger was
going, as go anywhere else. They had progressed some
hundred paces when The Gentle Anchorite turned his dark
piercing eyes on Fursey.

"Why are you holding your nostrils between your thumb
and forefinger?" he asked.

"I cannot abide the stench," replied Fursey.

"Nonsense," said his companion. "I am not conscious
of any stench."

"You're lucky," said Fursey.

Fursey had noticed that his new acquaintance held something concealed under his left arm. The sacking which the
anchorite wore, effectively hid it from sight. Fursey was too
polite to pretend to notice, even when a muffled clucking

became audible from the depths of the anchorite's habiliments ;
but when a hen suddenly thrust out her head and started to
croak desperately, Fursey could no longer pretend that he was
unaware of her presence.   He stopped on the road and faced
the hermit.

" You haven't been stealing poultry ? " he asked.   " I
cannot be a party to a crime."

" No," answered the hermit mildly.   " You can take my
word for it.   This bird is an offering from a client for whom I
performed a miracle yesterday."

" That's all right," replied Fursey quite satisfied, and they
continued on their way.

" I've had a gruelling day," volunteered The Gentle
Anchorite, " and I feel myself much in need of refreshment."

" Indeed ? " remarked Fursey politely.

" You must know," continued his companion, " that persons
like myself who are raised to an ecstatic intuition of the
Sovereign Good, are much pestered by the servants of the
terrible Emperor of Night.   I refer to Satan, whom nothing
tortures so much as the sight of a good man at his prayers."

Fursey nodded understandingly.

" It's nothing unusual for me," continued the anchorite,
" on waking of a morning to see my cavern flooded with a
dismal light, and to find a devil sitting at the foot of my bed
grunting like a pig.   Sometimes they come as ghouls and
harpies, and I have been followed around all day by a demon
in the form of a water-dog.   I have seen devils standing
upside down, and I myself have been thrown by them into
that unusual posture.   But, praise the Lord, I am always
well able for them, and I have no less than forty-eight demons
tied down in moorland pools on the mountain on which I
dwell."

This speech seemed to Fursey unduly boastful, but politeness demanded that he make a sound indicative of his admiration.   Thus, encouraged, the hermit continued his recitation.

" To-day I have had to struggle with a demon of more than
usual agility and guile.   I saw him first on awaking this

morning. He was furry and had snouted jaws; he looked dazed and languid and was peering in at me through the mouth of my cavern. Strange to relate none of the usual exhortation or adjurations had the slightest effect upon him. I chased him all over the mountainside, and while he seemed lumbering and slow in his movements, he was surprisingly nimble in dodging. I caught him at last a couple of hours ago. I admit it was more by luck than anything else. He tripped over an outcropping rock. The creature seemed by then exhausted, and I had no difficulty in fastening him to the bottom of a bog pool convenient to my cave. I must examine him further to-morrow as I have never before seen a demon quite like him. The chase has left me in almost the same state of exhaustion myself. That is why we are proceeding to an ale-house, where I can recoup my strength."

"Very interesting," commented Fursey, hoping that his companion would not discover that he was a wizard.

They had by now come to a low-sized, thatched house with some writing above the door.

"Here we are," declared the anchorite. "I cannot read myself, but the legend runs 'Cow's Head Select Tavern,' which is the name of the place. The inscription is in the Latin language, and was carved by a parish priest from Donegal who had been drinking for a week and was unable to pay his score. The work was accepted by the proprietor, who is a man sensible of the value of culture, in full discharge of the debt. The building is a very ancient one. The same inscription may be seen carved vertically on the left doorpost in Ogham, which was the way the learned wrote before the introduction of Latin lettering into this country."

Fursey expressed his admiration of these things, and the two of them bowed their heads and entered the low doorway. The interior was dark, but Fursey's eyes soon became accustomed to the half-light, and he saw that a long wooden counter ran down the middle of the room. Behind it stood the proprietor, who was bald and had neither beard nor eyebrows. There were several customers in the tavern in various stages of intoxication. They seemed upset by the entry of the anchorite and retired with one accord to the far end of the bar where they covered their mouths and noses with their hands. The proprietor hastily picked up a clothes peg from a neighbouring shelf and fixed it to his nostrils before approaching to enquire in what way he could be of service. The anchorite withdrew the hen from the depths of his clothing and placed her on the counter. From her long proximity to the holy man's person the bird seemed dazed and languid, and she seemed to find it difficult to keep her feet. She staggered once or twice and fell.

" The animal doesn't seem in very good condition," remarked the proprietor diffidently.

" She's all right," retorted the hermit. " She's a stranger here, and she's shy. You'll find her good eating."

The proprietor felt the bird's breast and wings while she gazed up at him mournfully.

" I'll allow you four beakers of ale or three of mead," he declared at last.

" Very well," replied the anchorite. " Mark me up four beakers of ale. And this gentleman has a loaf."

The tavernkeeper felt Fursey's loaf judiciously with his thumb.

" That's very good bread," he declared, " I'll allow you two beakers of mead."

" Right," said the hermit. " Give us the ale first."

At a signal from the proprietor a small boy whom Fursey had not noticed before, emerged from beneath the counter and with a piece of charcoal drew two columns on the whitewashed wall. In one of them he inserted four strokes and in the other two. He then crossed through two of the vertical strokes, and the proprietor produced two foaming beakers of ale and placed them on the counter. He then went to the door and drew in a few breaths of fresh air before replacing the peg on his nose and retiring to the furthest corner of the room. Fursey and the hermit took their beakers and seated themselves on a bench that ran along the wall.

" This is all of the highest interest to me," observed Fursey.
" I have never been in a tavern before."

The Gentle Anchorite took a long swallow of ale and
scratched the black rusty hair on his chest reminiscently.

" It's a very efficient system," he remarked, " though I've
been told that there are barbarous foreign lands too backward
to appreciate its merits. They have instead some highly
involved method which they call ' coinage.' They have little
bits of gold and other metal, on which is engraved the head of
the king ; and in their benighted ignorance the backward
inhabitants of those lands attach a disproportionate value to
the tiny amulets and use them for all purposes of exchange."

" I seem to have heard," replied Fursey racking his brains,
" that there were at one time big territories called Greece and
Rome which had some such complicated system."

" There were," agreed the anchorite triumphantly. " And
where are they now ? Wiped from the face of the earth forever,
while this country, the Island of Saints and Scholars, still
endures."

Fursey smiled happily and finished off the dregs of his ale.
His companion nudged him sharply.

" Listen," he whispered.

Fursey listened to the conversation which came up to them
from the far end of the tavern. A small man who was the
centre of an admiring group, was holding up to ridicule all
writers alive and dead, punctuating his witticisms and sallies
with bursts of cackling laughter which made Fursey shudder.
As Fursey glanced in his direction, he recognised with alarm
the gargoyle whom he had seen in Cuthbert's garden. The
creature caught Fursey's eye and gave him a friendly nod.

" Oh, you know him," remarked the anchorite apparently
relieved. " I feared from his appearance that he was a petty
demon of the trickier sort."

" I know him slightly," responded Fursey nervously.
" He's a minor man of letters."

" Oh, that explains it," answered the hermit, and he arose
to order another two beakers of ale.

Fursey glanced around the tavern covertly to assure himself that Cuthbert was not present. He told himself that the one person whom he must avoid above everyone else in the world, was the sexton of Kilcock Churchyard. Cuthbert's feelings towards him would certainly be not benevolent, in view of the disclosures he had made about Cuthbert at his trial before the Cathedral Chapter. It was bad enough to be burnt as a sorcerer, but it would be infinitely worse to be turned into a toad and kept indefinitely in a jar. But Cuthbert was not present. He had evidently turned the gargoyle loose on the world, or else the creature had escaped. Fursey washed down his relief with a long pull at his second beaker of ale.

"You can never be sure of whom you'll knock against," confided The Gentle Anchorite. "I was in here a few years ago, sitting where we are sitting now, having a drink with a most affable gentleman who insisted on paying for everything we drank. I was most favourably impressed by his demeanour and apparent piety, until glancing down suddenly I observed with some alarm that my companion had hands like the claws of a bird. Needless to say I immediately challenged him, and forthwith he turned into a spectre, badly-made and ill-dressed, very wicked-looking and stinking insupportably. His well-pressed cloak and kilt became all at once coarse black garments, dirty and singed by the flames. He made off through the doorway, and I would have followed him and transfixed him, had I not been prevented by the weight of the drink which he had forced me to consume. Nevertheless, the management was very grateful to me for having rid the house of him."

Fursey smiled with the left side of his mouth, and ruefully contemplated the empty bottom of his beaker.

"What would he have done if you hadn't discovered him in time?" he asked.

"It's obvious that he came here to tempt me," answered the hermit. "No doubt after we had put down another few drinks, he would have invited me round the corner of the house to meet some lively and engaging female that he had conjured up. Or he might have attempted to dazzle me with the offer of a kingdom in exchange for my soul."

" It just goes to show that a man must be very careful whom he talks to," asserted Fursey.

"Oblige me by taking that grin off your face," said the anchorite to Fursey, as he arose to indicate to the proprietor that it was time to serve the two beakers of mead.

" Was I grinning ? " asked Fursey.

"Yes, ever since you began your second mug of ale," replied the hermit severely. " It's not at all dignified."

As they sat in happy appreciation of the bouquet of the mead, Fursey watched with interest as a cow was driven into the tavern, and the small boy got a ladder and laboriously began to mark up a thousand beakers of ale on the wall, commencing high up in a corner near the ceiling. The cow was driven behind the counter, while her late owner, a melancholy-looking, ale-sodden farmer, sat down and began at once to reduce the number to his credit. A few moments later a little old woman entered, a shawl over her head, and placed two eggs on the counter. She was served with a half-beaker.

When The Gentle Anchorite had drunk his way through half his goblet of mead, he smacked his lips with satisfaction and plunged reminiscently into his life history.

" As a youth," he began, " I was a careless and indifferent fellow, much addicted to the sport of taws, a game played with round pebbles which one precipitates with the thumb, attempting to strike the taw of the opponent. Many a hen I stole from my mother's yard and gambled away at a taw-school. But I was saved early from a life of sin and entered the monastery at Cong. It was clear from the very first that I was marked out for a life of saintliness. As a novice my rapts and ecstacies alarmed the monks. It was not unusual for me during dinner in the refectory to be sometimes raised ten cubits from the ground, my spoon and knife still clutched in my fists, and landed in a height of passive contemplation where I experienced an ecstacy and an abstraction from the things of sense quite unobtainable by the less-favoured members of the community. At length the Abbot took me aside and advised me that I was far too pious for the smooth working of the monastery. I concurred with him in this : it was obvious to me that my extreme saintliness was leading my brethren into the sins of envy and jealousy. I wandered south and found a suitable cavern above the Cashel road. I drove out a family of wolves that had made it their habitation, and installed myself therein. I have been there nigh on forty years, and I can boast that never once have I indulged in the sensuous practice of washing.''

The anchorite raised a black claw and pulling back his sack-cloth, bared his chest for Fursey's inspection. Fursey moved along the bench away from the holy man, seemingly overcome by such evidence of piety.

'' I remember well,'' continued the hermit, '' the first demon who attempted to harry me. I had just placed on the slab that serves me as table, the handful of acorns which was to constitute my evening meal, when I heard him snorting at the entrance to the cave. I admit that I was not without fear. It was my first experience of demons, and I didn't know whether he was intent on taking my life, or whether he would rest satisfied with a bout of harrowing and attempted seduction. Uttering a passionate cry for strength I went to the cavern's mouth to encounter him. At first I could see nothing, and then about ten paces away a sort of black phantom with horns and tail presented itself and began to gambol about before me. He was a demon with burning eyes and claws upon his hands, and as he skipped about, he turned from time to time and grinned at me furiously. The uncouth sight was too much for me : I retired precipitately into the furthest corner of the cavern where I fell on my knees and gave myself over to prayer for strength in the fiery trial of martyrdom and for help in the hotter fire of temptation. I was awakened from my devotions by a scream like that of a screech-owl, and on looking up beheld the horrible enemy squatting on his hunkers before my table from which he had swept my handful of acorns. He had placed a hunk of succulent meat upon the stone, and before my eyes he took it up with both claws and devoured it bones and all. Being of a quick understanding, I speedily appreciated that his object was to tempt me to the sin of gluttony. It was Eastertide, and a paschal taper stood to hand. I immediately seized it and broke it over his head. I cannot truthfully say which of us chased the other out of the cave, but the two of us coursed back and forward over the hillside the whole night through. My memory again fails me as to which of us was the pursuer and which the pursued, but I do remember most distinctly that every time I found myself within his reach, I received countless slaps and blows from a stick with which he had armed himself. His sportiveness abated just before sunrise, and I was found in a debilitated condition in a furze bush by some peasants on their way to market."

"You must have been somewhat exhausted," remarked Fursey.

"Somewhat exhausted!" echoed the hermit indignantly. "I had just enough respiration left to prevent their burying me."

"Our beakers are empty," observed Fursey, who was beginning to tire of these reminiscences and was anxious to be allowed to speak himself.

"And likely to remain so," replied the anchorite gloomily. "We have nought left to trade for ale. Holy Poverty has its disadvantages."

"Leave it to me," said Fursey knowingly. He hitched his rope over his shoulder and made his way out of the tavern. He was back in a few moments, his arms loaded with food-stuffs, four loaves of bread, an aromatic cheese and a couple of pounds of best butter.

"Where did you get them?" asked The Gentle Anchorite suspiciously.

"Never you mind," said Fursey.

"If they've been stolen—" began the anchorite virtuously.

He seemed less inclined to press the matter when a few moments later three glistening pots of mead were set in front of him.

Fursey took his own three pots from the counter in a wide embrace and carried them over to where his companion was sitting. For some moments no word was spoken while each addressed himself seriously to the business of emptying one of the pots. At length Fursey took his face out of his beaker and languidly wiped a few amber-coloured beads of the liquor from his cheeks and chin. He sighed and putting his elbow on the table, rested his head on his hand. For some time he regarded his companion pensively.

" You're a man of great learning and piety," he said at last. " Perhaps you can help me in my trouble.'"

The hermit threw back the rusty hair that hung down over his face, so that he could see Fursey more clearly.

" If it's anything in the nature of a miracle," he replied, " I'll be glad to oblige you ; but a small offering is expected. The labourer is worthy of his hire."

" It's nothing like that," responded Fursey. " I only want advice."

" Oh," replied the hermit, and he seemed to be somewhat disappointed.

" Do you know anything about love ? " enquired Fursey.

" Of course I do," retorted the anchorite. " By God's grace I can see as deeply into the abyss of love as any man."

" How does one set about winning a woman's love ? " asked Fursey.

" I haven't the faintest idea," rejoined the anchorite haughtily. " You don't appear to realise whom you're talking to."

" I mean no offence," explained Fursey. " But there's an amiable young woman of my acquaintance, and I'm sore assotted on her."

The anchorite groaned aloud in anguish. " Seek not to follow after the daughters of iniquity," he quoted.

" She's the daughter of a man called Declan," replied Fursey.

"I don't care what her father's name is," retorted the anchorite. "I warn you that you're walking on the brink of Hell." And he began to exhort Fursey to be strong in faith and put his confidence in God. Fursey only half-listened to his exhortations. The conversation seemed to him to have taken a wrong turning, but he felt too happy and dreamy to bring it back. His mind wandered to past events, and he found himself regretting that he had not made better use of his stay in Cuthbert's cottage. He should at least have remained until he had learnt the ingredients, composition and use of love philtres. Fursey sighed as he thought of his lost opportunities. Here he was a fully-fledged wizard, and the only sorcery he knew was how to fly on a broom and how to produce food by pulling on a rope. He fixed his eyes dreamily on the anchorite's long rusty beard and wondered if he pulled it, would a loaf of bread fall on to the table. Probably not, probably only a colony of bugs. His thoughts drifted to Maeve and the last time he had seen her, standing against the evening sky waving her hand to Magnus as he rode down the track from the cottage. The muscles of Fursey's body jerked convulsively as he tore his mind away from the image which was so acid in his memory. What was the use of wishing for further magical knowledge? Magnus had Maeve, and it was too late.

He sighed and forced himself to listen to the anchorite, who was droning some story from the life of a lady saint, in the apparent hope of edifying Fursey and winning him from carnal desire.

". . . . her eyes," concluded the hermit, "no longer lit up with the wild delight of the delirium of vice and bacchanalian orgies, but glowed softly with the blessed peace of conscious forgiveness."

"This old fool wants to do all the talking," thought Fursey. "He won't let me get in a word at all. I'll show him."

Fursey emptied his beaker and waited for the mead to subside in his stomach. Then he plunged into a rambling account, punctuated by hiccoughs, of the life and times of

Blessed John the Dwarf, which he had heard read aloud in the
refectory at Clonmacnoise. Between his hiccoughs and his
faulty memory, the story of Blessed John, which should have
been edifying and exemplary, became, as Fursey related it,
very funny indeed. The good humour increased as The
Gentle Anchorite also became afflicted with the hiccoughs, and
Fursey had perforce to halt from time to time in his story to
laugh at his companion. Merriment is infectious, and soon
the hermit was emitting short melancholy barks, the sort of
laughter one might expect to hear coming up out of a grave.
He clawed his lank beard and asserted that Fursey was the
pleasantest fellow he had ever met. Fursey slapped the
anchorite jovially on the knee. A cloud of dust arose that
nearly blinded both of them. As they staggered around
sneezing and rubbing their eyes, their merriment nearly
reached the stage of convulsions.

A couple of hours passed in this manner. Fursey could not
afterwards recall the substance of their conversation, but he
remembered that it was the best and most brilliant talk
imaginable, scintillating with wit and good humour. When
at last they agreed that it was time to go, the tavern was
empty except for the proprietor asleep over the counter. They
let themselves out, but when they gained the roadway, the
fresh night air affected them powerfully. So uncertain was
Fursey's gait that he had perforce to lean against a tree, and
when he had secured its support, he was loath to leave it. He
stood, a tubby figure propped against the bole, smiling blandly
at the circular moon overhead, while The Gentle Anchorite
capered in the middle of the road trolling forth a song of
suggestive and improper import. When the hermit had
finished his bawdy lay, he succeeded in detaching Fursey from
the tree, and with old-world hospitality offered him accommo-
dation in his cave for the night. Fursey thanked him earnestly and shook his hand ; and the two of them proceeded
unsteadily arm-in-arm down the road.

It was a night of filmy moonlight, the sort of night on which
almost anything might well be abroad, one of those nights on

which the dead yearn to look on the living and to accost them. The stark trees laid their moon-softened shadows here, there and everywhere. Overhead the moon sailed among her stars, suffusing the fields and the roads with soft blue light and silence. But Fursey was not afraid : one is not afraid when one has as companion a man with forty years' experience of tying down demons. Fursey told himself that The Gentle Anchorite's fame must have spread far and wide in the world of shadows, and it would be a hardy demon or spectre who would venture to approach him, especially when he was drunk and belligerent.

The road was long. It seemed to Fursey that they walked for hours before scrambling through a hedge and making their way over the bare hillside. It was another hour at least, an hour of weary struggling uphill through furze and bracken, before they came to the stony place where the hermit had his habitation. It was a spot bleak enough to satisfy the most exacting anchorite, a low cave in the rocks, and beyond it the bogs. The air was moist, and a small breeze blew steadily across the waste. Fursey could see here and there the glint of a moorland pool.

The hermit had grown quiet and seemed plunged in a deep melancholy. Mead is a heady brew, but its effect soon wears off with exercise. Fursey was by now more tired than drunk, and he grunted bad-humouredly when the anchorite took him by the arm and insisted that before retiring to rest, he must see the hermit's latest conquest, the strange, shuffling demon who had been captured and tied in a bog pool that afternoon. The pool was not far removed from the cave, and after a few minutes clambering between the rocks and through the bracken they stood at its edge. The anchorite stretched out a black claw and directed Fursey's attention to a huge rock incised with a cross, which lay at the bottom of the pool. Fursey bent over the edge and peered in. The water was only about six feet deep, and the head and four paws of some creature were discernible projecting from beneath the boulder. The creature lay spreadeagled on its back with all the weight of

the rock on its chest.   Fursey gazed with quickening interest—
surely he had seen those bear's paws before and that body
covered with black hair.   A pair of red foggy eyes looked up
at him pathetically.   It was Albert !

Fursey stepped back quickly and allowed himself to be led
back to the cave by the hermit, who repeated his account of
the difficulty he had experienced in capturing the unusual
demon.   Of course, thought Fursey, Albert was impervious to
religious adjuration and exhortation for the simple reason that
he did not belong to the Christian order of things, but was a
creature of an older religion.   Fursey had not recovered from
his surprise, and his thoughts were still scattered when they
arrived back at the cave, and the hermit conducted him into
its depths.

" Now for our evening meal," said the anchorite.   Going to
a hole in the wall he drew out a couple of crusts and placed
them on a flat rock.   " Seeing as how you are my guest," he
continued, " we will make high festival," and with the conscious air of being a generous host, he produced a hazel nut.
" We will divide it between us," he said, placing it on the
stone slab.

Fursey stared gloomily at this meagre fare and essayed to
crack the crust between his teeth.   His efforts did not meet
with much success, and he replaced the crust upon the table
and wiped the blood from the corner of his mouth.

" Try the nut," advised the hermit, who was crunching his
crust with evident appreciation.   Fursey picked up the hazel
nut and gingerly brushed off the green mould that covered it.

" Ah, you're losing the best part," said the hermit deprecatingly.

Fursey smiled faintly and biting off half the nut, pushed the
other half over to his companion.   He found that it lent itself
to easy mastication, and he sat ruminating on its unusual
flavour until the hermit had finished his meal.

" Let us return thanks before retiring to rest," said the
holy man sinking on his knees.   Fursey chose a smooth spot
on the floor and knelt, resting his elbows on a rock and sinking

his face in his hands. The hermit prayed for almost an hour in a loud and terrible voice, accusing himself and Fursey of all the known sins and imploring forgiveness, while Fursey on his knees slumbered fitfully. When the hermit had brought his orisons to a conclusion in a final wallow of abnegation, he directed Fursey's attention to a neat row of disciplines hanging on the wall. There were about a dozen, and they varied in size from a narrow, lithe whip to a broad, leathern thong in which were embedded a goodly number of nails and shark's teeth.

"We must do a little penance before we retire," said the hermit, "a couple of dozen lashes apiece. We can confer them upon one another."

"I always do my penance in the morning," replied Fursey hurriedly.

"You might be dead before the morning," urged the hermit, "and you will have lost this opportunity of acquiring grace."

"I'll risk it," said Fursey stoutly. "Morning is my time for mortifying myself, and I'm not going to break the good habit of a lifetime."

"Have it your own way," answered the hermit huffily. "I'm not going to forego my nightly mortification of the flesh. Oblige me by giving me twenty lashes."

An odour of sanctity swept across the cavern like a wave as the holy man peeled off his upper garment and took up his stand, stripped to the waist, with his back to Fursey. Fursey inspected the row of disciplines.

"What size would you like?" he asked.

"One of medium strength," replied the hermit.

Fursey examined the row of disciplines judiciously, then he turned and looked at the hermit's back. A sudden image had come into his mind, a picture of the unfortunate Albert lying at the bottom of the moorland pool with two tons of granite on his chest.

"I venture to suggest," said Fursey, "that the thick hair with which your back is draped, affords you considerable protection against a discipline of medium weight. In a holy matter such as this, you must play fair with God. I suggest a discipline of greater striking power."

The hermit turned his head to gaze at Fursey. He seemed to think that his sanctity was being called into question, and his reply was short.

" Use your judgment," he said testily, and turning away once more, he hunched his back to meet the blow. Fursey picked down the weightiest discipline and tested the shark's teeth and nails with his thumb. Then he rolled up his sleeves and let fly with all his strength at the hairy back of the hermit. The snaky thong whistled, struck with a resounding smack, and wound twice around the holy man's body. The Gentle Anchorite emitted a howl and capered madly up and down the cave.

" What's wrong ? " asked the astonished Fursey. " You told me to hit you."

" I didn't tell you to take the skin and flesh off my bones," gasped the anchorite, turning on Fursey eyes full of bale.

" I'll use another discipline for the remaining nineteen strokes," replied Fursey comfortingly. " There's a nice one here with broken bits of razor embedded in the leather."

" I've had enough for to-night," muttered the hermit between his teeth. " Already I can feel my soul suffused and flooded with sanctifying grace, but in the morning," and his eyes met Fursey's, " I'll have the remaining nineteen when you are having your twenty. We shall confer them on one another. That is the most convenient."

" Certainly," agreed Fursey, quickly making up his mind that he would be gone before the morning.

The anchorite was still squirming as he indicated a heap of foul-smelling straw in the corner, which was to be their bed. He laid himself gingerly on his face as his back seemed to be still sore, and Fursey stretched himself alongside. Before long the cave was shrill with the hermit's catarrhal snores which forced their way through his beard in a muffled whistle.

Hour after hour Fursey tossed on the straw unable to sleep. When a man of determined sanctity has lived in a small cave for forty years, the insect life is apt to assume alarming proportions. Bugs, resigned for many years to the thin diet which the hermit's skinny frame provided, after one nip at Fursey scuttled off to tell their friends, and soon all the game in the cavern were making in his direction. They came in such myriads that for a moment Fursey thought that an attempt was being made to murder him. Plump fleas investigated different parts of his body in a series of gargantuan hops, while great strapping bugs fastened themselves to his arms and thighs. The smaller fry of the insect world, mites and the like, contented themselves with setting up colonies in unlikely corners of his anatomy where the competition was less keen. Fursey rolled and wallowed, but to no avail. To add to his discomfort The Gentle Anchorite woke up and seemed not only jealous of the attention his vermin were paying to Fursey, but to fear that there was a real danger of losing the external evidence of his forty years' sanctity, so he bent over from time to time to collect as many bugs as he could from Fursey's body and put them back on his own. This preposterous behaviour Fursey found in the highest degree exasperating. In his opinion it only encouraged the more mischievous of the bugs to greater liveliness, and it obviated all possibility of sleep. You couldn't possibly sleep if you were turned over every half-an-hour by your host and searched.

Towards morning the hermit's excursions became less regular, and he slept for longer intervals. When Fursey heard the muffled snores taking on a deeper note, he crawled from the straw on his hands and knees and dragged his wounded body through the mouth of the cave into the fresh air. There was a little patch of grey in the sky to the east, and realising that there was little time to spare, he hobbled quickly across the intervening space to the edge of the pool where Albert was imprisoned. He fell on his knees on the heather at the edge.

" Hello, Albert," he whispered.

A stream of bubbles issued from Albert's mouth. As they broke on the surface they resolved themselves into a string of very bad language.

" Sh ! " said Fursey. " Don't curse."

Albert made another effort, and the breaking bubbles indicated to Fursey that Albert was devoted to his service, that he was the best master Albert ever had, and for God's sake to get him out of the pool. Fursey cast a hurried glance over his shoulder to assure himself that the hermit was not yet abroad, before immersing himself in the pool, clothes and all. The cold water was a considerable relief to his bug-scarred body, and after herculean straining at the boulder he succeeded in rolling it to one side. Albert immediately bobbed up to the surface where he floated on his back. He seemed intact, though a little flattened. Fursey clambered out of the pool and taking Albert by one of his bear's paws, hauled him on to the bank, Albert shook himself like a dog, scattering water in all directions ; and then collapsed against a rock. He volunteered no word of thanks, but threw a terrified glance in the direction of the cave.

" If he comes out," he wheezed huskily, " order me to disappear. It's the only thing that will save me."

" Come on," said Fursey. " It's time we got away from here," and he set out at a trot down the hillside, with Albert staggering along at his heels. Fursey did not stop until they reached the road.

" I'm done up," gasped Albert, " You'll have to carry me."

" We're safe now," replied Fursey as he helped the ex-hausted Albert through the hedge. The familiar sat down in the dust of the road while Fursey seated himself on the grassy bank facing him.

" You should have ordered me to disappear up there at the pool," complained Albert. " Then I could have travelled down the hill with you in my capacity as an ætherial essence. It would have been far less tiring."

" I didn't want to let you out of my sight again," replied Fursey, " until I had found out how you got into that predicament. I think you owe me an explanation."

Albert looked uneasy.

" Come now," said Fursey severely. " I summoned you on the road yesterday, and you failed to appear. How was that ? Don't you realise that you are bound absolutely to my service ? "

Albert assumed a hang-dog look, and his eyes failed to meet his master's.

" It's all very fine," he answered sullenly, " If you had a rock as big as a mountain on your chest, you'd be slow in answering a summons."

" Don't quibble," said Fursey primly. " It's not a question of slowness in answering a summons ; you didn't answer it at all."

" I couldn't come," bleated Albert indignantly. " That mad fellow up there, the long, thin fellow, had got hold of me and fixed me in the pool. I couldn't get out. You saw it yourself ; what's the use of asking silly questions ? "

" You're avoiding the issue," retorted Fursey. " You're bound to my service, and you're supposed to be at hand all the time, ready to appear the moment you're summoned. What were you doing gallivanting round the countryside getting into trouble ? "

Albert fixed his foggy red eyes on his master and glared balefully, but did not reply. Fursey flushed and stamped his foot on the ground.

" If you don't answer me," he said, " I'll punish you. I'll think up something terrible to do to you. I'll turn you into something extraordinary, a lizard or something like that. You don't appear to realise that I've inherited The Grey Mare's powers, and I'm a very formidable wizard."

" Garn ! " interjected Albert contemptuously. " You're the most hopeless wizard I've ever encountered. Why, you don't know how to do anything."

" Don't be impertinent," shrilled Fursey.

" If the marrows of an unbaptised babe were put into your hands," said Albert raising his voice so as to shout his master down, " I don't believe you'd know what to do with them. Can you even turn milk sour ? Do you even know how to plough a field with four toads harnessed to the plough ? Why, you don't even know how to do the simplest things."

Fursey did not reply, but sat for a moment thinking of his deficiencies. When the eyes of sorcerer and familiar again met, both seemed rather ashamed of their loss of temper. At last Fursey spoke.

" How did it happen ? " he asked simply.

" I'm that starved," replied Albert sulkily, " through your refusal to supply me with my proper meed of blood, that I became desperate. I wandered off hoping to find some quiet human whom I could have a nip at when he wasn't looking. I didn't expect to run into a wild character like the hairy fellow up above, who chased me around the whole afternoon shouting Latin at me."

" Let it be a lesson to you," said Fursey reprovingly. " You shouldn't try to bite people."

" It's all very well for you to talk," growled Albert. " You look well-fed enough, but I've grown that meagre that if I stand sideways you can hardly see me. Really, master," he said with a throb of emotion in his voice, " you'll have to do something for me. My coat is all falling out. Soon I'll look like an old, mangy, moth-eaten dog. Look."

He put a shrunken paw to his chest and pulled out a handful of hair, which he held out for inspection. When Fursey answered, his voice was sad and far-away.

" Maybe, Albert," he said, " you won't be bothered with me much longer. I'm on my way to Cashel to surrender myself to the authorities."

" Why should you do that ? " asked Albert astonished.

" I've tried life," said Fursey, " and I've found it wanting."

" So now you're going to try death ? "

Fursey thought for a moment before replying.

" Aye," he answered at last.

" You know that you'll be burnt ? "

" Yes," replied Fursey.

A look of genuine happiness spread over Albert's countenance from his red eyes to the tip of his snout, but he tried manfully to hide his satisfaction.

" Maybe it's best for us both," he said consolingly. " You'll be rid of the cares of living, and when you're dead, I'll be able to secure another master, some young wizard with a promising career ahead of him, who is fully cognisant of the care which he should bestow on his familiar."

" I'll miss you," said Fursey sadly. " It's not that you're an engaging companion, but I've sort of got used to you."

" You won't feel the sense of loss for long," replied Albert somewhat impatiently. " They'll have you burnt in a couple of days."

" I don't imagine that we'll see one another again," declared Fursey. " I think farewells should be quick. It's best that way."

Albert rose from his hunkers and held out his paw. Fursey took it and shook it sadly.

" Goodbye," said Fursey.

" Goodbye," replied Albert. " Don't forget," he added anxiously, " that you've to order me to vanish."

" Disappear," commanded Fursey ; and as Albert dissolved, Fursey waited to utter a final word of melancholy valediction to a single smoky red eye which hung alone in the air for a few seconds after the rest of Albert had gone. Then he turned hurriedly on his heel and made off down the road that led to Cashel.

CHAPTER X

ABOUT an hour later Fursey's unwilling feet brought him to New Inn Cross. A crossroads is at all times a place of foul repute, a point where watchful fiends are apt to lurk, and a spot likely to be used for nocturnal dances and all classes of witchery. Fursey would have hurried by, but he was suddenly rooted to the road at the sight of a familiar figure in black leaning nonchalantly against a gate. It was Cuthbert! A dark lock of hair hung over his forehead obscuring one of his eyes. The other eye was fixed upon Fursey. A witchhazel wand was propped against the gate beside the sexton. In his hand he held a silken bag, and a red cock was perched upon his shoulder.

Such was Fursey's terror that he stood in the middle of the road bereft of the power to move either forward or backwards : his legs had become like two rods glued to the ground. His heart gave one mighty whack in his chest and then seemed to stop beating altogether. He struggled to regain his breath, his mind the prey of the most painful imaginings. He saw himself turned into a toad and imprisoned in an earthen jar for the duration of Cuthbert's life ; and on the sexton's demise, perhaps handed down to generation after generation of sorcerers as an interesting specimen. The intolerable boredom of such an existence was borne in powerfully upon him and filled him with the strongest disquiet. It might well be that many thousands of years would elapse before some accident occurred to break the spell and effect his release. Through a film of mist he observed the sexton detaching himself from the gate and sloping across the road towards him. He became aware that his limp hand had been lifted from his side and was being warmly wrung.

"My dear friend Fursey," came the sexton's voice, "You have no conception of the pleasure this encounter affords me. I located you in my crystal about an hour ago and travelled here to intercept you, as I desire to have some discourse with you in private."

Fursey was not conscious of what happened next ; but when he became once more aware of the world about him, he found himself propped against the gate while the sexton fanned him anxiously with his hat.

"That was a bad turn you took," purred Cuthbert. "My poor friend, wait here for a moment while I procure you a stimulant."

The sexton grabbed Fursey's length of rope and hurrying to a neighbouring tree, flung it over one of the branches. He gave it a sharp jerk and deftly caught the cup of mead which fell from the foliage. He came running back without spilling a drop, and having prized Fursey's teeth open with his witch-hazel wand, he poured the entire contents down Fursey's gullet. Fursey hiccoughed and recovered full consciousness.

"Are you all right ? " asked Cuthbert.

"I'd like to sit down," responded Fursey feebly.

Cuthbert helped him into a sitting position with his back supported by the gate, and stood over him cracking his fingers nervously. Fursey gazed disconsolately from the red cock perched on the sexton's shoulder to the small silken bag which swung from his hand. Then a seemingly interminable spate of words fell from Cuthbert's lips. Fursey's wits were too scattered to follow the sexton's flow of talk, which seemed to be about Fursey's health. Fursey was not concerned about his health : what he was worried about was his future ; but as Cuthbert's deluge of words flowed over his conscious-ness, odd words and broken sentences began to form a sediment, which he turned over slowly in his mind and began to examine. The sexton appeared to be trying to explain away the part which he had played at Fursey's trial, and to convince Fursey that he felt for him only fraternal goodwill and benevolence. Fursey pricked up his ears and began to listen. Then he fixed his gaze on Cuthbert's face. There could be no doubt about it. The sexton's manner was ingratiating ; the emotion that lit his countenance was the desire to please. Could it be that the tremor in Cuthbert's voice was due to fear ?

" You understand," concluded Cuthbert, " that no other course was open to me. I had no idea that Satan held you in such esteem that he was prepared to conduct your defence in person."

So that was it. Cuthbert, far from wishing to destroy him, was eager to placate him ; not through any love for him, but because he was, as Cuthbert saw it, under the Archfiend's powerful protection. Fursey sat looking at his toes reflecting on the strangeness of things, while the sexton shifted his feet nervously, apparently anxiously awaiting Fursey's judgment. At length Cuthbert spoke.

" Tell me," he begged, " that you forgive me and that we are friends again."

Fursey cocked his eye at Cuthbert's face.

" Yes," he replied, " I forgive you. Now, help me to my feet."

Cuthbert hastened to comply and assisted in massaging the hinges of Fursey's knees, from which the weakness had not yet quite departed.

" Remember," said Cuthbert, " that if I can at any time be of the slightest assistance to you in any matter great or small, I am entirely at your service."

" Thank you," replied Fursey, " I think I must be going now."

" Not that I wish to imply," continued Cuthbert, " that a man of your lively and subtile temperament, who has the added advantage of being so highly connected, should ever stand in need of the assistance of a man in such a humble line of wizarding as myself. You are a man who has it in his power to confuse and dazzle tigers, but I shouldn't wish you to depart without realising to the full the depth of my esteem."

" It's very nice of you," answered Fursey, " but I really must be going. I've an important appointment in Cashel."

" Before you go," protested Cuthbert, " I insist that you honour me by accepting from me a small gift."

Fursey looked at him uncertainly.

" What is the nature of the gift ? " he asked suspiciously.

" You are going to Cashel, a place dangerous to such as you on account of the prevalence there of religious jugglery. I shall provide you with a protector so that none will presume to approach you, let alone lay hands on you."

The sexton's eagerness was such that before Fursey could reply, Cuthbert had shaken on to the road from the silken bag which he carried, a variety of curious objects, human knuckle-bones, nail-parings, moles' paws and elf-shots, things which immediately suggested to the startled Fursey that an operation of a magical character was imminent. Cuthbert then seized the red cock which was perched on his shoulder, and before the luckless bird had time to do more than give an indignant croak, its neck was wrung and its corpse flung on the ground. In a twinkling the sexton had drawn in the dust of the roadway with his witchhazel wand a circle with four divisions and four crosses.

" Stand inside," he commanded.

The trembling Fursey deemed it safer to obey. He watched with horror as Cuthbert deftly arranged the objects that had fallen from the silken bag.

" You have no occasion for fear," the sexton assured him, " I shall also draw with charcoal the Star of Solomon and the Sacred Pentagram."

This operation was completed before Fursey found his voice.

" What are you going to do ? " he quavered.

" I'm going to conjure up a poltergeist," replied Cuthbert, " and instruct him to accompany you everywhere you go, and cast around you the cloak of his protection. By magic I shall constrain him to appear."

Fursey opened his mouth, but no sound came out.

" The thing to remember," declared Cuthbert as he briskly completed his preparations, " is that it is the double tail of the serpent which forms the legs of the solar cock of Abraxas."

" I really have to go," gasped Fursey.

" You can't go now," said Cuthbert sharply. " If you step outside the circle, you are likely to be subtly consumed and altogether destroyed. The terrible citizens of the spiritual world are all about us, and but for the judicious precautions which I have taken, I would not be able to answer for the safety of either of us."

Fursey felt his knees weakening again. He closed his eyes and tried to pray while Cuthbert made mysterious passes with his wand and began to mutter strangely. Suddenly Cuthbert raised his two arms above his head and yelled three times in honour of triple Hecate. Fursey crumpled up and fell at his feet. As Fursey grovelled on the ground, he observed a thickening of the air at a spot just outside the circle. Something was slowly taking shape. At first the form was shadowy and strange, but before long it took on flesh, until it stood there in its entirety, a huge creature some eight feet in height with powerful, hunched shoulders. Its swinging arms were so long that the knuckles of its hands almost touched the ground. In general appearance it resembled a man, save only that it was green in hue. As its eyes, alight with hot, unholy fires, fixed themselves on Cuthbert and Fursey, its features became distorted in a sardonic grin. The creature was bald, and a fine steam arose from its polished green skull.

" Eminently satisfactory," said Cuthbert rubbing his hands. " What's your name, my good fellow ? "

The grotesque creature answered with its tongue hanging half-a-foot out of its mouth.

" Joe," it said.   " Joe the Poltergeist."

" Very good, Joe," said Cuthbert briskly.   " You see this gentleman here at my feet ? "

" Ay," replied the poltergeist.

"Well, listen carefully to your instructions. You will, when I tell you to do so, resume your invisibility and attach yourself to this gentleman as his protector. You are not to leave him for a moment. If aught menaces him, you will take immediate steps to ward off the danger. It is anticipated that it is from human beings that the danger will threaten. You will deal with those human beings as you think fit. Do you understand?"

"Ay," said the poltergeist.

"Now, disappear," ordered Cuthbert. "Do you hear me? Disappear."

Fursey clambered to his feet and got behind Cuthbert. When the sexton spoke again, Fursey was aware of a new note in his voice. It seemed to Fursey like a note of anxiety.

"I'm addressing you, Joe the Poltergeist," enunciated Cuthbert with severity. "I command you to vanish."

For a moment there was silence, then as Cuthbert turned to him, the terrified Fursey saw that the poltergeist still stood in the roadway, with an obscene leer creasing his unattractive countenance and his long talons twitching alarmingly.

"Something has gone wrong with the spell," muttered Cuthbert out of the corner of his mouth. "He declines to vanish. For your life, do not stir outside the circle."

The master sorcerer made several passes in the air, but they in nowise served to relieve the situation. The sexton seemed puzzled; then he turned and fixed a suspicious eye on Fursey.

"Have you by any chance," he enquired, "crosses or religious amulets about your person, which may have interfered with the smooth working of the spell?"

"No," replied Fursey.

"Are you sure?" asked Cuthbert sharply as he noticed Fursey's hesitation.

"I admit," faltered Fursey, "I admit that I said a prayer while the spell was in the course of being woven."

Cuthbert greeted this intelligence with a sharp intake of breath.

"Nice mess you've landed us in," he hissed. "Such a *contretemps* is altogether outside my experience. I haven't the faintest idea how we'll get rid of him."

"Couldn't we make a run for it," suggested Fursey hopefully.

"Don't attempt anything of the sort," snapped Cuthbert. "If we as much as put a foot outside the circle, he'll tear us in pieces."

Fursey shivered as the poltergeist began to lumber around the edge of the circle grating his teeth horribly.

"It's a tricky situation," commented Cuthbert. "Of course I could try to undo the spell by reciting it backwards, but such an operation is fraught with danger. The magic is liable to stick in one's throat. I think the best thing that I can do, is begin again and weave the spell once more, and we'll see what happens."

"Is there not a danger that if you pursue such a course, the net result may well be that we shall have two poltergeists to contend with instead of one?"

"There is wisdom in what you say," answered Cuthbert thoughtfully. "There's really only one thing to do. I shall have to fly home on my witchhazel wand and consult my books. I have no doubt but that Camerarius will have something to say in the matter."

"Can't you take me with you?" enquired Fursey anxiously.

"I regret that my wand is too light to carry two," replied Cuthbert. "You can await my return in perfect safety provided you remain within the circle. I expect that I shall be back before nightfall. Do not let the phantom coax you into leaving the circle."

"You need have no anxiety on that score," Fursey assured him.

"Very well," said Cuthbert, and throwing his leg nimbly across his wand, he shot vertically into the air to a considerable altitude. Fursey saw him peering to left and right to get his direction before making off over the tree-tops towards the north. Joe the Poltergeist was apparently taken by surprise, and he manifested in no uncertain manner his chagrin at the loss of one of his prey. For some minutes he ran up and down roaring horribly, then to relieve his feelings he pulled up a couple of trees by the roots and tried to tear up a length of road. At last he came back and opening his mouth, displayed before the quaking Fursey two magnificent sets of grinders, which he gnashed horribly.

How long Fursey could have endured the proximity of the dreadful creature without breathing his last through sheer fright, it is impossible to say ; but at that moment the sound of many voices striking up a hymn was heard from round the bend of the road. All at once the poltergeist seemed to forget Fursey, he turned immediately on his heel and lumbered off to investigate. The moment he had turned the corner and was out of sight, Fursey shot like a bolt from the circle, burst through the hedge without seeing it, and made off across the fields.

A party of a dozen monks from Clonmacnoise, pilgrims to the shrine of the saintly Gray Mare, moved slowly along the southern road. They had walked twenty miles since morning ; and as they plodded along, they leaned wearily upon their staves. It was with a view to whipping up their flagging enthusiasm now that they were nearing their destination, that the Master of Novices, who was in charge, ordered them to strike up a hymn. The monks sang lustily, for the hymn was well-liked, having a jovial swing. As they approached a bend in the road, little Brother Patrick made frantic attempts to pitch his voice above the musical baying of Father Sampson, so as to convey to his brethern the alarming intelligence that he had just espied a flying wizard in career over the tree-tops. But Brother Patrick failed to make himself heard, and the hymn continued for several minutes until it was brought to a sudden close by the appearance of Joe the Poltergeist round the bend of the road. The band of pilgrims stopped dead and stood huddled together in the centre of the track as the grotesque monster lumbered in their direction. Their first instinct was to take to their heels ; but the Master of Novices, always a cool man, succeeded in staying the panic. A small stream crossed the road about fifty paces from where they stood.   The ungainly stranger continued towards them until he reached the middle of the stream, and there he took his stand facing the pilgrims, a horrid and fearsome sight with the water flowing over his hairy, green ankles. It was apparent from his menacing demeanour that it was his intention to oppose their progress. In the unearthly silence that seemed suddenly to have fallen over the entire countryside, Brother Patrick at last made himself heard. His report of the flying wizard did nothing to allay the apprehensions of his brethren, who shifted nervously as they realised that there was devilry afoot.

" What is he ? " asked Father Placidus in a thin voice. " Is he an arch-vampire ? "

" A poltergeist by the look of him," replied Father Sampson.

This opinion was substantiated a moment later when the horrid spectre stooped down suddenly and, picking up an armful of stones, began to pelt the monks mercilessly.

" Stand where you are," commanded the Novice Master. " In a struggle between Good and Evil, the Good must never give ground."

" I observe that he has taken his stand in south-flowing water," said Father Sampson, who had an eye for strategy. " I doubt if we shall succeed in overcoming him with spiritual weapons, for it is a well-known fact that south-flowing water has magical properties."

" We can only try," answered the Novice Master, and taking his book of exorcisms from under his arm, he advanced ten paces towards the poltergeist.

The exorcism was unsuccessful. The poltergeist laughed uproariously during the first part of it ; and before the Master of Novices had got as far as the adjuration, Joe swept the book from his hand with a well-aimed lump of rock. The Novice Master retreated precipitately to his brethren on the roadway.

"Perhaps we should essay the fulmination of an anathema," said Father Placidus, who was so beside himself with terror that he scarcely knew what he was talking about. In fact, the general fright was such that the monks would very likely have bolted only for the powerful influence of Father Sampson. The ex-wrestler was not only unafraid, he was spoiling for fight. His ire increased when he received a blow of a stone on the forehead. He tore off his monk's habit and revealed a frame knotted with muscle.

"Father Novice Master," he begged, "give me leave to assail this offensive demon. I am confident of my ability to weaken and annihilate him."

The Novice Master blenched. "It is a perilous undertaking—," he began.

"When I was a wrestler at the Court of Thomond," snarled Father Sampson, "no man, save only Father Furiosus, ever stood successfully against me. Why did God give me bodily strength, save only that I should use it in His service?"

"I must admire your manly and aggressive spirit," replied the Novice Master, "but I should not wish you to lose your life."

"Please," begged Father Sampson. "I assure you that my many years' experience as a wrestler has given me a suppleness of limb which almost places me in the contortionist class. I'm confident of my ability to apply as efficacious a stranglehold as in days gone by. All the more effective methods of choking an opponent are very well known to me."

"Bravo!" shouted Brother Patrick, who loved the sight of blood, having been much addicted to attendance at cockfights in his youth.

The Novice Master hesitated. "Very well," he said at last. "Our blessings will go with you. In the meantime we others will intone a hymn by way of encouraging you and confusing the demon."

Brother Patrick gripped Father Sampson by the arm.

" Try and get him with a hammer-lock or a crutch-hold,"
he advised, " and then when you have him, kick him in a vital
spot."

As Father Sampson, clad only in his singlet, moved down
the road to meet the poltergeist, the monks under the direction of the Novice Master began a heartening hymn.   All sang
lustily, save only Brother Patrick, who was too excited to
join in: The diminutive laybrother capered up and down
wrestling with an imaginary opponent.

For some time the monk and the poltergeist circled one
another warily.   Then Father Sampson suddenly closed and
attempted to trap the poltergeist's torso between his legs in
the scissors-hold, but the demon, gripping the monk's foot,
hugged the captured leg closely to his chest before passing it
around the back of his neck and throwing Father Sampson
heavily.   Quick to seize advantage, the poltergeist tore a
block of granite from the bed of the stream and flung it at his
opponent, missing the latter by inches.

" Dirty foul ! " screeched Brother Patrick.   " Play the
game, you filthy demon ! "

Father Placidus shook his head despondently.   " And there
are some," he remarked, " who impudently proclaim that it is
folly and ridiculous beyond words to believe these marvellous
happenings."

Father Sampson was again on his feet and had delivered a
couple of rabbit punches before the poltergeist realised what
was happening.   Then the monk essayed some of the traditional strangleholds and chokelocks, but the extreme plia-
bility of his opponent's body made it extremely difficult to
keep him in a tight grip.   Joe seemed to be able to slip out of
everything.   At one moment Father Sampson had the demon's head trapped between his knees and was essaying a
simultaneous three-quarter nelson and a kidney-squeeze, but

the poltergeist escaped by making a half-turn so that he rolled
over the back of his opponent. While they faced each other
again, the monks shouted the final verse of the hymn and
began another without pausing for breath. Both adver-
saries were covered with sweat and breathing heavily. Father
Sampson was apparently planning to cross-buttock the phantom with his left leg, but Joe rushed in first and succeeded
in trapping the monk's forearm under his left armpit. Father
Sampson replied with a short-arm scissors followed by an
ingenious toe-hold, and in a moment both of them had fallen
and were involved in a struggle in the bed of the stream. At
first Father Sampson was content to apply pressure with his
thumb against a point immediately below the lobe of the
demon's ear, but then with a quick movement he succeeded
in capturing his opponent's right leg. For some minutes he
worked on the leg to the extreme discomfort of the demon,
who yelled hideously. The excitement was too great for
Brother Patrick. He burst away from the band of monks
and, running to the stream, gave the poltergeist a resounding
kick in the ribs before scuttling back to safety.

It was obvious to the onlookers that the struggle was between the skill of the trained wrestler and the brute strength
of the poltergeist. At one period things looked bad for
Father Sampson. The demon sprang into the air and landed
heavily seated astride the monk's chest. With his foot on
Father Sampson's face he dug his thumbs into the monk's
windpipe as an additional means of persuasion. But Father
Sampson escaped from his perilous situation by bending the
demon's arm back in a painful angle so that Joe had perforce
to release him. When they faced one another again, the green
sweat was running down the demon's face. With a sudden
forward movement Father Sampson gripped the poltergeist
by the wrist and in a moment had flung him backwards over
his head. The demon landed on his back with a sickening
crash. It was the famous Irish Whip! A wild shout of
applause arose from the watching monks, and they started to
run down the road towards the stream. Joe the Poltergeist

lay among the rocks totally uninterested in the subsequent proceedings. The monks under the direction of Father Sampson strained at a huge rock and strove to roll it over on top of the poltergeist so as to pin him down for all time ; but before they could complete the operation, the demon struggled to his feet, and assuming the form of a water spaniel with the head of an ox, he ran limping down the road, pursued by the maledictions of the whole body of clergy.

*   *   *   *

When Fursey arrived at the southern gate of Cashel, the guards on duty took to their heels. No attempt was made to oppose his entry into the settlement, nor was his progress through the streets impeded. The inhabitants fled before him, spreading on all sides the terrible news that the arch-sorcerer was once more in the city roaming about seeking whom he might devour. This dire intelligence caused a considerable exodus of citizens through the northern gate. Before taking to flight some hurried to their cabins to collect their few possessions. Aged parents were dragged from their inglenooks and flung across the broad shoulders of their sons. A stream of refugees, bowed beneath these burdens, poured through the northern gate, their eyes bloodshot, their only anxiety to put as great a distance as possible between themselves and the terrible Fursey.

The sorcerer himself plodded through the streets unaware of the commotion of which he was the cause. He observed that the settlement was singularly deserted, but he was too taken up with his own affairs to ponder overmuch on such matters. At the foot of the incline which led to the Bishop's Palace, he hesitated, but it was only for a moment : then with a thumping heart he began to climb the hill. When he reached the head of the track, he knocked timidly on the Bishop's door. The bronze panels opened before him, and it became immediately apparent that the news of his advent had preceded him. The hall was lined with armed men ; in the centre stood Father Furiosus with Bishop Flanagan

trembling behind him. Fursey observed that the friar was
well-equipped with spiritual weapons. On his right was a
cask of holy water, and half-a-dozen underlings stood by with
buckets, ready at a moment's notice to form a living chain
so as to keep it replenished. On the friar's left stood a table
with an open book of exorcisms upon it. The table was piled
also with crosses, handbells and other evidences of an extensive religious armoury. But most formidable of all was the
red-faced friar himself as he stood in the centre gripping
his blackthorn stick menacingly. For a moment no one spoke.
Then Fursey stepped forward.

"I have come," he said haltingly, "I have come to surrender
myself to justice."

As he spoke, he gazed anxiously at the friar's hard, green
eyes set deep beneath his ginger eyebrows, eyes that seemed to
Fursey to resemble the points of two screws already in position
to bore into his brain. Father Furiosus returned his gaze
unwinkingly. Fursey's eyes dropped, and he contemplated the
blossoming, strawberry-like nose of the friar and the thin lips
drawn tight across the determined jaw. The phrase "The
Church Militant" came to his mind, and he shuddered.

"How are we to know?" said the friar at last, "that you
have not been guided here by demons with the object of
further wizardy and malice?"

"You have only my word," replied Fursey, "that I've
come here and placed myself in your power of my own free
will. Witchcraft is as detestable to me as it is to you."

"Why have you come?" asked the friar.

"I've come that I may be released one way or another from
my present unhappy state, the state of being a wizard."

"So you admit that you're a wizard?"

"Yes, I freely admit that I'm a wizard, an unwilling one,
but nevertheless a wizard."

"Come into the other room," commanded Furiosus. "We
will talk further."

As they moved into the interior of the Palace, the Bishop
plucked the friar's sleeve nervously.

" If this goes on much longer," he whispered, " we'll all fall into a lunacy.   Why not have him put to death forthwith ? "

" I'm managing this," replied the friar roughly.   " It's a most involved case.   I must probe it to its depths."

The Bishop's Adam's apple vibrated anxiously.

" But if we permit him to move about thus freely, how shall we escape his devilry ?   Let me have him well thrashed and pelted with stones while the fire is being prepared."

" No," said Furiosus shortly.

" Well, don't blame me," snarled the Bishop, " if he suddenly throws a bridle over your head and changes you into a horse.   I observe that at the present moment he is mumbling something which may well be a spell."

They had reached an inner room, and the three of them were now alone.   Father Furiosus glanced sharply at Fursey.

" What are you saying ? " he asked.

" A prayer to blessed Kieran for help in my affliction," replied Fursey.   " I hope you don't mind."

The friar motioned Fursey to a chair and then sat down himself.   Bishop Flanagan declined to sit, but hovered in the neighbourhood of the door lest it should be necessary to summon help.

" I may as well tell you," began the friar, " that his lordship and I have on many occasions during the past month discussed your case with Abbot Marcus of Clonmacnoise.   The Abbot is fortunately in Cashel at present ; and on receiving intelligence of your arrival, I sent a slave across to the library with a request that he should attend here as soon as his studies permit.   So we may expect him at any moment."

" I see, " said Fursey.

" It may interest you to know," continued Father Furiosus, " that your case is bristling with difficulties.   For instance, you told us just now that you have voluntarily surrendered yourself ; but how am I to know whether that statement proceeds from Fursey, late monk at Clonmacnoise, or from the demon that possesses him ? "

" But I assure you that I'm not possessed by a demon."

" That's all very well," said the friar carefully, " but if you are possessed by a demon, I should expect him to deny his presence, for lies would come more naturally to his tongue than truth."

" It's a clear case of deadlock," interjected the Bishop impatiently. " The truth in the matter is not obtainable. In the meantime we cannot have you moving around the countryside roaring after your prey, or at least inflicting an innocent peasantry with wasting diseases and fits."

" I wish you wouldn't interrupt," said Father Furiosus.

"It's all very well for you," retorted the Bishop. " A roving friar has few responsibilities ; but I'm bishop of this diocese, and I have responsibilities to the lambs of my flock. This man Fursey is a self-admitted sorcerer. His contention is that his dread powers were innocently acquired. Be that as it may, he has those powers, and he must be burned before he turns them to malefic ends."

Father Furiosus seemed determined to ignore the Bishop. He turned his steady gaze on Fursey once more.

" How did you escape from your prison ? " he asked. " By sorcery ? "

" No," replied Fursey. " Satan got me out."

" Satan ! " ejaculated the friar.

" Yes," admitted Fursey. " I've always found him very helpful, though a little headstrong."

The friar's eyes widened, but he made no comment. Bishop Flanagan vented a horrified moan and edged nearer the door. The friar continued his examination.

" Is it the case that on departing from this city you stole all the gold so generously donated by Prince Apollyon of Byzantium, together with a high-stepping hound of superior pedigree which was my particular possession ? "

" No," replied Fursey. " The gold was spectral gold and vanished with Prince Apollyon, who was Satan himself. The hound to which you refer, was no doubt one of the lower orders of imps, and, I expect, followed his master, as is proper."

Nothing was said for a few moments while the friar and the Bishop tried to grasp the implications of this alarming intelligence. They had the information only half-digested when there was a sudden stir at the door, and Abbot Marcus entered. He bowed gravely to Bishop Flanagan and Father Furiosus, and nodded kindly to Fursey. Fursey in his chair felt suddenly uncomfortable.

" This wretched man," gasped Bishop Flanagan, " has just had the effrontery to inform us that the noble and generous Apollyon, Prince of Byzantium, is none other than the Archfiend Lucifer himself. Did you ever hear such nonsense ? "

" I'm a man," replied the Abbot, " from whom the years are creeping away faster and ever faster. What avails me my coming old age unless it finds me wise ? A lifetime's study and observance has convinced me that in the land of Ireland anything may happen to anyone anywhere and at any time, and that it usually does."

" But such a preposterous suggestion ! " exclaimed the Bishop. " Apollyon is a man of great wealth and influence, most solicitous for the well-being of the Church, and most generous in his contributions to the support of its pastors—"

" I suggest," interrupted Marcus, " that we three seat ourselves here and listen carefully to Fursey's story of all that has befallen him since he first made acquaintance with the forces of Evil in his cell at Clonmacnoise. Let him relate all, bringing his narration up to the present moment."

Thus encouraged, Fursey related his strange story. Father Furiosus listened intently, nodding his head occasionally at some marvellous happening or impish trick which was borne out by his own experience of the world of shadows. The only time he manifested impatience was when Fursey recounted his experiences in the cottage of The Gray Mare. The friar's impatience at this part of the story was understandable, for it was obvious to any man of sense that the martyred lady, at whose shrine so many miracles had recently taken place, could not possibly have been guilty of the unprincipled behaviour which Fursey attributed to her. Again the friar shook his head doubtfully when he heard Cuthbert accused of being a sorceror of a hue deeper than is usual. Cuthbert was so obviously a man of sterling piety ; and by private enquiry the friar had ascertained that Cuthbert performed the responsible duties of sexton with diligence and probity. It was hard to understand for so much of what Fursey related had the ring of truth. The friar began to wonder whether in these two matters of The Grey Mare and Cuthbert, Fursey was perhaps the victim of hallucination. When Albert came to be spoken of, the Abbot interrupted the flow of Fursey's tale.

" So you govern and maintain a familiar ? " he said with interest.

" I've attempted to govern him," replied Fursey," but unfortunately he's not readily amenable to discipline. As for maintaining him, I fear that I have not. The poor fellow has shrunk to a mere shadow of his former self."

Fursey continued the faithful relation of his experiences, save only that when he came to speak of the employment he had obtained in Declan's cottage in The Gap, his heart failed him ; and he forebore to mention that there had lived in the cottage as well as Declan a good-natured girl who was always laughing. He left Maeve out of his story altogether.

Bishop Flanagan evinced the greatest impatience during Fursey's recital. He shifted constantly in his chair, his under-lip twitched, and his Adam's apple was in constant motion in his throat. It was obvious that he considered Fursey's story to be no more than the recital of unnecessary and uninteresting detail. To his mind, the only important point was that Fursey was a sorcerer, and as such should be burned. When Fursey brought the tale to a conclusion, the Bishop could no longer contain his impatience.

" How long must we listen to this creature's maunderings ? " he burst out. " Let us proceed at once to bring his wicked career to a conclusion before he has us all wasted and consumed."

There was a moment's silence, then the Abbot spoke.

" Strange and wonderful as is his story, I believe that Fursey is telling us the truth."

Fursey threw a look of dumb gratitude at the Abbot, and his eyes brightened with tears. It was obvious that Father Furiosus respected Abbot Marcus' opinion, for when he had contemplated the Abbot for a few moments, he too spoke, slowly and gently.

" I'm inclined to agree with you. I believe that while this unfortunate man is suffering from a moistening of the brain in regard to certain persons and incidents of which he has spoken, his intention is good, and he has striven to tell us the whole truth. He's to be pitied, not condemned."

The Bishop squinted from the Abbot to the friar, and then across at Fursey. He opened his mouth as if to speak, but he ran his tongue across his lips instead and said nothing. Father Furiosus sat for some moments in thought before turning again to Fursey.

" I'm convinced of your penitence," he said, " and I'm sure that you are afire with anxiety to make amends to Heaven for your sins. Isn't that so ? "

" Yes," replied Fursey carefully.

" Well, an opportunity for atonement is at hand. Abbot Marcus and I are practical men, and we have discussed at length measures whereby this land may be rid forever of the pestilential demons which everywhere infest it."

" Are things as bad as that ? " asked Fursey, hoping to gain time, for he had an uneasy feeling that he was cast for a leading part in the task of purging the land of its unwelcome visitors.

The friar's brow furrowed.

" Things are very bad. Only yesterday a parish priest not two miles from here eloped with a visiting vampire. Great scandal has been caused, for he was much respected by his flock, being a man of outstanding piety and one of the largest bullock owners in the territory. The carcase of the unhappy man, sucked dry of blood, was found this morning in a ditch, where his phantom paramour had flung him. In the trading towns on the western seaboard there has been a deplorable outbreak of loose living, and I don't doubt that it is Hell-inspired. The 'bad disease' is so rampant that if you enter a house in those territories and clap a citizen on the back, all his teeth fall out on the table.''

" It seems a perilous thing to be alive at all,'' murmured Fursey.

"The worst feature,'' continued Furiosus, " is that the demons which lately infest the land, are all of foreign origin. It's a well-authenticated fact that the native Irish demons, whether they be banshees, fairy pipers, leprechauns or pookas, are far superior to the foreign brands. Our demons may be mischievous, but they are admitted all the world over to be as upright and pure in their manner of living as demons can be. The chastity of the Irish demon is well-known and everywhere admitted.''

Fursey nodded patriotically.

" Unfortunately the same cannot be said of the foreign demons which are now rampant. They are not only clad in a manner offensive to decency, but they seem to specialise in inciting men to lechery. It is therefore,'' continued the friar, " a national as well as a religious duty to rid the land of these pestilential hordes. That is where you can help.''

" Me ? '' said Fursey.

" Yes, you. From evil will come good. We must cash in on your friendship with Satan. It will be necessary for you to get in touch with him at once and persuade him to lead his entire forces to a lake in the north called Lough Derg. In that lake there's a small island known as Saint Patrick's Purgatory, on which you must persuade Satan to encamp with all his forces, two-legged, four-legged and those that crawl on their bellies. When you have done that, the clergy of Ireland who will be lying in ambush, will surround the lake and bless it, thus converting the entire lough into a vast stoup of holy water. The happy result will be that Satan and his angels will be imprisoned for all time on that island, and will therefore be no longer in a position to range abroad seducing the faithful from their allegiance."

The sweat broke out on Fursey's forehead.

" How am I to get them on to the island ? " he squeaked.

" By the exercise of ingenuity. You can think up a plausible plan at your leisure. You might suggest, for instance that it would be a safe base from which they could harry the surrounding monasteries and settlements."

" I see," said Fursey.

" If you do this," put in the Abbot, " we can promise you your pardon and a safe berth in a monastery."

" We might even be able to arrange a canonry in the Chapter," said the Bishop eagerly. " Think of that, the best of feeding and drinking and no more work for the rest of your life."

" It will be a resounding victory for the Irish Church," concluded the friar, " and such a good act on your part will no doubt obtain for you divine forgiveness for your sins and sorceries."

" Suppose," said Fursey, " that before the operation is complete, they discover that I'm not playing straight with them ? "

" Then you will die a blessed martyr. What more could any Christian ask for ? "

" It's a good plan," commented Abbot Marcus. " We three have discussed it during the past month, but the difficulty was how to coax the demons on to the island. Your advent offers the ideal solution and seems to solve the problem."

Fursey grew alternately hot and cold. It seemed to him that the ecclesiastics were underestimating the difficulties inherent in assembling some thousands of fearsome creatures and then persuading them to take up their abode on a minute island on a small lake ; but the word " forgiveness " had been used, and Fursey's heart bounded at the thought of escaping the funeral pyre, which certainly awaited him if he refused.

Moreover, he was filled with a great exaltation at the thought
of being once more on the side of Good in the battle with Evil.
And even if he fell, wrestling manfully with a score of cacodemons and hippogriffs, it would be a glorious end and one
befitting a Christian.

" I'll do it," he said sticking out his chin determinedly.

" Well said ! " commented Abbot Marcus, smiling across
at him.

" You won't forget," added Fursey anxiously, " to rescue
me from the island before you pin the demons there forever ? "

" That will be attended to," answered the friar placing a
friendly hand on Fursey's shoulder.

At that moment a flourish of trumpets was heard and a
sudden cheering. Before the ecclesiastics had time to enquire
as to the cause of the commotion, an excited slave burst into
the room.

" My lord Bishop," he announced breathlessly, " the noble
and most generous Prince of Byzantium has entered the city."

With one accord the three ecclesiastics hurried to the door
of the Palace. Fursey trailed along behind them, his heart
thumping like a hammer. From their vantage point in the
doorway they could see Prince Apollyon approaching down the
street, gracefully casting handfuls of gold to the frantically
excited populace. Now and again he paused to pat a child on
the head or to enquire courteously as to the present state of
some old gaffer's rheumatism. Then he proceeded on his way
bowing left and right to his frenzied admirers. Bishop
Flanagan's eyes nearly fell out of his head as the debonair
figure began to ascend the incline towards the Palace.

" Such generosity ! " he breathed. " Every inch a gentleman ! "

" He can well afford it," muttered Fursey. " They'd be
well-advised to spend that gold quick before it disappears."

This remark of Fursey's jarred the ecclesiastics considerably,
reminding them of Fursey's assertion that the noble stranger
was none other than the Prince of Darkness himself. Furiosus
and the Bishop glanced doubtfully from Fursey to the ap-

proaching Prince. Fursey felt a slight pressure on his arm
and, looking around, he saw that the Abbot Marcus was close
beside him. The Abbot drew Fursey back a couple of paces
from the others.

"Tell me the truth, Fursey. Is this gentleman really
Lucifer, the terrible Emperor of Hell ? "

"Yes," replied Fursey ; and for some reason the word
seemed to stick in his throat.

The Abbot regarded him doubtfully.

"If that's so, I wonder why he has come."

"I know why he's come," ejaculated Fursey with a sudden
sob. "He knows that I'm in danger, and he's come to
rescue me once more. He's the only one who really cares
what becomes of me ; and I've repaid his kindness by undertaking to betray him."

Slow horror crept across the Abbot's face.

"Fursey, you owe allegiance to Heaven, not to Hell."

The Devil would have been a fool indeed if he had failed to
notice that his welcome was a lukewarm one. The Bishop
shrunk back behind the door, and even Father Furiosus was
pale as he took the demon's proffered hand. The Abbot
contented himself with a distant bow, and the face which
Fursey turned to his old acquaintance, was streaming with
tears.

"Let us go inside and talk," said Apollyon quietly, and he
led the way into the inner room. As the ecclesiastics followed,
Father Furiosus dexterously hooked a stoup of holy water
with his forefinger from the table in the hall, and carried it in
concealed behind his back. The ecclesiastics seemed still
doubtful of Apollyon's real identity, but the first words which
he spoke, confirmed their worst fears. Apollyon was the only
one of the five who was wholly at his ease. He crossed the
room and seated himself in the Bishop's favourite chair.

"You've no occasion to weep, Fursey," he said quietly.
"I know that you've betrayed me, but you forget that I'm
the Father of Lies, Deception and Double-dealing. Your
conduct in that regard affords me the highest pleasure. I

find myself in the debt of these gentlemen : they have thrown you and me closer together."

Fursey's mouth fell open, and he sat down suddenly in a chair. Father Furiosus produced the stoup of holy water from behind his back and began shakily to take aim.

" Please," remonstrated the Archfiend. " Do not forget your country's age-old reputation for hospitality. Oblige me by putting down that weapon. I'm not here as an enemy. I've come to make terms with the clergy of Ireland."

Father Furiosus did as he was bid and sat down looking rather dazed.

" Abbot Marcus," continued the Devil, " you seem to be the only one who is retaining his wits. Oblige me by summoning the canons of the Chapter. I'm satisfied that they and you three gentlemen are sufficiently representative of the clergy of this country to ensure that any treaty I conclude with you, will be acceptable to the clergy as a whole. In the meantime, perhaps his lordship Bishop Flanagan will bestir himself and see that food and drink are provided for his guests."

The Bishop staggered to the door and gave a few husky commands. When the ale and meats were borne in, the Bishop retained only enough presence of mind to see that Fursey got nothing except a plate of hard food. One would have imagined that natural curiosity would have constrained the canons of the Chapter to hurry over to the Palace to see such an important personage as the Archfiend, of whom they had read and heard so much ; but a strange reluctance on their part manifested itself when they received Abbot Marcus' message. It needed all the Abbot's powers of persuasion and his insistence that perhaps the future of the Irish Church was at stake, before they climbed the hill to the Palace and came sidling round-eyed into the room in which the conference was to be held.

" My Lord Bishop and very reverend fathers," began Satan. " I'm well aware that you regard me with a certain prejudice. Nay, do not, in the excess of your courtesy, shake your heads and strive to look as if it were otherwise. Let us be honest and face facts. You don't approve of me. Isn't that so, Canon Pomponius ? "

The broad-bellied doyen of the Cathedral Chapter manifested considerable alarm at being thus singled out. He shifted jerkily from one expansive ham to the other.

" You must make allowances, sir, for our upbringing— the tales remembered from childhood—the effect—," his voice trailed away into a whisper.

The Devil sighed understandingly.

" Let me explain myself," he said. " I'm a person cursed with a sense of freakish humour. I'm well aware that it interferes seriously with my effectiveness as a demon. You may assert that my humour is depraved. I freely admit that it is. For centuries it has spoiled my best-laid plans. I cannot conquer this boyish desire of mine to see monks, anchorites and other holy men startled out of their wits by an apparition, preferably a female one. It affords me the keenest amusement, but it's a vice which is rendering me more and more ineffective as a demon. While I'm splitting my sides laughing, the gentleman whom I'm tempting, has immediate recourse to prayer and other spiritual weapons, the very last thing which I wish him to do. The net result is that he always wins, and when I've recovered from my paroxysm of merriment, I find that there is nothing left for me to do but retire chagrined and baffled."

The canons shifted uncomfortably, moistened their dry lips and wondered what was coming next.

" Father Furiosus," said the Demon ingratiatingly, " answer me a question. Which is the greatest of all sins ? "

The friar's honest face betrayed his embarrassment.

" Everyone knows that," he replied. " It's not considered proper among decent people to put a name on it."

The entire body of clergy nodded in agreement.

" We're all adult men," said the Demon persuasively. " We're not likely to incur injury by mention of the mere name."

The canons shook their heads doubtfully.

" Come now," urged Apollyon. " Tell me which is the most grievous of all sins, so that the conference may proceed."

The friar flushed slightly.

" The most heinous of all crimes," he said, " are those which may be summed up by the word ' sex '."

The assembled clergy nodded in agreement, and then looked uncomfortably at the walls and ceiling.

" Exactly," said the Archfiend with a sudden quick glint in his eye. " Well, I offer this country immunity from such temptation, if you on your part promise me something in return."

The clergy sat up in their seats and for the first time looked really interested.

" What do you want in return ? " asked Father Furiosus carefully.

" I should expect that the clergy in their teaching would not in future lay undue stress on the wickedness of simony, nepotism, drunkenness, perjury and murder."

" These sins which you mention," said the friar after a long, cautious pause, " are but minor offences when compared with the hideous sin of sex. What you somewhat exaggeratedly term drunkenness, perjury and murder are perhaps but the exuberance of a high-spirited and courageous people. Nepotism is, after all, merely an offshoot of the virtue of charity. As for simony, we know all about that. The cry of simony is usually raised by evil-minded persons who are unwilling to subscribe to the upkeep of their pastors."

" You think then that we can perhaps do business on these lines ? "

Before replying Father Furiosus glanced along the rows of eager ecclesiastical faces.

" I think we can," he said at last.

The conference dragged on hour after hour. Fursey fell asleep and when he awoke, Apollyon was delivering his final oration.

" I promise the clergy of this country wealth and the respect of their people for all time. When a stranger enters a village, he will not have to ask which is the priest's house. It will be easy of identification, for it will be the largest house there. I promise you that whenever priests are sought, it will not be in the houses of the poor that they will be found. And as a sign that I will keep my part of the bargain, I will stamp the foreheads of your priesthood with my own particular seal— the seal of pride."

The Archfiend's voice was lost in the tumult of applause, and the assembly broke up. The Canons of the Chapter left the building in small groups chattering excitedly to one another. Every face was aglow with animation save only that of Abbot Marcus, who sat crouched in his chair, his face shadowed with doubt and indecision.

" They have compromised with Evil," Fursey heard him muttering, " They have compromised where there can be no compromise."

Father Furiosus and the Bishop had walked out into the hall with the canons, and Fursey found himself alone with Apollyon, alone except for the motionless figure of the Abbot sunk in his chair in a far corner of the room. The Archfiend seemed tired as he moved towards the door with Fursey.

" Well," he said pausing on the threshold, " it's over now— a most satisfactory arrangement, in which both sides are convinced that they have gained substantial benefits. Do you realise what has happened, Fursey ? "

" No, I was asleep."

" Well," said the Archfiend carefully, " unless my sense of humour has again betrayed me, I appear to have the souls of the Irish clergy in my bag for all time. It'll give Hell a considerable Irish ecclesiastical character, and I suppose the other damned won't like it. They'll say that they've enough to put up with as it is."

He sighed and seemed to become very depressed as he meditated on the future.

" Life will be very difficult in the coming centuries," he said. " Before long Hell will hardly know itself. It will bear an extraordinary resemblance to an Annual General

Meeting of the Catholic Truth Society. It's a terrible prospect for a demon of sensitiveness and breeding like me."

Fursey had not the slightest idea what the Archfiend was talking about ; but as politeness demanded it, he made a sound indicative of his sympathy. The Devil started suddenly, possessed by a new idea.

"Fursey," he said eagerly. "I've a proposition to make to you. I have the Irish Church in my bag for all time. I'll exchange the souls of all of them, born and unborn, for your soul."

"No," retorted Fursey. "Certainly not."

The Demon's face fell. "I suppose you're right," he replied gloomily. "Your soul is the only thing which your country has left you, and I suppose you're right to stick to it."

Grimly he hummed one of the psalms backwards for a few moments. At last his face cleared, and he turned to Fursey once more.

"It's unlikely that I'll see you again. Before I go, I'd like to know how you're placed for the future."

"I don't know. I expect they'll let me back into Clonmacnoise."

"I'd advise emigration," said the Devil. "The future of the Irish race lies in emigration."

"Ah, the country isn't as bad as all that," protested Fursey.

"The country is all right," replied the Devil. "The only thing that's wrong with it, is the people that are in it."

"I don't agree with you," said Fursey patriotically.

"Maybe," sighed the Devil, "maybe I should have said that the country and most of the people are all right ; what's wrong with this land is the hard-fisted few that have and hold it. Forgive me if I seem to be carping," he continued, "but I'm rather out of patience with the Irish race. Your countrymen have no real sense of humour as the phrase is understood by other peoples. They never laugh at themselves."

"Maybe," replied Fursey.

"Goodbye now," said the Devil, "and don't get yourself into any further trouble."

" I won't," said Fursey. " Are you not going out through the front door ? "

" No. I'll take my departure through the smoke-hole in the roof. I don't want to have to shake hands with Bishop Flanagan. Damn it, I have my pride."

The Archfiend waved his hand to Fursey in melancholy valediction, and streaking up to the ceiling, made a perfect exit through the smoke-hole, just as Father Furiosus and the Bishop re-entered the room rubbing their hands and evincing every sign of satisfaction.

" Is our friend gone ? " asked the friar.

" Yes," replied Fursey pointing to the ceiling. " He went that way."

The Bishop laughed tolerantly as if the Devil's choice of exit was an understandable boyish freak. He turned genially to Furiosus and the Abbot.

" Well, everything is fixed," he said, " most satisfactorily. The only thing that remains to be done, is to burn Fursey."

Fursey glanced incredulously from the Bishop to Father Furiosus. When he saw the friar nodding gravely, he turned and fled to the far corner of the room where Abbot Marcus was rising stiffly from his chair.

" Father Abbot," he cried, " They say that they're going to burn me. It's not true, is it ? "

The Abbot looked at him sadly.

" Of course it's true. You know as well as any of us that the only way to cure a sorcerer is to burn him. I understood that you appreciated the position when you surrendered yourself. After all, we can't allow a wizard to be at large in the territory, nor can we allow your soul to be eternally lost for the want of a little cleansing fire."

" That's all very well," quavered Fursey, " but I thought that now that everything is fixed—."

Before he could utter another word Father Furiosus, who had approached him from behind, seized him suddenly by the arms and flung him forward on his face on to the floor.

" Call the guards," commanded the friar.

Fursey, not unnaturally incensed at this high-handed proceeding, bounded to his feet, and before the three ecclesiastics, who apparently did not expect resistance on his part, had grasped what he was about, he darted through the door into the hall. A damp-souled servingman was gloomily sweeping the floor with a broom. Fursey did not stop to ask his permission, but snatched the broom from him ; and running to a corner, tore the box of ointment from his pocket. He had thoroughly smeared the shaft before the clerics burst from the room into the hall.

" Stop ! " shouted the friar.

Before they could reach him, Fursey had flung his leg over the broom and shot towards the ceiling. As he flew in circles around the hall, his head brushing the rafters, Father Furiosus sprang from table to table aiming blows at him with his blackthorn stick.

" Resistance will avail you nought ! " shrilled the Bishop.

Fursey did not answer : he was too preoccupied in steering the broom in the limited space available so as to avoid collision with the walls. It was a difficult task, for the constant circling made him dizzy.

" Come down, Fursey," urged the Abbot. " These antics can have only one end. Please come down."

" Yah ! " retorted Fursey. " Come down and be burnt ! What kind of a fool do you think I am ? "

The Bishop tore open the great door of the Palace with the apparent object of summoning assistance. Fursey saw his opportunity. He swooped suddenly, snatched a flint and taper from a table, banked sharply, and shot through the open doorway like a bullet. When he reached the open air, he swerved once again and alighted on the roof of the Palace. A large crowd of townspeople who had waited for hours before the Bishop's dwelling in the hope of further financial benefit from the visit of the generous Prince Apollyon, raised a shout of surprise as they beheld the marvel and saw Fursey perched on the ridge of the roof. Their astonishment changed suddenly to rage as they beheld Fursey lighting the taper and setting

fire to the thatch of the roof in half-a-dozen different places.
It was borne in powerfully on the citizens that it would be
incumbent on them to contribute generously for a new palace
for their pastor. A storm of maledictions was hurled at Fursey,
but the more practical were quickly disciplined by Father
Furiosus and ran in all directions for ladders and buckets.
Fursey regarded the creeping flames with satisfaction, then a
thought seemed to strike him. He peered down at the
howling mob as if to select a victim. His eye fell on a small,
flaxen-haired slave on the edge of the crowd, who was gaping
up at him with his mouth open. Fursey flung his leg over the
broom once more and suddenly swooped. The crowd panicked
and gave way before him, allowing Fursey as he swept over
their heads, to grip the diminutive slave by his long hair and
fly back with him on to the roof of the Palace. The slave lay
across the ridge of the roof with his eyes turned up to Heaven,
fully convinced that his last hour had come. Fursey took
him by the throat.

"What day of the week is this?" demanded Fursey.

"What's that you said, sir?" gasped the slave.

"I asked you what day of the week it was."

The slave closed his eyes and started to say his prayers.
Fursey thumped his head a couple of times against the crossbeam so as to make him stop. The treatment was efficacious.
The wretched creature was silent and looked up at Fursey
with his eyes bloodshot and his tongue hanging out.

"What day of the week is it?" repeated Fursey applying
additional pressure to his gullet.

"Saturday," gasped the slave.

"I thought so," muttered Fursey grimly, and with a mighty
heave he yanked his prisoner into a sitting position.

"Point out the position of Kilpuggin Church," snarled
Fursey, baring his teeth.

The slave raised a trembling hand and pointed.

"Thanks," said Fursey, immediately releasing him.

There was a howl of horror from the crowd as the slave slid
down the roof and fell to the pavement below with a crunching

sound that spoke of broken limbs. The flames were crackling merrily as Fursey once more mounted the broom and sped like a bolt across the housetops of the settlement and away over the green fields. Not once did he falter in his course until he sighted the little church of Kilpuggin. He circled the building once to reconnoitre. He saw horses tethered outside, but there were no human beings. He made a second circuit just for safety, and then made a smooth landing at the church door. He propped his broom carefully in the entrance, and tiptoed in. It was as he had hoped. In the nave in the centre of a small group of friends stood Magnus and Maeve, and behind them Declan and the Widow Dykes. The double wedding had not yet commenced.

" Why, it's Flinthead come to my wedding ! " cried Maeve. " Welcome, Flinthead ! " and she advanced a pace to meet him. Fursey brushed by her, his eyes fixed on Magnus, who was smiling down at him in amused contempt. Fursey did not waste any words, but promptly kicked the bridegroom in the stomach and sent him sprawling. Phineas the Clerk pushed himself forward through the horrified group of guests.

" Flinthead ! " he exclaimed. " Are you mad ? "

" I'm not Flinthead. I'm Fursey, the most powerful and terrible sorcerer that this land has ever known."

" I always knew that there was something strange about you," breathed Maeve.

" Are you mad ? " repeated Phineas shrilly.

" Look through the door," shouted Fursey, " if you don't believe me. I've just set fire to the Bishop's Palace, and the flames of Cashel are roaring into the sky."

Magnus sat up on the floor, more astonished than angry, until Fursey put him once more into a recumbent position with a deft kick under the chin.

" I'm now going to turn you all into toads," asserted Fursey, " and keep you in jars for my amusement."

There was a gasp of horror, and the little group withdrew a couple of paces.

" Nonsense," declared Declan, coming forward and peering closely into Fursey's face. " You're not a sorcerer. You're Flinthead, my farmboy, who ran away last week with a suit of my second-best clothes."

" What would you like for your wedding ? " asked Fursey fiercely. " Wine ? "

" Yes," replied the old man.

Fursey swept the coil of rope from his shoulder, and flinging it over a beam in the roof, jerked it sharply. An immense beaker of wine fell out of nowhere and smashed in pieces on the floor at his feet. The guests retreated precipitately with cries of horror, save only Declan, who clambered on to a chair and began to inspect the rafters to see whether there was anything else concealed there. A priest had appeared among the startled guests. Fursey heard the word " weapons " and saw that the men were scattering towards the back of the church. He immediately seized Maeve by the arm and ran with her to the door.

" Oh, Flinthead," she gasped. " What are you doing ? "

" I'm eloping with you," explained Fursey. " We're going to a better and a freer land."

" But I can't elope with you," she said. " I've got to marry Magnus."

" You can't want to marry that big, boastful bully," insisted Fursey.

" But the priest has been paid and all the guests invited," she objected faintly. " What will people say ? "

" Let them say what they like," asserted Fursey stoutly. " Your friends have run for their weapons. You wouldn't want to see me cut to pieces at your feet."

" Of course not. But I can't marry a sorcerer."

" Why not ? It's as good a profession as any other."

" But what would we live on ? You've no property."

" We'll fly to Britain," declared Fursey, " and open a grocer's shop. It's the easiest thing in the world, I'll spend the mornings pulling on the rope, and the afternoons selling off the goods."

" I hear them coming," declared Maeve, throwing a terrified glance over her shoulder.

" If you don't come with me," declared Fursey, " I'll have to stand here and fight them ; and however manfully I fight, I'll be cut to pieces."

" But have we a steed on which we may escape ? "

" Yes," replied Fursey, producing the broom.

" You're such a precipitate man," gasped Maeve.

" The man of action rules the world," declared Fursey. " Throw your leg across."

" Oh, I couldn't," said Maeve modestly, " I'll ride side-saddle."

As the guests burst from the church clutching their swords, they saw Fursey bent intently over the broom as it rose, while Maeve sat behind, clinging to him desperately and emitting little terrified screams. Thrice Fursey circled the church shouting derisively, while the terrified guests ran hither and thither. Then Fursey, fearing that they might start ringing the church bell, and so bring him to earth, rose high into the air and turned his face towards the east. He glanced over his shoulder only once to gaze with satisfaction at the billowing smoke that crept upwards into the sky over Cashel. Then he flew eastwards, over the grey-green fields, the crooked roads and the sluggishly rolling mountains of Ireland, the first of many exiles for whom a decent way of living was not to be had in their own country.

THE RETURN OF
FURSEY

To RIA MOONEY

my good friend these many years

CHAPTER I

IT is not generally known that the first Letters of Extradition issued in Western Europe were those addressed to the court of Mercia by Cormac Silkenbeard, King of Cashel ; and that they related to the notorious sorcerer Fursey, recently fled across the Western Sea to Britain. They set out in elegant Latin his manifold crimes and villainies, and politely requested that he be returned to Ireland for judicial burning. The Civil Service of Mercia was a small, bald-headed man, whose administrative cares increased yearly as his warlike master pushed conquest further and further into the neighbouring territories, but the Civil Service of Mercia was tenacious, and after three weeks' study came to a full understanding of the document and of its implications. He appointed a day for the reception of the Irish delegation and carefully coached the King of Mercia in what was expected of him.

Ethelwulf was a gloomy, big-boned warrior, at home only in the saddle. He had begun to realise the drawbacks of conquest. It was very pleasant to overrun and annex territories during the summer months, but during the autumn and winter you had to settle down and give your time and energies to arranging for their administration ; and this work he found in the highest degree tedious. Other things, too, contributed to the steady decay of his temper. He was blessed with a wife shapely of body and gracious of address, but her extravagance was past all belief. To keep her clothed in the latest Byzantine fashion cost more than would maintain an army of the hardiest warriors. And on the day on which he received the Irish delegation, he had even more than usual cause for moroseness and gloom. His only son,

on whom were based the hopes of the dynasty, had but a
few days previously disgraced himself by eloping with a
molecatcher's daughter. The molecatcher had been immediately seized and hanged, but this act of tardy justice had

afforded but little solace to the afflicted father. So it was with a brow of more than usual sternness that Ethelwulf entered his Hall of Audience on the day appointed.

On his entry the assembly of nobles and warriors rose to its feet as a mark of respect to their sovereign, and a flock of long-haired harpers in a corner struck up a welcoming tune. Ethelwulf stalked across the hall, mounted the dais and seated himself gingerly on his carbuncle-studded throne. When the company had once more resumed their seats, the Civil Service cleared his throat and began to read the day's manifestos and proclamations prior to passing them up to the monarch so that the royal mark might be made at the bottom of each.

During these preliminaries Ethelwulf rested his black chin on his fist and gazed gloomily along the rows of forked beards that filled the hall. How he hated the silks and effeminate trappings of peace ! How ridiculous they looked, those fierce swordsmen of his, dolled up in coloured cloaks and ribbons ! His eyes travelled the length of the hall and came at last to rest on a little group of strangers near the door. His face brightened with a momentary gladness as he bent his gaze upon the group of tall, fierce-looking men with lank locks tucked into their belts—the Norse traders. They had come a few days before and from their long dragonship in the harbour had discharged a cargo of salted hogs. The king smiled slightly. *They* were no traders. He noted the twitching fingers on the pommels of the great swords, the scars, the broken noses and the places where ears had been lopped off. Those were not accidents that befell simple traders on board ship. Unless he was very much mistaken they were men after his own heart, Viking raiders, some of the few who had so far escaped Christianising. He wondered what they had in mind. The cargo of salted hogs was obviously a blind. It paid their expenses, of course, and brought them thus far into the Western Sea. Doubtlessly they would slip away some night without a return cargo, but with an empty dragonship to cruise along the coasts with irregular and villainous purpose. Despite the Viking raids of the previous centuries there must still be many a fat Irish monastery worthy of their attention. Hardy warriors, he told himself. He could use such men in the coming spring, when he planned to burst like a hurricane into the kingdom of Strathclyde.

The shrill droning of the Civil Service ceased, and Ethelwulf awoke from his day-dreaming. He turned his eyes to where the Civil Service was bowing and smiling blandly so as to secure his attention. When the little man saw that Ethelwulf was listening, he puffed out his chest importantly, unrolled a scroll of parchment, and announced in ringing tones : " Request from Cormac Silkenbeard, King of Cashel, for the extradition of the unspeakable sorcerer, Fursey, recently fled to Mercia in Britain."

" Where's Cashel ? " asked the King suddenly.

" I have searched my encyclopaedias," replied the Civil Service, " and discovered that it's a small kingdom in Ireland."

" Where's Ireland ? " enquired the King.

" It's an island lying far distant in the Western Sea."

" I've heard of it," said Ethelwulf grimly. " A land of abhorred pirates, who constantly raid these coasts for the purpose of carrying off honest men into slavery."

The Irish delegation stirred uneasily. The Civil Service, well aware that the King was as likely as not to order the immediate removal and hanging of the delegation, proceeded hurriedly :

" Cashel is an inland kingdom many miles distant from the seas. The delegation is a most respectable one. Step forward, gentlemen, and state your name and condition."

Two men moved forward to the foot of the throne. The elder was an ecclesiastic, whose dress proclaimed him a man of some rank. Although he was advanced in years, he held himself upright and moved with simple dignity. His face was the face of a student ; there were tiny lines about his eyes, the legacy of long hours spent by taperlight poring

over illuminated manuscript and obscure scroll. Ethelwulf
noted the gentle dignity of the face and the noble carriage
of the head. When the King spoke again, his voice was
subdued.

" You are welcome," he said. " You may speak without
fear."

The ecclesiastic bowed slightly. " My lord king," he began,
" there is in the island of Ireland a great river which we call
the Shannon. Beside that river, in a lonely countryside of
marsh and low green hills, a place remote from men, there
is a famous monastery called Clonmacnoise, where for more
than four hundred years simple men have sought to serve
their God in quiet, far from the strife of mankind. My name
is Marcus : I am the abbot of that monastery."

There was a hush throughout the hall. There seemed to
flow from the silver-haired abbot a winning grace, which
affected every one of the savage warriors present. They, to
whom gentleness was weakness and old age a joke, looked
across at the stranger, their fierce countenances strangely
softened as they watched the changing light and shade in
his face.

" My companion," continued the abbot, " is Magnus, an
honest soldier. We have come to your court, my lord king,
he to request the return of his bride lately carried off by a
deplorable sorcerer named Fursey ; and I to request the
surrender of the sorcerer's person so that he may pay the
penalty of the law for his crimes and for his misfortunes."

Ethelwulf glanced from the abbot to the brawny young
soldier who accompanied him. Then he sat back in his
great chair.

" Relate your story," he commanded.

" What I shall relate," began the abbot, " is a strange and
marvellous tale. Scarcely three months ago the terrible
Emperor of Night, Satan himself, grown rabid with hatred
of our holy settlement, launched a determined and sustained
attack upon the monastery. To forward his unhallowed
purposes he drew on all the dread forces which surround

mankind. The assault began with certain curious and
unaccountable happenings. By daylight showers of fish fell
from the heavens like hail. At night the bedclothes were
suddenly switched away from the beds in which my monks
were peacefully slumbering. The monastery echoed to the
baying of giant hounds, a sound all the more dismal in that
it appeared to proceed from some invisible source. As these
happenings are out of the course of Nature, we began before
long to suspect that there was devilry afoot. It was not,
as you may imagine, that the monastery is situated in a
particularly sorcerous neighbourhood. On the contrary, a
clear, cool air of unmistakable sanctity pervades the entire
territory. We gave ourselves to fasting and prayer, but the
Evil One in his struggle for empire redoubled his efforts.
In every corner of the monastery pestiferous demons could
be heard snorting and snuffling most hideously. There were
no bounds to their detestable behaviour. An unspeakable
company of female devils of the most luscious character
imaginable strove sedulously to tempt my hard-praying
brethren to improper thoughts. When this damnable
behaviour proved ineffective, we were plagued with demons
of hideous aspect in the form of loathsome worms and hydras.
Ounces and pards came sloping down the corridors and used
my unfortunate brethren most foully. For three long weeks
Satan haunted the settlement, contriving all manner of
wickedness, until at last by prayer and exorcism we drove
him and his evil-working minions forth."

As the abbot paused to wipe from his forehead the small
beads of perspiration which had broken out at the recollection
of these terrible happenings, his fascinated audience stirred
and breathed again. The abbot's voice dropped as he turned
once more to face the King.

"I have said that we succeeded in ridding the monastery
of these unwelcome visitants. That is not altogether true.
In one cell they remained. There was in Clonmacnoise at
that time a laybrother named Fursey, a man of sparse intelligence, though nimble and courteous in the performance of

his duties. It's my belief that he was a good man, but definitely thin-minded. This unfortunate fellow had an impediment in his speech ; and being so circumstanced, was unable through sheer fright to pronounce the necessary words of exorcism, so that in Fursey's cell the demons knew themselves to be safe. There was only one practical solution : we expelled Fursey from the monastery. He went ; and their bridgehead gone, the demons went with him."

Once more the abbot paused, whether to weigh his own responsibility in the matter or to conquer his emotion, his hearers could not say. When he took up the thread of his story again, he spoke so low that only those near at hand could hear him.

" He was an unfortunate man, this Fursey. After he had left the monastery, he permitted himself through stupidity to be married to a witch, an aged, spent and decrepit hag ; and, through a deplorable lack of attention to what was happening around him, he inadvertently inhaled her sorcerous spirit as she lay dying, and so became unwillingly a sorcerer himself. That is the story which Fursey tells, and I believe it. Others, including my companion Magnus, deny its truth and assert that Fursey has been a complicated villain from the very beginning."

Magnus the soldier spoke for the first time. His words came out in a low growl.

" I don't believe that tale. Fursey is nothing but a malevolent wizard of the lower sort. Didn't he carry off my bride on the very day of her marriage ? The whole countryside saw the two of them ambling and capering through the air on a broomstick as they flew eastwards to this country."

Ethelwulf stirred so as to obtain a less uncomfortable position on his carbuncle-studded throne before addressing himself to the abbot.

" I don't quite understand the character of this man Fursey," he said. " From what you assert he appears to

be some sort of doting monk, yet he has enraptured at least
two women in as many weeks. Is he then a man of such
resistless charm that no woman can look on him and preserve
her virtue ? "

" On the contrary," answered the abbot gloomily, " he's
a man whose brain is naturally moist. I have said already
that he's thin-minded. Nor can it be truthfully claimed
that he's a model of manly beauty. He's about forty years
of age, small and plump. His hair is snow-white, and his
visage is one of exceptional foolishness."

" How then," queried the King, " do you account for the
fact that in the course of several weeks he won for himself
a wife, albeit she was a witch ; and succeeded in so enchanting
the bride of this well set-up young man that she fled hither
with him from your interesting country ? "

" His wife," replied the abbot, " was nigh on eighty years
when she married him, and was very nearly blind. How he
persuaded the maiden Maeve to flee with him, passes my
comprehension."

" He beguiled her with his extravagant wizardings,"
growled Magnus.

" Do you know aught of this remarkable man Fursey ? "
enquired Ethelwulf, turning to his Civil Service.

" Yes," answered the Civil Service importantly. " I have
had diligent enquiry made. He runs a small grocery business
at the edge of the wood just beyond the town. I detailed
two graduates from our College of Spies to watch him over
the fence for the past couple of weeks. He seems to be
plentifully supplied with foodstuffs, though where he procures
them nobody can say. He does little business, due, I am
informed, to the science of economics, which is defined as
the relating of supply to demand ; but he has every appearance of prosperity. He is always prepared to undercut our
own traders by producing, seemingly from nowhere, vast
quantities of food and drink, which he readily exchanges for
articles of lesser worth. Last week he deprived a passing

charcoal burner of a pair of pigskin trousers, giving as pay-ment countless hogsheads of wine."

" These things I can explain," interrupted the Abbot Marcus. " Fursey, although he possesses the powers and capabilities of a sorcerer, has only learnt how to practise two forms of sorcery. He is able to fly on a broom, and he can produce an infinite quantity of food and drink by the simple operation of throwing a rope over the branch of a tree and pulling on it. In all other forms of wizardry he is quite helpless. These things he has confessed to me himself."

" Does he present in his manners or conversation any symptoms of frenzy ? " enquired the King.

" No," replied the Civil Service. " I've seen and spoken to him myself. He is friendly, anxious to please, and of a somewhat scattered intelligence."

" Remarkable," said the King.

" Yes, Your Majesty," concurred the Civil Service.

" Have you aught more to add ? " asked Ethelwulf, turning once more to the abbot.

" I have, my lord," answered Marcus. " As long as Fursey continues to live, my people in Cashel will shake and sweat with fear. We are civilised men, and we live according to the rule of law. It's a well-known fact that to cure a man of being a wizard is beyond the competence of the most skilful leech or surgeon. Only by the cleansing action of fire can a cure be effected. Fursey surrendered himself to the authorities of the Kingdom of Cashel, and made a full confession of his affliction, asserting that he had become a sorcerer by accident ; but no sooner did we inform him of our charitable intention of securing the safety of his immortal soul by burning him on a pyre, than he began to behave in a manner altogether at variance with his known character for gentleness and humility. He immediately proceeded astride a broom to the roof of the Bishop's Palace and set flame to the thatch with such thoroughness as to gut com-pletely that valuable and desirable residence. Not content with having wrought this great mischief and evil, he swooped on a neighbouring church, interrupted a marriage ceremony, disabled the bridegroom by a sudden kick in the stomach, and carried off the bride to the great distress of her friends and relations."

" Maybe," said the King mildly, " he was not unnaturally incensed at your high-handed proceeding in deciding to burn him without consulting his convenience in the matter."

" But, my lord king," remonstrated the abbot. " It is the law. We are a civilised people living according to the rule of law. Surely in your enlightened kingdom you also put sorcerers to death by fire ? "

" Not always," said Ethelwulf absently. " Sometimes they have their uses."

" Uses, my lord ? "

" In warfare," answered Ethelwulf. " Let us suppose a king were contemplating warfare, a wizard might be useful in raising an enchanted fog on the battlefield. Even the sight of a sorcerer muttering spells powerfully affects the morale of the opposing forces."

" I have no more to say," replied the abbot shortly. " I demand the extradition of the sorcerer Fursey, that he may return with me for condign punishment in his own country."

There was a silence in the great hall. Ethelwulf sat back slowly in his chair and contemplated the abbot.

" No doubt your suggestion is," he said sweetly, " that I should send twelve of my hatchet-men to apprehend him."

" Something of the sort," replied the abbot, " but permit me to add that my studies have taught me that in order that wizards may be bereft of their execrable powers, it is necessary to remove them from contact with the earth. Therefore, when Fursey is arrested, he should be carried away in a basket or on a plank."

The King sat suddenly upright.

" Presumptuous cleric ! " he thundered. " Do you realise that you have used the word ' demand ' to me, Ethelwulf the Unconquerable ? Your request is refused. Fursey remains in my dominions. Show the gentleman out."

The abbot seemed about to remonstrate, but four of the royal hatchet-men moved in upon him and conducted him to the door. Ethelwulf watched, and the thundercloud slowly drifted from his brow. When he turned his head again he saw that the soldier Magnus was on his knees before the throne.

" My lord king," pleaded the soldier, " do what you will with the unspeakable Fursey, but give me permission to take my bride back with me to my own country."

Ethelwulf looked at Magnus. He noted with approval the great hands and muscles, the broad shoulders and the bullock-like simplicity of countenance of the born soldier, the sort of man he understood and with whom he felt at home.

" Marriage is a folly," he said sympathetically, " but it's a respectable one. Take the woman if she is willing to go with you, but do the sorcerer no violence."

.   .   .   .

Beyond the town, but not quite as far as the fringes of the forest, a small, plump man sat under a tree pondering the problem of human happiness. He was a tubby man with a fresh-complexioned face, round and moonlike, crowned with a wealth of prematurely white hair. Nearby was a snug cottage with walls of cunningly interwoven rods and twigs carefully plastered over with clay. A trickle of smoke drifted meditatively from a hole in the thatched roof. The track from the town passed the door and wound away into the forest, already aglow with the mellow loveliness of autumn. Some hundred paces from where Fursey sat were the cliffs, which fell sheer into the untranquil sea.

For some moments the little man sat listening to the seas fussing among the rocks, then his thoughts came back again to the problem that was exercising him. " I have a neat house," he said to himself, " the best of food and drink, and a pleasant woman on whom I am sore assotted. And yet I am not conscious of being actively happy." He sighed, and his eyes strayed across to the long line of cliffs against

which the sea was tossing its white breakers, and thence to
the winding track and the chequered countryside, coming to
rest finally on the stretch of nearby trees, the outposts of
the forest. He noted appreciatively the autumn colouring,
green, amber and gold. " Nature is beautiful," he said to
himself. " If any man should be happy it is I, who possess
all that I can possibly desire—and yet I am not conscious of
happiness. I am only conscious of sitting under a tree
thinking about these things."

He shook his head gloomily and began to think about his
friend the molecatcher. It had been a beautiful friendship.
Twice a week he had walked over to the molecatcher's hut
to sit at the molecatcher's feet and listen to him talking
philosophy. But on the previous Wednesday when he had
gone over to put to his friend the problem of human happiness,
he had been surprised to find the molecatcher hanging from
the crossbeam over his own front door. Fursey, knowing
that it was unlucky to meddle in matters which did not
concern him, had crept away without a word. But for the
past few days a certain depression had weighed upon his
spirit. He had begun to worry not only about human
happiness, but about the uncertainty of continued existence.
His thoughts were interrupted by a clear, pleasant voice
from the cottage :

" Fursey ! Supper's ready."

Fursey rose obediently and ambled across the grass to the
little wickerwork hut. He ducked his head in the low doorway
and entered the cottage. Inside there was a woman bending
over the fire, her face somewhat flushed from the heat. She
straightened herself and glanced around as he entered. She
was about thirty-two years of age, fresh and gracious in
appearance.

" What's for supper ? " enquired Fursey pleasantly.

" I have made you a pie of escallops," she replied, pointing
with the ladle to the place where he was to sit at the table.
Fursey rubbed his little, plump hands contentedly.

" A beaker of ale is needed to make smooth its passage

to the stomach," he remarked, and going to the corner he gave a sharp chuck to a rope which hung from the rafters. Immediately a beaker of ale appeared from nowhere, slid down the rope, was caught deftly by Fursey and conveyed to the table. Maeve threw a glance at him over her shoulder, a slight frown upon her face.

" I hate to see you engaging in sorcery," she said.

" Why ? " asked Fursey blithely. " Isn't it the foundation of our fortunes ? Anyway, producing food is practically the only sorcery I know. I know nought of conjurations or any kind of complicated wizardings."

" Sorcery of any sort doesn't seem to me to be very respectable," retorted Maeve.

" But we'll starve unless I produce food and drink."

" You could get a job."

" A job ! " ejaculated Fursey, his mind becoming immediately engloomed.

" Yes," continued Maeve determinedly. " Now that the molecatcher is dead, I'm sure you could get his job if you asked for it."

" But I don't know anything about catching moles," bleated Fursey.

" You could learn," replied Maeve tartly as she turned once more to the fire. " At least it's much more respectable than being a wizard."

Fursey relapsed into abstraction, his spirits much affected by this sudden suggestion. He ate his pie in silence, for he could think of nothing profitable to say. Besides, he had learnt during the two months he had lived with Maeve that a woman fussed by her household duties is a different sort of creature altogether from the girl one remembered standing beside a lake with the wind blowing through her hair. But the silence in the room became at last so painful that when he had finished his beaker of ale he ventured to speak once more.

" I was talking to the charcoal burner yesterday," he said,

" and he told me that the world is going to end in the year 1000. It's the talk of the town, he says."

" It'll probably last out our time," snapped Maeve.

" It's a very serious thing for humanity," said Fursey, shaking his head.

Maeve did not deign to reply, but sweeping the pie dish from the table, began to scour it thoroughly. When she spoke again, she astonished Fursey by her sudden change of subject.

" I wish you wouldn't sit round on the grass," she said. " You'll ruin your new pigskin trousers."

It was Fursey's turn to be silent, and he sat for a long time brooding on the sore change that had so suddenly befallen their relationship. He was aroused from his thoughts by a sudden commotion outside the cottage. All at once the door was kicked open and, as the startled Fursey rose to his feet, he beheld the man whom he had wronged, outlined in the doorway. Magnus appeared to be struggling to break from the restraining grip of the two other men, the Civil Service of Mercia and the Abbot Marcus.

" Is this the abode of the accursed sorcerer ? " shouted Magnus. " Let me go. I am resolved to make a skeleton of him."

At these alarming words, Fursey sprang across the kitchen as if to burst through the far wall and so make his escape ; but, finding no exit that way, he fled into the corner and hid behind Maeve. Magnus continued to give tongue to the most gross and horrid epithets of abuse and insulting comparison, but made no real attempt to break from the feeble grip of the two elderly men and precipitate himself into the sorcerer's cottage. He seemed to be struggling in the most furious and formidable manner, but in fact he deemed it wise to keep as great a distance as possible between himself and a man of such unwholesome fame as Fursey.

" Go in and restrain Fursey," said the abbot to the Civil

Service. " I fear me that if these two come to grips the combat will be terrific beyond all description and will doubtless result in their mutual destruction."

The Civil Service did as he was bid, but when Fursey felt the persuasive hand laid on his arm, his confusion of mind was such that he fell on the floor. When Magnus beheld the sorcerer on his hands and knees he did not doubt but that an operation of a magical character was imminent, and he was with difficulty restrained by the abbot from taking to his heels. In this scene of indescribable confusion, Maeve seemed to be the only one to keep her head. She stepped lightly across to the door.

" You are welcome, gentlemen," she said. " Won't you come in and take a seat ? "

Marcus inclined his head politely and, keeping a tight grip on Magnus' arm, entered the kitchen. The soldier was put sitting on the edge of a chair, panting heavily. Fursey was helped to his feet and stood leaning against the far wall, from which he cast agonising glances across at the door. Fursey knew himself to be in evil case. He knew that one cannot carry off a bride from the foot of the altar, live with her for two months, and then on one's next encounter with the outraged bridegroom expect him to behave with courtesy and reason. He knew Magnus to be a man of hard temper, and he was under the most painful apprehension as to the outcome of the affair. It seemed to him that he would be lucky if he escaped with no worse hurt than a couple of broken limbs.

" Yes," said the abbot to the Civil Service of Mercia, " this is Fursey, the unfortunate man to whom the Devil manifested himself in Clonmacnoise, and who afterwards became unwillingly, he asserts, possessed of sorcerous powers. Those powers are fortunately of a very limited nature."

As the Civil Service contemplated him with interest, it was borne in powerfully on Fursey that his one hope of safety lay in convincing his hearers that he was a man more formidable than they imagined. He passed his tongue over his dry lips and addressed himself to the abbot.

" My lord," he quavered, " since we last had the pleasure of meeting I beg you to believe that I have become most learned in occult devices. I regret to say that my disposition has altered for the worse, and I am now a man prompt to violence. I am subject to sudden storms of rabid fury."

The abbot stared at Fursey doubtfully, but the Civil Service moved back his chair hurriedly.

" It may be," he said in an awestricken whisper, " that this man, to all appearances tame and tranquil, is in fact possessed of a wily, treacherous and fierce disposition."

A ghastly smile spread over Fursey's visage as he strove to assume a look of preposterous depravity. Magnus rose shakily to his feet.

" Let us go," he whispered. " His countenance and complexion are scarcely of human aspect."

Maeve laughed suddenly, and Fursey experienced a stifling feeling as he felt the tension in the room relax.

" What is this nonsense, Fursey ? " said the abbot, bending forward. " Sit down, Magnus. Would you forego your bride ? "

" I can ill endure his presence," muttered the soldier. " He seems to me to be forming some atrocious design, he sits there so still."

The abbot shook himself impatiently. He arose and taking Maeve gently by the arm, drew her into a chair.

" My dear lady," he said, " why did you run away with this man ? "

Maeve glanced up at him with surprise. There was such a winning kindness in the old man's face that she suddenly knew that she could not tell him a lie. She flushed slightly and looked down at the floor.

" It all happened very quickly," she answered in a low voice. " I thought he needed me. He seemed so helpless and without friends."

The abbot nodded understandingly.

"You know," he said gently, "your life with him here is not very respectable."

Maeve flushed again. "I suppose not," she admitted in scarcely audible tones.

"Not respectable at all," repeated the abbot. "If people thought you went with him voluntarily, they'd be inclined to talk."

Again Maeve looked up at the old man with surprise.

"Do they not know that I went voluntarily?" she asked.

"Oh, no. They believe he bewitched you by an insidious spell and carried you off against your will. Everyone has the greatest sympathy for you. If you return to Cashel, no one will think any worse of you."

Maeve put her head down suddenly on the abbot's shoulder and began to cry. He patted her arm soothingly.

"Respectability is a very precious thing. The good opinion of our neighbours is worth more than gold. This young man, Magnus, is willing to take you back."

Maeve raised her head and looked with streaming eyes at Magnus, who nodded to her awkwardly.

"Do you think that Fursey still needs you?" whispered the abbot.

"No," wept Maeve. "He can get everything he wants with that magic rope of his. And I don't know that he even cares for my company. He spends half his evenings out drinking with a disreputable molecatcher."

The abbot made a sign to Magnus, who arose and put his arm around the weeping girl.

"Take her to the boat," said the abbot. "I will follow you."

As they went through the doorway, Maeve threw one glance back. Through a film of tears she caught a glimpse of Fursey sitting dead still in the corner, his face ashen and his forehead damp with sweat. Then the door closed behind them.

"Our journey to this land has not been altogether in

vain," said the abbot. "One wrong at least has been righted. Fursey, I have little to say to you. I demanded of the stiff-backed ruler of this territory that you should be surrendered and go back with me to Cashel, there to stand trial ; but my reasonable request has been refused. The King seems to think that he can make use in warfare of such knowledge of the darker arts as you possess, though I did my best to persuade him that you possessed none worth talking about. I must now take my departure ; but before I go I urge you once more to repent of your manifold crimes. Goodbye, Fursey."

When the door closed behind the abbot, Fursey gave vent to a moan that accorded with his forlorn situation. The Civil Service of Mercia coughed importantly and addressed himself to the little figure huddled in the chair.

"With reference to what has just taken place," he began, "I am instructed to inform you that the application for your extradition to the Kingdom of Cashel has been refused. I am to inform you further that you are forbidden to quit this territory under pain of His Majesty's displeasure. You will hold yourself in readiness at all times to give service and to perform such duties as may be assigned to you."

"I'm afraid I don't understand you," replied Fursey. "My spirits are in too great disorder."

The Civil Service regarded him disapprovingly. Then he relaxed and seated himself on a chair.

"If you will oblige me by removing that wild and vacant look from your face I shall endeavour to explain your position to you. His Majesty has saved you from the fate of most sorcerers, death on a funeral pyre, an end which is without comfort or honour. You will be grievously lacking in courtesy and gratitude if you fail to place at his service the experience which you have gained in the practice of the darker arts."

"But I'm no good as a sorcerer," wailed Fursey. "All I can do is produce food by pulling on a rope."

THE RETURN OF FURSEY

" Is that all ? " asked the Civil Service suspiciously. " I find it hard to believe you."

" I can fly on a broomstick if it's ready prepared and anointed for me. But I've no magical oils or ointments, and I don't know how to make them."

The Civil Service breathed severely through his nostrils as he rose to his feet.

" You would do well to make rapid progress in your studies," he said coldly. " The King has little patience with charlatans. Last summer he employed a most well-spoken wizard with a satchelful of testimonials, but the wretched man failed lamentably to live up to our expectations. In the first battle in which he was employed, although he succeeded after much labour in inducing a shower of thunder-stones, they fell, not on the enemy, but on our own com-missariat two miles in the rear. His ability to produce an enchanted fog when required cannot be called into question, but the poltroon was unable to control it, and it kept floating up and down the line of battle, impeding the vision of our slingsmen."

" I suppose His Majesty was annoyed," ventured Fursey.

" Annoyed ! The fellow was nothing but a quack, and he got his deserts—a fate worse than death."

Fursey swallowed. " I see," he said.

The Civil Service paused at the door. " I'd brush up my magic if I were you. You know not the day nor the hour when the King may call upon you."

Alone in the cottage, Fursey rested his arms on the table and buried his face in his arms. He sat for a long time thus ; then he stirred and placed his right hand on his heart as if to support its intolerable weight. It felt like a heavy stone in his chest.

" For a week," he said dully; " I was so idle that I had nothing better to do than try to explain to myself the nature of happiness. Now I know. Happiness is no more than the absence of unhappiness, and it is a sufficiently blessed state."

As he sat alone hour after hour the realisation of his

grievous loss waxed until it possessed his whole body. He squirmed as he thought of the woman he loved so dearly, and he beat his fist impotently on the table—hard, hopeless blows. Then he was still, and bitterness crept into his mind as a thin sliver of light creeps across the surface of a lake. He remembered what she had said, that she had only gone with him because he seemed helpless and without friends. It was pity that had stirred her, not love. For a moment he felt that he hated her, but something suddenly broke down inside him. The tears coursed down his cheeks and he knew that he could never hate her. But feeling the necessity to hate someone, his thoughts stretched out and encompassed Magnus—a strong, self-confident bully, he told himself. And he began to hate himself for his weakness. " I'm a born coward," he reflected bitterly, " without the strength or the courage to put out my hand and take what the world has to offer, without even the resolution to hold what I already have." But self-hatred is a whip from which we turn and twist until we escape, and Fursey began painfully to justify himself in his own eyes. After all, he had never in his life willingly done any wrong. He had been expelled from his monastery, released from his vows and flung into the un-friendly world because a horde of unwelcome demons had attached themselves to him. Through no fault of his own he had swallowed the sorcerous spirit and powers of a witch, and when he had made known his misfortune, the authorities, instead of striving to cure him by spiritual or surgical means, had coolly set preparations in train to burn him. And at last, when he had seemed to find happiness in another land with a dear, good woman, they had coaxed her away from him with talk of respectability and virtue.

" Damn respectability and virtue ! " exclaimed Fursey, and suddenly took his resolution. " Henceforth I will serve Evil. I'll become a most depraved character. I'll turn really wicked."

He sat for a moment, his troubles forgotten as he turned over in his mind this new idea. After all, his entire life had been spent in the pursuit of goodness, and where had it got him ? Into a proper fix, with the probability of having to face at any moment " a fate worse than death." He rose to his feet and swaggered across the room. He looked around the kitchen as if challenging opposition. Then he seized the pie dish and smashed it to pieces on the floor. He was rather startled at the crash it made and skipped hastily out of the way of the flying pieces. But he recovered himself quickly and kicked the broken shreds across the floor. Then he seized the ladle and flung it into the fire.

" I'll show them," he said. " I'm tired of being the football of destiny. I'll earn for myself a terrible reputation as an evil-working fellow. I'll behave in a preposterous manner so that people will say that my like for depravity has never been seen in the world before."

He took up a chair and, opening the door with one hand, flung the chair out on to the grass outside. Then he came back and seated himself at the table so as to think out a plan of campaign.

" There are three things I must do," he said. " I must recover Maeve. I must do Magnus an injury, and I must remove myself and Maeve to some place where we shall be secure. No, there's a fourth thing, most pressing of all— I must remove myself with the utmost despatch from the dominions of this monarch before he starts asking me to do magical sleight-of-hand for him. The results of any such attempts on my part would certainly be deplorable."

Fursey shuddered as he remembered the beady eye of the Civil Service as the words " a fate worse than death " were enunciated. He spurred on his thoughts to think out a course of action, but despite the simmering inside his head, of which he was conscious, no plan presented itself. Then he remembered that he was a sorcerer and as such never entirely alone. He bent forward and whispered a name. " Albert ! "

For a moment nothing happened. Then there was a thickening of the air beside the fireplace, and ever so slowly

there appeared a creature like a large dog, covered all over
with rusty black hair. It was tailless and had the paws of a
bear. The creature was of an unnatural leanness and seemed
in very poor condition. It fixed on Fursey a pair of smoky
red eyes of unutterable melancholy.

" Is that you, Albert ? "

The stranger opened his snout, and his voice came out in a
hoarse croak.

" Who the hell do you think it is ? Haven't you just
summoned me ? "

" Don't be impertinent," said Fursey.

" You called my name," the creature insisted obstinately.
" What did you expect to appear ? A buck rabbit with a
ribbon round its neck ? "

" See here," said Fursey severely. " You'll have to learn
to be more respectful. You're my familiar, and a sorcerer's
familiar should treat his master with respect. It's not
sufficient that you should always be at hand to carry out
my orders. I expect you to be courteous as well as nimble
in my service."

Albert's smoky red eyes regarded Fursey mournfully, but
he volunteered no reply.

" What have you been doing with yourself during the two
months since I last saw you ? " enquired Fursey. " You've
allowed yourself to become very emaciated."

The light of indignation flickered for a moment in Albert's
red eyes and then was suddenly drowned in a look of watery
despair. Two large tears welled up and ran down each side
of his snout.

" Oh, Albert," said Fursey, bending sympathetically
towards his familiar.

Albert took an uncertain step forward and laid his chin
on Fursey's knee. Great husky sobs came up from the
depths of his shrunken chest and he slobbered all over
Fursey's new pigskin trousers.

" Accursed be the black day on which I first became

attached to you as your familiar. I'm slowly starving to death."

"But I thought," said Fursey diffidently, "that spirits feed on quintessences and other matters of an ethereal nature."

The look which Albert threw at him was so full of pathos that Fursey's heart turned over within him.

"You know perfectly well," said Albert heartbrokenly, "that a sorcerer must feed his familiar with his own blood. I explained it all to you when you first became a wizard. It's your criminal neglect that has reduced me to my present lamentable state."

For a little while Fursey sat brooding sadly while Albert slowly mastered his emotion. At last the familiar raised one of his bear's paws and dried his eyes.

"Things are going to be different from now on," said Fursey gently. "When you first introduced yourself to me and informed me that I had inherited you as well as a magician's powers, I was so revolted at the thought of being a wizard that I could not bear the sight of you. Nor did I entertain sympathetically your repeated demands for my blood. But things are going to be different from now on. I am resolved to live a life of unexampled depravity."

"If you wanted to do me a good turn," suggested Albert, "you could either sell me or make a present of me to some full-blooded enthusiast who is embarking on a career of sorcery. That's my only chance of survival."

"No," said Fursey determinedly. "I won't part with you. You're the only friend I have."

Albert emitted a despairing moan.

"To others," said Fursey, "you may be a terrifying citizen of the spiritual world, but to me you are my familiar, personal to myself, and my very dear friend."

"That's all very fine," said Albert lugubriously, "but as things are going at present, I don't think I'm long for this world."

"But I need you," insisted Fursey. "Never have I stood so much in need of advice and assistance. My affairs have taken a very sinister turn and are at present in a state of grave detriment."

"It's no use expecting nimble service from me," replied Albert. "At present I haven't the energy of a ninepenny rabbit."

"Will my blood restore you?" asked Fursey.

Albert raised his head expectantly. And then in the half-light of the cottage Fursey deliberately did evil for the first time in his life. He took a knife and, making an incision in his thumb, fed some drops of his blood to his familiar. When the ghastly ceremony was over, Albert sat back on his hunkers, far from satiated, but filled with optimistic expectation of brighter days to come.

"Now," said Fursey, "to business. I am much in need of advice."

Albert had no tail, but he wagged his hindquarters courteously.

"I have an enemy," began Fursey. "He has just carried off an amiable young woman on whom I am sore assotted. How will I get even with him?"

Albert thought for a moment.

"You don't happen to have a hairless cat?" he enquired.

"No," replied Fursey. "I'm sorry."

"If your enemy was here," said Albert, "you could imprison him in a leather bottle, or alternatively you could spread the venom from a toad, or other baleful juices, on his linen. But, of course, he's not here."

"No," said Fursey. "I don't know where he is."

"If we had some eggs," said Albert, "we could labour them in a pail of boiling water and see what happens. But, of course, you'd need to know how to do it. Unless a wizard is very expert in the weaving of a spell he cannot always be certain of immunity from danger to himself."

Albert paused and gazed for a moment thoughtfully into the fire.

" I have it," he said suddenly, slapping one clenched bear's paw into the palm of the other. " You should hide under his bolster a rope composed of the hairs torn from the head of a raging hyena. That will cause his fingers and toes to rot and fall off."

" I wish you'd be practical," replied Fursey shortly. " I haven't got the head of a raging hyena."

" Well, have you got the marrows of an unbaptised babe ? They're very useful in inducing delusions and insanity."

" I haven't," said Fursey peevishly. " I haven't got any of those things."

" Well, why not simply afflict him with a lingering and painful disease ? "

" Because I don't know how."

" Do you not even know enough," enquired Albert hopefully, " to afflict him with a lameness ? "

" No," replied the exasperated Fursey. " You know perfectly well that the only magic I'm competent to perform is the production of food and drink by pulling on a rope."

" And I heard you this evening," said Albert, shaking his head reprovingly, " telling Abbot Marcus that you had become most learned in occult devices. I'm afraid you're an extreme liar."

" That was a defensive stratagem," answered Fursey.

" Do you even understand the powers of seven and nine ? "

" No."

Albert shook his head despondently. " I'm afraid you're a sad sorcerer."

They sat for a while in silence, Fursey watching his familiar's face anxiously, while Albert gazed broodingly into the fire, occasionally shrugging his shoulders and muttering to himself as he dismissed some plan that had suggested itself to his mind. Finally he raised a hairy paw and scratched his head.

" I can't think of anything," he said. " After all, if you don't know any sorcery, there's nothing to be done in that line. You'll have to proceed by ordinary natural means."

" You're not much help to me," said Fursey.

"What's the use of trying to help a shiftless fellow like you?" snapped Albert. "You've been a sorcerer for three months and you've learnt nothing. I don't know what you've been doing with your time."

Albert rose and shook himself like a dog. Then he shambled over to the door and back again.

"Of course, there's one thing you might do," he said.

"What's that?" enquired Fursey eagerly.

Albert threw a quick look at his master. "There's an old acquaintance of yours in the neighbourhood," he said slowly.

"Who?"

"Satan."

Fursey sat back slowly in his chair and his eyes met those of his familiar. Albert was squatting on his hunkers and gazing steadily at his master.

"I'm not acquainted with Satan myself," he said diffidently. "We belong to different mythologies. But I understand that he is an affable gentleman, always willing to oblige a friend."

Fursey said nothing.

"I don't want to seem inquisitive," continued Albert, "but it would clarify matters considerably if you would tell me the exact relationship in which you stand to the dread Emperor of Night."

Fursey had become suddenly wan. He passed his tongue over his dry lips before he spoke.

"When I was a laybrother in the monastery, Satan appeared to me and sought to persuade me to sell him my soul. I refused. He appeared to me several times afterwards before I fled to this country, and each time he repeated his offer. He always treated me with courtesy, asserting that he had taken a liking to me, but how do I know whether or not to believe a being whom mankind calls 'The Father of Lies'? He insisted on doing me several services, in order, I suppose, to ingratiate himself with me. It is sufficient that I have always rejected his offers."

" Would you reject them, now that you have determined to live a life of iniquity ? "

Fursey said nothing for a long time, but sat brooding on his forlorn situation. His mind hardened as he remembered how the good and the pious were seeking his destruction.

" How do you know he's in the neighbourhood ? " he asked at length.

" You forget that I'm an elemental spirit," replied Albert. " In my capacity as an ethereal essence I get to know a lot of things."

Still Fursey hesitated. Then he suddenly envisaged the exasperation of the King of Mercia on discovering that the wizard whose life he had saved was unable to perform the simplest magical operation. He did not doubt but that a wealthy monarch like Ethelwulf had in his dungeons a repertoire of the most exquisite tortures. He shuddered.

" Yes," he said huskily. " I'll seek out Satan and ask his help. Where is he to be found ? "

" There are things happening in the forest to-night," replied Albert darkly. " He is there—with his friends."

" The forest is vast," quavered Fursey, " and it is an uncouth place in which to wander alone and after nightfall. How will I find my way to him through the profound darkness that will obtain ? "

" The moon is full to-night. You will find your way by moonlight. You know the broad track that enters the forest ? "

" Yes."

" Four hundred paces along that track a bridlepath branches off to the left. You must follow the windings of that bridle-path until you penetrate deep into the wood."

" Wait a minute," interrupted Fursey. " The week before last a merchant who had lost his way took the track of which you speak. The unfortunate man had to run a distance of five miles, pursued by a numerous banditti."

" It is true," admitted Albert, " that the forest abounds in dishonourable fellows of the robber class, but you will be lucky if it is only human beings that you encounter."

" What do you mean by that statement ? " demanded Fursey. " Is the woodland frequented by wolves and wild boars ? "

" They are present in force," conceded Albert ; " but it was not such creatures that I had in mind."

" Please be explicit," said Fursey. " I may as well know the worst."

" I said that there were things happening in the forest to-night," replied Albert. " You may find your road incommoded by the presence of ghouls."

Fursey looked at him. " Maybe it would be as well to call the thing off."

" Nonsense," rejoined Albert, " you're not the sort of man to be alarmed by a vague wraith or two."

" Amn't I ? " interjected Fursey. " I'm glad you think so."

" The truth is that certain tenants of the tomb are abroad. As you proceed along the woodland path you will probably be conscious of unseen intelligences about you. If they materialise, you would do well to have no conversation or dealings with them, as all spirits are of a variable disposition and inclined to deceit."

" You needn't fear," retorted Fursey, " that I'll force conversation on them. I'm not proceeding into the forest at all. I'd prefer to surrender myself to the King and let him torture me into a knot."

" Don't be silly," rejoined Albert. " All you need is a stout heart."

" But that's a thing I haven't got."

" I wish you wouldn't always be making such capital of your poverty," said Albert crossly. " It may be effective in argument, but it gets you nowhere in life. I'm only trying to help you."

" You're a great help," snapped Fursey. He sat for a while gazing into the fire in much dejection of spirit.

" Suppose," he said at last, " suppose I do commit myself
to the dangers of the forest, and succeed in escaping destruction by bandits, wild boars, wolves and the ghastly inhabitants
of the tomb, what happens after that ? "

" Deep in the forest," replied Albert, " you will come to a
rude bridge of hurdles flung across a chasm."

" And I suppose," said Fursey gloomily, " there'll be a
couple of poltergeists waiting there to throw me over."

" I don't think the matter is a suitable one for joking,"
said Albert huffily.

" I assure you that I don't feel a bit like joking," replied
Fursey. " All that you tell me is most dismal to my ear.
What will I encounter at the bridge ? "

" You may not encounter anything," said Albert stiffly,
" but in its neighbourhood you will very likely espy a dark,
low-sized fellow with the face of an ape."

Fursey breathed heavily through his nostrils. " You seem
to be acquainted with all the riff-raff of the World of
Shadows," he said severely. " What is he ? Some class of
unclean spirit, I suppose ? "

" He's the demon Elemauzer," said Albert with dignity.
" You will have no difficulty in recognising him. He has a
pair of boar's tusks, which are in the highest degree formidable,"

When Fursey spoke again it was in a strange hollow voice :
" The whole affair seems to me to wear a dismal aspect."

" You mustn't let ideal terrors influence you," urged
Albert.

" In the long run," replied Fursey, " the adventure might
well prove a bootless undertaking."

" You must act in the matter as suits your convenience
and pleasure," answered Albert coldly. " Take thought."

" I'm taking thought," said Fursey, " and the whole
business seems to me to be in the highest degree unwholesome."

" I admit that once you are in the forest it will be necessary
for you to behave with uncommon caution."

" You're very glib," said Fursey, " but it seems to me that I'll be very lucky if I succeed in advancing one hundred paces into the forest without being torn into small pieces by someone either spectral or mundane. As for you, there's no need to maintain that black and sulky aspect ; it's I, not you, who must face these manifold dangers."

" So you're going to go ? "

" I don't see what else I can do," responded Fursey. " I'm in imminent danger of destruction at the hands of the Christian monarch who rules this territory, and it seems that Satan is the only one who can advise me. I feel moved to much cursing and swearing, but unfortunately I don't know how."

" When you encounter the demon Elemauzer, you should address him courteously and ask him to direct you to the Prince of Darkness. He will not hesitate to do so."

" I will," said Fursey glumly, " if I get that far. I'll enter the forest well charged with ale. It may serve to allay my trepidation."

" Before you order me to disappear," said Albert, " I would remind you that I will be due for another feed of your blood at latest the day after to-morrow."

" Kindly vanish," ordered Fursey, " and don't bother me further. I've enough worries of my own."

Albert disappeared slowly with a wriggle of indignation, and Fursey was once more by himself.

CHAPTER II

IT is unlikely that Fursey would have ventured into the forest at all that night but for the courage artificially induced in him by the consumption of large quantities of ale. Although it was not yet dark when he left the cottage, he held a lighted lantern high above his head. He had a length of rope slung over his shoulder and his gait was somewhat uncertain. It was a couple of miles to the edge of the

woodland, and by the time he arrived among the occasional trees that were the outposts of the forest, he had sobered considerably. The shades of evening had deepened between the trees and, as Fursey stood peering into the green gloom, an indefinable fear gripped him. Even the trees seemed to him to wear a look of conscious mystery. The path which he must take was murky and in the highest degree uninviting. He stood in an agony of indecision. He was sorely tempted to retrace his steps, and it was only by keeping constantly before his mind the elaborately equipped torture parlours of the King of Mercia, that he hardened his courage sufficiently to enter the forest. He told himself that he would be wise to hasten so as to complete as much of his journey as possible before the light faded altogether from the sky. This thought seized on his mind so powerfully that he began to run. It seemed an age before he reached the spot where the fatal bridlepath wound off to the left. Here he paused, the prey of the most painful imaginings. With a shaky hand he flung his rope over one of the lower branches of a tree.

" A large beaker of ale," he whispered.

The beaker slid down the rope, and Fursey took a long pull, half emptying the vessel. Then he secured himself a second beaker, made an attempt to damp down his terror, and started to tiptoe down the bridlepath, filled with dismal foreboding. It seemed to him a profound forest and very dusky, but he did not dare let his mind dwell on its secrets. Instead he sought to conjure up an image of himself being introduced to a company of the King's most expert torturers. Once, as the pale glimmer of his lantern lit up a space between the trees, he thought that he saw something very frail moving in the black depths of the wood ; but in the dubious twilight he could not be certain. He stopped to take a swig from his beaker before hurrying on. He had gone a long distance along the crazy track when he was brought to a standstill by the sudden appearance of a dingy phantom leaning against a tree. It turned on the quaking Fursey an eager, frenzied eye, and contemplated him for a moment before suddenly springing eight feet up the bole. The wonder was that Fursey retained his wits. As it was, he staggered uncertainly and with difficulty kept his feet. The phantom was of peculiar aspect. He seemed a sullen, rancorous fellow and had piercing eyes like those of a water-rat. It was quite apparent to Fursey that he was a demon of the lower sort, but in spite of his uninviting aspect he seemed to be a knacky and ingenious fellow, for before the eyes of the startled Fursey he began to climb the tree with his teeth. This unusual behaviour was little calculated to allay Fursey's disquiet. He became suddenly galvanised into action and began to run with such violence that he dashed himself against a tree. In a flash he was on his feet again and scuttled down the track as fast as his legs would carry him. He was conscious of mad laughter accompanying him as he ran. It seemed to come not only from behind the trees and from the undergrowth, but to be all around him. Fursey ran faster than he had ever run in his life before, and as he ran he raised the beaker to his lips and strove to drink at the same time, spilling most of the liquor in his efforts. He had turned a corner and run right through a meagre gentleman in a shroud before he noticed him. When Fursey realised what had happened, he did not pause to make any explanations, but ran all the harder. When he stopped at last through sheer exhaustion, the blood was pounding in his temples and his heart felt as if it might at any moment burst through his chest. He leaned against a tree to recover his breath.

" By God," said Fursey, " this is a sombre business."

The wood was quiet. Between the treetops came the random light of the moon, shedding over all a dismal sepulchral illumination. But the wood was quiet, and Fursey allowed himself to hope that he had passed successfully through that area of it which was haunted. But before long his hopes were dashed, for he had no sooner recovered his breath than he observed something approaching him, flitting from tree to tree. Whatever it was, it seemed of flighty and unsettled character, and very bristly. Fursey did not wait to scrutinise it further, but hastily finished his beaker of ale and took to his heels once more.

It was fortunate for Fursey that he was drunk during the latter part of his progress through the wood. It was true that he was inclined to see the subsequent phantoms and demons as pairs of twins instead of singly; but the alcohol seemed to give him an unexpected second wind at the moments when he most needed it. Moreover, it served to dull his senses. Had he to run such a gauntlet when sober, it is unlikely that he would have succeeded in doing so without becoming deranged in his intellects.

All at once he found himself in a small clearing. Now that he was clear of the trees it was less dark, and Fursey stopped to peer left and right around the open space ringed irregularly by the black forest. The atmosphere of the place, the air tremulous in the twilight, filled him with peculiar foreboding. As he stood hesitating, he was suddenly conscious of a furtive breeze that seemed to come slipping around a mass of lichen-crusted rock which lay athwart his path. A chill breath of air struck him in the face, and a moment later he became aware of a small wind of an uncommonly pestilential character. Above the whispering of the forest he could hear the sound of water close at hand. As he stood with a beating heart listening, his senses strained to the utmost, there came suddenly skipping around the pile of rock a strangely disreputable-looking demon. It was covered with matted hair and seemed to Fursey an apparition of a particularly unlucky looking character. It paused on the path about ten paces from where he stood and, fixing its eyes upon Fursey, displayed a double set of teeth. Then it bent down and started whetting its fangs on a stone. Fursey was much affected by this baleful sight, and it was borne in powerfully upon him that the creature was bent on doing him a personal mischief. He felt that it was no empty phantom, and the conviction grew in him that this was something he had better not have seen. The creature suddenly wagged its head in Fursey's direction.

" What would you have ? " it asked.

Fursey grew pale about the lips and was too overcome to vouchsafe an answer. The demon, its fangs having now been sharpened to its satisfaction, stood once more upright and began to skip and gambol to and fro among the rocks, round and round Fursey, in ever diminishing circles. Suddenly as the phantom wagged its head, the soft moonlight fell full upon its face, and Fursey noticed that from its countenance sprouted a formidable pair of boar's tusks. A flood of relief swept over him.

" Stop," he said in a thin voice. " Aren't you the demon Elemauzer ? "

The hideous apparition ceased its capering and stood stock still.

" Yes," it answered, surprised. " Who are you and what are you doing in the forest on a night such as this ? "

Fursey, as he answered, made a mighty effort to interlace authority with his words.

" I do not tell my business to underlings. Kindly take me to your master Satan, who is present in this forest to-night."

The demon seemed startled. It stood looking at Fursey for a moment rather crestfallen.

" Follow me," it said at last, and, turning, made off across the clearing. Fursey followed, quaking.

They came to a narrow rustic bridge, beneath which a torrent sighed and roared. Fursey hurried across in the wake of his guide, not daring to glance down at the white water foaming in the hollows between the thirsty crags. They continued across another stretch of open ground until they came to a long, low grassy mound. Fursey recognised it as a barrow, the burying place of some old pagan king, who, before the beginnings of history, had been here laid to rest with fabulous ceremony. The demon stopped and turned its unattractive visage to Fursey.

" Satan will manifest himself here, sir," it said. " You have only to call upon him."

" All right," replied Fursey, eyeing the apparition with considerable trepidation. " You may go now about your business. I shall not require you further."

Elemauzer still hesitated.

"I hope it's nothing in the nature of a complaint to the Boss," he said ingratiatingly. "I had no idea you were a friend of his. Anyway, I wasn't really going to harm you. I was only joking."

"That's all right," gasped Fursey. "Please go away."

"Goodbye, sir," said Elemauzer humbly, and he touched his forelock. "I wish you a successful outcome to your business."

He spun himself suddenly on one toe and was gone. Fursey peered left and right to convince himself of the fiend's departure before venturing to lean against a rock and wipe the sweat from his forehead with the tail-end of the hempen rope which he still carried.

"If there's much more of this," he said, "I'll fall into a lunacy."

He let his eyes travel about him so as to ascertain the exact nature of his surroundings. He seemed to be still in the clearing, which was apparently larger than he had at first imagined. It was an area of tumbled rocks and bracken, enclosed by the wide circle of the forest, black, rustling and muttering, never still. In the light of the moon the clearing was filled with a misty splendour. Here and there were grey pools of shadow, but in general the night was blue and luminous. Fursey looked at the low green barrow a few yards away and thought of the pagan king only a few feet down, the black earth packed tightly against his fleshless face. He shuddered; it was surely a place of ill-omen. He remembered his errand and his heart shrank within him. He had endured so much to-night already that he began seriously to doubt his ability to support a prolonged interview with as formidable a personage as the Archfiend Lucifer himself. He was sorely tempted to leave the Devil undisturbed and stay where he was until morning. He could then retrace his steps through the forest by daylight when its dread visitors would presumably have gone. This course of action appealed to him very powerfully, but he forgot completely that the demon Elemauzer had no doubt hastened away to acquaint the Lord of Hell with the fact that a gentleman had called to see him. He was therefore considerably startled when there was a sudden flash of blue light, accompanied by a smell of a very sulphurous character, and a voice addressed him affably.

"Good evening, Fursey. I trust that you find yourself in the best of health."

When Fursey turned his head a yellow vapour was dispersing and creeping away along the ground; and there, lounging against the barrow, was no less person than the Prince of Darkness himself.

"Thank you," ejaculated Fursey nervously. "The truth is that I find myself in the utmost solicitude and agitation, but I trust that you're keeping well yourself."

The Devil inclined his head politely, but said nothing. As he and Fursey gazed at one another Fursey got a sudden shock. On the couple of occasions on which the Enemy of Mankind had previously appeared to him, seeking to purchase his immortal soul, Satan had manifested himself as a suave, debonair personage, dressed in the latest fashion and irradiating good fellowship and *bonhomie*. Fursey recognised the lineaments of the Prince of Darkness, but it was with difficulty; for the dark-complexioned fiend presented the appearance of a very decayed gentleman indeed. His countenance seemed tarnished with malignant vapours and his black cloak was singed and smelt abominably of brimstone. In fact, the Archfiend was a hideous piece of wreckage, very rickety as to his legs, and generally very much in need of repair. Fursey gazed at him in amazement. A melancholy smile played about the Devil's aristocratic features; then he emitted a sigh that seemed laden with all the heartbreak of history.

"Nay," he said gently, "do not enquire solicitously about my health or as to whether things are not going right in Hell. It's true that things are rather disturbed below. We have had our first Irish ecclesiastical contingent, and they are making things hot for the whole of us ; but that is only a small part of my troubles."

He gazed into the distance, a look of unutterable sadness shadowing his fine, dark eyes.

" I fear," he continued, " that I grow wilted and old. Soon people won't believe in me any more."

" Oh, you must cheer up," said Fursey. " Things aren't as bad as all that. There will always be some to believe in you."

" I suppose so," replied the Devil, but without much apparent conviction.

There was silence between them for a while. The Devil gazed at the turf between his feet. He looked like a man in whom hope had died. He didn't seem to have a jig left in him. Fursey was suddenly struck by the strangeness of the situation. He watched the Devil round-eyed, and all at once stirred nervously. His companion looked up.

" I may as well tell you," the Devil said heavily. " It's a relief to talk to someone. Sit down on the sward."

" On the what ? " queried Fursey.

" On the sward," repeated the Devil.

Fursey sat down on the sward.

" Since I last saw you," began the Archfiend, " I've just missed having *finis* put to my career. And it would have been a pity, for it's been an interesting and adventurous career. It was one of your countrymen that nearly did for me. He was very adroit, far too adroit for me. He comes from your part of the country ; maybe you know him. He's called The Gentle Anchorite."

" I've met him," said Fursey hoarsely, " and broken bread with him."

" With a mallet, I expect," replied the Devil gloomily. " He lives on a crust a day, and he's always about two months in arrears with his meals. He's a man of the most formidable sanctity."

" Was he unkind to you ? " asked Fursey inadequately.

The Devil's visage assumed a very peculiar character.

"You probably know," he began, "that people of every class and condition come to Hell, but the most numerous are those who have sinned as I have sinned, through pride. And the greatest sinners in this category are those who pride themselves on their virtue. The righteous and the presumptuous are packed into every tenement in Hell in such myriads that the housing problem is becoming very acute. But I always find room for more, and it has ever been a point of honour with me to provide a warm corner for those who have passed their lives presumptuously convinced of their own virtue. Such a one is the man who likes to be called The Gentle Anchorite. Forty years ago he took up residence in an unhygienic cave on a waste and windy hilltop some miles south of Cashel, and there he has since lived on a sparse diet, every day increasing in sanctity. He is a most hardened anchorite, and for many years has subsisted entirely on an occasional crust or a handful of nettles, washed down by a mouthful of water every Saturday night. Some of my liveliest demons tried their hand at tempting him, but all to no avail. Succulent meats were passed to and fro beneath his nostrils, attempts were made to dazzle him with showers of gold and the promise of kingdom, whole platoons of the most engaging females were perambulated up and down before his eyes, a series of poetry readings were initiated in an attempt to beguile him ; but for all the success we met with we might as well have been trying to interest a bullock in the intricacies of classical music. He didn't pay the slightest attention. He just sat in front of his cave meditatively prosecuting his researches for fleas, of which he harboured untold myriads. The most alluring visions had no meaning for him. What matter if he had continued to sit there until his death, in this state of pious stupefaction ; but he is an ambitious man, and many years ago he decided to take the offensive himself and carry warfare down the avenues of the world of shadows. In short, it became his practice to fling aside his passivity when one least expected

it, and hit back at any demon foolhardy enough to approach
him.   In the course of many years he has become a man
very expert at dominating devils.   Experienced fiends give
him a wide berth, but the fascination of what is difficult
has proved an irresistible bait to many of my younger and
more adventurous subjects.   The net result has been that
Hell has suffered grievous casualties at his hands—some
fifty of my nimblest and most daring imps have been tied
down by him in sundry bog pools in the unattractive moorland on which he dwells."

" I've heard of these things," said Fursey softly.   " Prudent
demons eschew the neighbourhood."

" The young are always reckless," said the Devil, " and
even the most needle-witted imps have fallen a victim to
him.   Would that I had learnt from their example ! "

" Did you venture yourself," queried Fursey, " to knit
the issue with him ? "

" Unfortunately," sighed the Devil, " I knitted it.   I have
no one to blame but myself.   I knew The Gentle Anchorite
to be a sapient man and a performer of many remarkable
miracles, but my accursed self-confidence betrayed me.
You know," said the Devil, turning a piercing eye on Fursey,
" that I am of Jewish origin ? "

Fursey thought for a moment.   " Of course," he replied.

" Well," continued the Archfiend, " I have all the faults
and virtues of my race.   I possess in a high degree the ability
to take punishment and come up smiling.   You may try to
subdue me by insult, you may think you've rid the land of
me and my companions, but you might as well try to put a
cork permanently under water.   The moment your heavy
hand is removed, I bob up again.   This quality I account
a virtue.   I am one who recovers heart quickly, therefore
I can truly boast that my spirit is indestructible.   But there
is another side to it.   I am artistic and wayward, qualities
the possession of which I account a vice.   As far as The
Gentle Anchorite was concerned, I should have left well
alone ; but the danger attracted me.   What artistry, I

thought, to bring about this man's ruin by giving him cause
for such pride as never Christian heart had felt before. He
has overcome some fifty minor demons, I said, and his pride
in his achievement is great. Let him imagine that he has
wrestled with and overthrown the dread Emperor of Hell
himself, and his very heart and brain will burst with over-
weening vanity. So confident was I of success that before
I set out upon my mission I ordered a special pit to be dug
in Hell and paved with glowing anthracite for the reception
of the man who had wrought such havoc among the battalions
of the lost. Then I winged my way to Ireland, and for a
whole week I hovered in the air above the hermit's cave.
I watched him as he squatted on his lean hunkers in the
cavern mouth, a long rusty beard enveloping the lower part
of his face, and the rest clothed with dirt of various kinds
and colours. I watched the tawny wolves who came from
the holes in the hillside and sat at his feet without fear.
I saw him take his daily exercise, an amble around a nearby
crag and back. I endured with fortitude for seven days
the chill winds of the upper air, while, with all the will power
which I have at my command, I insinuated into his mind
the insidious temptation. ' You have tied down nearly fifty
filthy demons,' I urged. ' Why not tie down the Prince of
Darkness himself, and so gain the glory of having rid mankind
of him forever ? ' At length my efforts were rewarded. I
saw him dismiss his friends the wolves, bidding them go as
he wished to meditate.   I saw him walk up and down thoughtfully with tempered gait. I saw him dig a mighty cavity
in the ground to hold me. I watched his preparations, and
at the proper moment I manifested myself. I came as
Lucifer, striding across the mountains in all my panoply
of terror, while the miserable hermit in his rags took his
stand on the bare hillside to receive me, quite unafraid.
I had a clever plan. I meant to allow him almost to overcome me, and it was my intention at the last moment to
substitute an airy phantom in my place."

"The combat must have been of a nature terrific beyond all description," remarked Fursey, round-eyed.

"It wasn't," said the Devil lamely. "I rolled the thunder around the sky a bit in keeping with my dignity, but I was afraid to make too much noise for fear of frightening him. Also I reduced myself to my natural size and took my stand ten paces distant from him."

"What happened then?" asked Fursey with bated breath.

"To tell you the truth, I don't exactly know," replied the Devil gloomily. "I only know that I got the worst of it from the very beginning. He had some religious sleight-of-hand up his ragged sleeve, and he shouted something at me in Latin, which had the effect of rendering me earthbound. I found myself suddenly bereft of my power either to rise into the air or to disappear, nor was I able to transform myself into a hare or other animal noted for its speed, which would have enabled me to make my escape. He then ran at me and smote me about the head so shrewdly with a club, with which he had armed himself, that to the present day I have a singing in my ears. For his age he was remarkably agile, and no matter how I doubled and ran, every time I turned my head, there he was cantering close behind. He seemed full of advantageous devices; that is, they were advantageous to himself. Finally he caught up with me, and with his club struck me a buffet that left me all bemused. While my brain was still beclouded, he tripped me and set about rolling me in a bed of furze. I need not tell you that by this time I was in a state of sore vexation but I was in no mood to grapple with him : my sole concern was to make my departure with the utmost despatch. I succeeded at last in this, and fled down the hillside with The Gentle Anchorite in close pursuit. I had to endure the indignity of precipitate flight along many miles of country road. All the children of the countryside were waiting for me, and they pelted me mercilessly with stones. At last the hermit's wind gave out, and he fell exhausted at the fourth milestone. One little brat of about seven years of age kept following me for a mile further, but fortunately his aim was poor. He only registered one hit, when he took the tip off my ear with a piece of slate."

Fursey sought to assume a sympathetic cast of countenance and shook his head disapprovingly.

"One thing is certain," concluded the Archfiend as he looked down at his torn and shabby garments. "Never again will I put a foot in the holy land of Ireland." He bent a steady gaze upon Fursey. "I don't like your countrymen," he said. "They're too rough."

There was a silence between them for a few moments. The Devil shifted himself on the barrow so as to attain a more comfortable position, and crossed his knees nonchalantly. He glanced at Fursey and then began to study his finger nails, which emitted pale sulphurous flames. Fursey, sitting on the sward with his parted legs stretched out before him, gazed at his toes and said nothing.

"I assume," said the Devil at last with a show of indifference, "that you didn't come here through courtesy merely to enquire about my well-being. Am I correct in assuming that it was business brought you?"

"Well, yes," conceded Fursey awkwardly. "In a way."

"I suppose you want something of me," said the Devil, with a trace of hardness in his voice. "No one ever seeks me through a desire for my company. I suppose you want me to do something for you."

"I have put the pursuit of good behind me," burst out Fursey. "I have come over to your side. I am determined to become a man of violent and atrocious character."

The Devil glanced at Fursey's innocent, moon-round face, and a slight smile flickered across his own countenance and disappeared beneath one of his pointed ears.

"Why?" he asked solemnly.

"The virtuous have done me great injury," replied Fursey. "They're still intent on tying me to a bundle of faggots and burning me with colourful ceremony. Any moment the King of Mercia may decide to demand impossibilities of me ;

and when I disappoint him, as I undoubtedly will, he will mete out to me a fate worse than death. I understand that he is very practised in meting out such fates."

" He is," grinned the Devil. " Ethelwulf is a playful lad, and very ingenious."

This remark seemed to Fursey to be in bad taste, having regard to his unenviable situation ; but he ignored it and continued :

" Lastly, they have taken from me and carried away to Ireland the woman without whose company life seems to me dull and unprofitable."

" Wait now," said the Devil. " Are you certain you want her back ? "

" Of course I want her back," retorted Fursey.

" Do nothing rash," advised the Archfiend. " You have lived with her for two months, and it's not as if your heart was still palpitating with the first tumults of love."

" I want her back," replied Fursey determinedly.

The Devil shook his head disapprovingly. " I advise you not to be too hasty," he urged. " You may be in love with her now, but cast your eyes twenty years ahead. Just imagine the old muzzle of her staring across the table at you three times a day. It gives one furiously to think."

" I don't care what you say," asserted Fursey. " I am determined to recover her."

The Devil shrugged his shoulders.

" May I ask a question ? "

" Certainly," replied Fursey.

" Was your union consummated ? "

" Certainly not," said Fursey indignantly. " We both had a good Irish Catholic upbringing, and we don't know how."

The Devil seemed impressed and lapsed into silence.

" Her laughter was part of the loveliness of the world," said Fursey, striving manfully to overcome his emotion. " The taking of her from me was a maimed business. But I mean to become apt in the practice of sorcery, so that I may transfix and utterly destroy Magnus, who has carried her off to Ireland to make her his bride."

"Sorcery," said the Archfiend meditatively. "You mean learning how to sweep the dust of the street towards his door so as to inflict him with the palsy or something equally unpleasant. You may succeed in annihilating him by sorcery if he's a man accessible only to coarse influences. I don't set much store by magic myself. It's old-fashioned stuff and belongs properly to a period prior to my era, though it survives here and there."

"I possess the spirit of a sorcerer," replied Fursey. "My trouble is that I'm lamentably inept in the practice. In fact, I may as well admit that I'm acquainted with no occult devices whatever. I'm no good at wizarding at all."

"I suppose that there's a certain amount to be said for sorcery," said the Devil. "One may learn the most arcane secrets and wander at will through the abysses of the unseen world. But time passes. What do you want of me, Fursey?"

"I want to know how to get to Ireland, how to recover Maeve, how to consume subtly and altogether destroy the baneful Magnus (or at least how, by the operation of magic, to afflict him with monstrous boils and warts), and lastly how to escape and live happily ever after."

"You're asking a great deal," replied the Devil testily. "I can neither recover Maeve for you nor instruct you in conjurations and charms. I might also add that the recipe for happiness is unknown to me. All I can offer you is two pieces of advice. I can advise you how to get to Ireland and I can advise you as to the present whereabouts of the master sorcerer Cuthbert, to whom you would do well to apprentice yourself. The rest is up to you."

"I suppose I must be satisfied with what I can get from you," replied Fursey hesitantly. "The state in which I find myself at present is so benighted that any help is welcome."

"You realise, of course," continued the Devil, looking at him hard, "that I am first and foremost a business man.

You must pay my price. I shall require your soul in exchange for my advice."

" That's barefaced robbery," ejaculated Fursey indignantly. " My soul is worth more than two pieces of advice. Not so long ago you offered me in exchange for my soul, kingdoms, troops of females of the most lively and amiable character, and even a reputation as a man of letters."

" My poor Fursey," replied the Archfiend sympathetically, " you have little wit. Is your brain so moist that you do not realise that circumstances have changed? On those previous occasions when you refused my offers for your soul, it was I who was the petitioner. Now it is you who stand in need, and are the bidder. You need my advice. I fix the price. Take my offer or leave it."

" It's a black market operation," muttered Fursey.

" I don't know why you hesitate," said the Devil irritably. " Just now you told me that you were determined to become a man of violent and atrocious character. What better beginning can you make to a life of iniquity than the sale of your soul to me ? "

" That's true," said Fursey despondently.

" Well ? "

" All right," said Fursey glumly. " I suppose I have no choice. What do I do ? "

" Well, we should really begin the ceremony by devouring the boiled bones of a black cat," replied the Fiend ; " but as I don't suppose you have a black cat about you, we can dispense with that preliminary."

He raised his hand and made a mysterious pass in the air. Immediately a thick, dun vapour came rolling from behind a rock and came to rest at his feet. The Devil pulled up his sleeve and plunged his arm into the vapour. When he withdrew his hand, Fursey saw that he was holding what seemed to be a small chunk of sulphurous mist. This he parted delicately and drew out two pieces of goat's skin parchment, an iron pen and a small knife.

" It's necessary," he explained, " that the agreement be
written in your blood. Are you not feeling well ? "

" I don't know why," replied Fursey, " but I begin to feel
peculiarly indisposed."

" The night airs and the damps of the forest affect some
people adversely," said the Devil smoothly. " Oblige me
by rolling up your sleeve."

The quaking Fursey did as he was bid. He emitted a
short, sharp yelp of pain as the Devil, wielding his knife
dexterously, made a small incision in his arm.

" Can you read or write ? " enquired the Archfiend.

" No," replied Fursey mournfully.

" Then I'd better indite the agreement. All that will be
necessary will be for you to affix your mark."

The Devil wrote assiduously for a few minutes.

" I wish you wouldn't keep jabbing the pen into my arm,"
complained Fursey. " If you do it again I'll call the whole
thing off."

" I've got to dip the pen in the ink," retorted the Devil.
" Will you kindly stay still. I never knew such a complaining fellow."

At last the documents were completed, and the trembling
Fursey affixed his mark to each.

" Why do there have to be two copies ? " he enquired.

" It has to be in duplicate," explained the Devil. " One
copy is filed in my closet in Hell and the other must be
swallowed by you."

" Swallowed ? " repeated Fursey faintly, fixing his eyes
on the thick goat's skin parchment.

" Yes," said the Devil briskly, " and swallowed entire.
No chewing or biting bits off. I once let a robber captain
from the County Cork consume his agreement in bites ; and
when I wasn't looking he bit his signature off and spat it
out. Oh, he was a tricky fellow all right."

Fursey gave a wan smile and continued to contemplate
the bulky parchment.

" It will have a most adverse effect on my digestion."

" Nonsense," rejoined the Devil, " you'll have it down in
no time. Go on, try."

A moment later Fursey was lying across the barrow
choking while the Devil thumped him on the back.

" Is it up or down ? " queried the Fiend, turning Fursey
over.

" Up," gasped Fursey.

" This is very vexatious," said the Devil. " Try it again.
Grip it firmly with your gullet and give a sudden swallow."

Fursey tried again, while the Devil pushed hard at the
rolled end of the parchment which protruded from Fursey's
mouth. A corncrake-like rattling came out of Fursey's
throat, and he evinced every sign of imminent suffocation.
The Devil removed the parchment and peered down Fursey's
throat.

" The passage seems somewhat narrow," he said in disappointed tones. " I'm afraid I'll have to let you tear it
into pieces and swallow a little at a time."

Fursey seated himself on the barrow and addressed himself
to this unappetising meal.

" I don't see why all the chewing is necessary," declared
the Devil, who was watching him closely. " You'll have
all the ink washed off."

Fursey turned on him eyes full of pathos and slowly
swallowed the last fragment.

" How do you feel ? " asked the Fiend when the operation
was complete.

Fursey did not answer for some time, but sat staring in
front of him with his eyes glassy.

" I admit to a certain depression of spirit," he said at last.

" That's nothing," answered the Devil, giving him a hearty
slap on the back. " Now for my part of the bargain. You
may succeed in recovering this woman to whom you are so
honourably attached, by learning the ingredients and use of
love philtres from the sorcerer Cuthbert, who as a wizard is
at the very summit of his profession. Similarly, you can
learn from Cuthbert how to overcome and demolish your

rival Magnus. But you must be assiduous in your magical studies, otherwise you will never succeed in quenching Magnus."

" I'll apply myself with the utmost zeal," declared Fursey earnestly. " I'm determined to quench him, preferably with the greatest pain and inconvenience to himself."

" You are already acquainted with Cuthbert," continued the Devil. " For many years people believed him to be a highly respectable sexton, most sedulous in the performance of the duties of his state in life ; but recently strange happenings of a magical nature in the neighbourhood of Cashel, enchanted cats and the like, gave rise to suspicion. Accusations had been levelled against Cuthbert, and the authorities, deeming it wiser to be sure than sorry, decided to burn him forthwith. He succeeded, however, in making his escape into the mountains twenty miles south of Cashel. He has now set up residence in a damp, unhealthy cave in the hillside over a place called ' The Gap '."

" I know ' The Gap '," replied Fursey.

" Well, seek him out and ask him to take you on as an apprentice sorcerer. You may mention my name if you think it will help."

" Very well," answered Fursey. " But how do I get back to Ireland ? I came here flying on a broom, but brooms require to be anointed with a magical ointment. The little I had is exhausted and I don't know how to manufacture a further supply. Moreover, I doubt if flying conditions are now favourable in view of the approaching equinox."

" Have you not heard," enquired the Devil, " that there are at present some alleged Norse traders in port ? "

" I have," responded Fursey. " In fact, I've seen some of them."

" How did they seem to you ? "

" To tell the truth, they looked to me men of gloomy and ferocious disposition."

" So they are," the Devil replied happily. " They are

Viking raiders, intent on a sudden onslaught on the Irish coast."

" I hope you're not going to suggest," put in Fursey nervously, " that I should have dealings with them ? "

" I am," replied the Devil dreamily. " They would welcome a man like you, who knows the country, to guide them to some sleek Irish monastery."

" But," said Fursey shakily, " will I not be in certain danger from them ? They are men of proud temper, who look as if they might be unkind."

" Sigurd the Skull Splitter is their captain," continued the Fiend, ignoring Fursey's feeble objections. " It will be a most promising start for you in your life of depravity. Tell them that your one ambition since you were a boy has been to become a Viking, and offer to pilot them to the rich monastery of Clonmacnoise. A little exaggeration will be advisable. Tell them that the monastery is piled high to the roof with gold plate and similar valuables. You can confide in them and tell them that you're a wizard and that through your control of the winds you can secure them a smooth sea passage."

" But," protested Fursey faintly, " I don't control the winds."

" You're a terrible man for raising difficulties," said the Devil shortly. " What matter whether you do or not as long as you succeed in convincing them ? Bring a few stones with you wrapped in a piece of cloth and tie it to the mast with due ceremony. You can inform them that you have favourable winds tied in the cloth."

" But if they should discover the deception," objected Fursey. " Is it not the case that these Northmen are rather hasty of temper ? "

" A little snappish sometimes," conceded the Devil. " But I don't know any other way you can get to Ireland. I'm afraid you've no choice."

He regarded Fursey for a moment, and then added sympathetically :

"Would you like a few minutes to let your thoughts dwell on the King of Mercia's College of Torturers before you make up your mind ? "

" No," responded Fursey hurriedly. " I've made up my mind. I'll do it."

" Good," said the Devil briefly. " Goodbye now, Fursey. I have other work to do. I advise you to get back through the wood to your cottage and make your preparations."

" Just a minute," said Fursey.

The Devil, who had begun to disappear rapidly from the feet up, manifested himself once more in his entirety.

" What is it now ? " he asked impatiently.

" As I came here," said Fursey nervously, " the wood was populous with shadows of most uninviting aspect. I would be greatly obliged to you if you would convey me rapidly to my own door and thus free me from the painful necessity of proceeding once more through the forest on foot."

" Certainly," replied the Fiend, and seizing Fursey by the hair, he sprang two hundred feet into the air. Fursey emitted a scream of mingled pain and fright.

" I declare to goodness," muttered the Devil between his teeth, " I never knew such a complaining fellow. Some people are never satisfied."

He glanced to left and right, and then shot across the ceiling of the forest, still holding Fursey by the hair. Fursey thought his last moment had come, and he kicked wildly as his dangling feet trailed across the treetops. It was a painful and terrifying journey, but it had at least the merit of celerity. He found himself suddenly deposited on his own doorstep, his legs too weak to support him. The Devil did not stay to bid him goodbye a second time, but returned the way he had come, in a delicate streak of lightning.

" By God," said Fursey, as he arose shakily to his feet,
" I appear to be embarked on a business of strange and
fearful import."

CHAPTER III

IT was the turn of the tide, an hour before dawn, and the
Vikings were preparing to launch their long dragonship
on to the waters. Fursey cast an apprehensive glance
at the never-tranquil seas and, summoning all his courage,
approached the group of Norsemen that stood on the shore.
By the fluttering torchlight he could see that they were
hardy fellows, in aspect wild, brutal and terrific beyond
description. They wore coarse woven cloth beneath their
armour. Their helmets were distinguished by horns and
wings, and their corselets of thick leather were covered with
chain mail and iron scales. Those in authority wore necklaces
and armrings of gold, while the ratings had to be satisfied
with heavy beads of amber and glass. Shields, swords, spears
and battleaxes were piled suggestively on the beach. But
it was not their barbaric appearance which dismayed Fursey ;
rather it was their intent visages, which seemed to him
devoid of candour and kindness. But he knew there was
nothing for it, and he approached with a quaking heart.

" I beg your pardon," he lisped. " I want to speak to
Captain Sigurd the Skull Splitter."

Dark eyes were turned on him, dull and heavy. A man
pushed his way forward and confronted Fursey. His limbs
were large and uncouth, and there hung from either side of
his mouth a pair of moustaches so long that he had their
ends tucked into his belt. When Fursey looked up at the
visage furrowed with cunning, he felt his blood turning to
water. He dropped his eyes, unable to bear the Skull Splitter's
scrutiny.

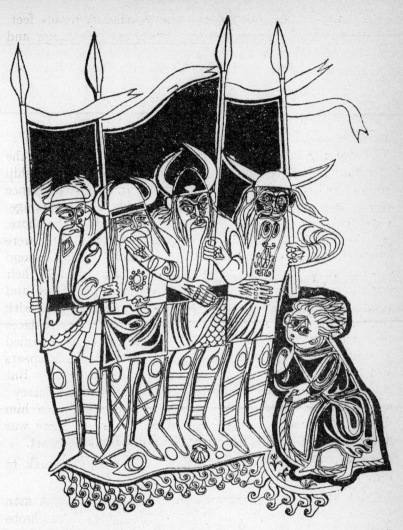

"Well," demanded that personage, "what do you want of me?"

Fursey moistened his dry lips.

"I want to become a Viking," he quavered.

There was a moment's silence, then Fursey heard a series of short, gruff barks, which he took to be laughter; but

when he glanced   round the circle of fierce faces they were
all regarding him impassively.

" Have you run away from school ? " asked Sigurd at last.

There was another series of brief barks, and Fursey saw
that they were all looking at him, waiting for an answer.

" I'm afraid I'm not making myself clear," he said. " I'm
forty years of age and a very formidable wizard. I can be
useful to you."

" A wizard ? " queried Sigurd.

" Yes," answered Fursey. " Just watch me."

He walked a few paces up the beach to a withered thorn
tree which stood beyond the line of shingle. The Norsemen
followed him and stood in a circle watching. Fursey uncoiled
the rope from his shoulder and flung the end of it over one
of the gaunt branches. With a wave of his hand he directed
their attention to the boughs naked of leaves.

" You will observe," he said, " that I have nothing up
my sleeves. What would you like me to produce for you
in the way of food or drink ? "

For a moment no one spoke, then a hoarse voice growled
from the back :

" A vat of the best Spanish wine."

" Certainly," said Fursey. " A vat of the best Spanish
wine."

He gave the rope a sharp chuck and immediately an
immense tun fell out of the tree and rolled down the beach
into the water. Fursey skipped out of the way just in time
to prevent his legs being broken, and the Norsemen scattered
in all directions. Sigurd did not run, but Fursey noticed
that he bent down and picked up a battleaxe.

" Don't do anything hastily for which you might afterwards
be sorry," pleaded Fursey. " Maybe you'd like some mead ?"

He pulled the rope, deftly caught the beaker and presented
it to Sigurd, who sipped it gingerly.

" It's mead all right," he admitted.

" Maybe we ought to be getting on board ship," said one of the sea rovers nervously.

" I have here," continued Fursey, " a bag in which I have tied up half-a-dozen favourable winds. Fixed to your mast they may come in very useful."

" What is your proposition ? " demanded Sigurd.

" I want passage to Ireland in your ship," explained Fursey. " In return my magical knowledge is at your disposal. Furthermore, if you should think of calling at a place called Clonmacnoise, I will be your pilot and guide. I know that country and the monastery intimately, having been a laybrother there until three months ago, when they expelled me and relieved me of my vows."

The Vikings gathered around again, their faces quickened with interest.

" Why were you expelled ? " asked Sigurd carefully.

" A flock of mischievous demons attached themselves to my person. It wasn't really my fault. I couldn't get rid of them."

" So the monks got rid of you ? "

" Yes," replied Fursey dolefully. " I was most unjustly treated."

In the silence that followed, Fursey heard a battle-scarred veteran muttering : " He looks like a monk all right. I should know. I've killed scores of them."

Noticing their hesitation, Fursey proceeded hurriedly :

" It would be an exaggeration to say that you can't move around Clonmacnoise without tripping over piles of gold and other valuables ; but gold is there, nevertheless, in great quantities. The monastery is situated in the interior on the River Shannon, and the religious settlements on the coast have for many years past sent their treasures inland to Clonmacnoise for safety."

" Describe the exact location of the monastery," commanded Sigurd.

" It's situated many miles inland from the sea and above

the Danish city of Limerick," replied Fursey, "but it lies on the Shannon, a great river, readily navigable by ships of shallow draught such as yours."

Sigurd motioned a warrior to step forward. He was a tall, spare man of most uninviting aspect, with only one eye, which was a large, melancholy one. Fursey noticed that he had only two teeth, big, yellow fangs, which dwelt apart.

"Snorro," Sigurd addressed him, "you've heard what the stranger says. Is it true?"

"Yes," replied Snorro. "It is even as he says. I've been in the Danish settlement called Limerick, and I've heard the monastery Clonmacnoise spoken of. It lies in the vicinity."

"Why do you want to lead us to Clonmacnoise?" said the Skull Splitter, turning suddenly to Fursey.

"I want to get my own back on the monks who expelled me."

Sigurd nodded to Fursey and withdrew his men to some distance, where they conversed in guttural whispers. Fursey noticed with foreboding that some of the warriors drew their fingers across their throats before contributing their opinion, while others spoke first at length and then drew their fingers across their throats. He decided that this meant that there were two schools of thought among the Vikings, the first lot was persuaded that it was proper to slit his throat without further delay, while the second school deemed it more sensible to defer the slitting until he had led them to Clonmacnoise. He made up his mind that if the first school prevailed, he would try to make a run for it ; but that if they were out-voted by the second school, he would make a run for it the moment the ship touched Irish soil. At length the group broke up, and Sigurd came back to Fursey.

"You can come with us," he said, "but we carry no passengers. You must become a Viking."

Fursey hastily assured him that to become a Viking had been his dearest wish ever since he was a small boy.

"All right," said the Skull Splitter. "You're under the care of Snorro. He's responsible for you."

Sigurd went off to see his men aboard, and Fursey, by direction of Snorro, went down on his knees and swore allegiance to Thor and undying hatred of the Christian faith. Then Snorro helped him into a corselet of mail and a pair of greaves. It was rather difficult to fit Fursey, who was small and tubby; but Snorro managed it at last, except for the helmet. Even the smallest helmet fell down over Fursey's eyes when he nodded his head, but he found that by throwing his head well back and keeping his eyebrows raised he could keep it in position. Then Snorro girt on him a long, dangerous looking sword, which incommoded Fursey greatly in his walking. He found that it took all the strength of his two arms to lift the weighty battleaxe, but after several efforts he managed to raise it and rest it in a soldierly manner on his right shoulder. Thus accoutred he marched down in Snorro's wake to the dragonship. Willing hands helped him, stumbling and falling, to a place in the narrow waist of the ship, and Snorro clambered in after him. At Sigurd's request he tied his bag of favourable winds to the mast, hoping earnestly as he did so that they would not be required during the voyage. Back in his place beside Snorro, he raised his helmet from over his eyes and looked about him. The first grey of the dawn had lightened the sky in the east. Fursey took off his helmet altogether and contemplated the two ox horns with which it was ornamented. Then he wiped the sweat from his brow.

"It should be a pleasant trip," he said to Snorro, who only grunted by way of reply.

"Will there be much murderings?" enquired Fursey anxiously.

"Don't worry," replied his gloomy companion. "You'll get your share of fun. These monks don't fight, but they squeal a lot when you cleave them. Of course we may run into fighting men. That's another matter altogether."

" I expect so," said Fursey. " In that eventuality how would you advise me to comport myself ? I have never wielded lethal weapons before."

" Irish fighting men don't fight with any discipline or artfulness," replied Snorro. " They're strangers to wile. They just run straight at you and hit you with whatever they've got. I've known them with one blow to drive a warrior's helmet so far down into his breastbone as to render it impossible of extrication."

" And where was his head ? " asked Fursey anxiously.

Snorro turned on Fursey his one melancholy eye.

" I don't know," he said. " We could never find out. It must have been in his stomach."

Fursey turned away his face and looked longingly at the receding shore.

" The best thing to do when you encounter an Irish fighting man," said Snorro, " is to receive his first blow on your shield. Then you must hew off his feet at the ankles. This upsets his balance and, as he falls, you can, if you're any good, sweep off his head with a back stroke of your sword. There's nothing difficult about it."

For the first day and a half, during which the dragonship rode up and down across the swelling seas, Fursey lay in the bilge water on the floor of the boat hopelessly seasick. It was only on the afternoon of the second day that he dragged himself up on to his seat in the slim waist of the ship and cast a jaundiced eye over the waters.

"You'd better have something to eat," said Snorro, passing him a hog's foot and a pannikin of metheglin. Fursey averted his gaze.

" No, thank you," he replied. " I fear that my stomach is in a state of consolidation."

" I never heard such retching," asserted Snorro, looking at him curiously. " And the queer things you brought up !

What did you last have to eat anyway ? It wasn't a goat's skin overcoat by any chance ? "

Fursey shook his head despondently. He pondered Snorro's words for some time, and at last realised that he had probably rid himself of the goat's skin parchment on which was inscribed his agreement to sell his soul. Its loss cheered him considerably, until he remembered that there was a duplicate copy filed in the archives of Hell.

An hour passed, and it became late afternoon—a lazy September afternoon, soaked through and through with sunlight. He had been dreamily watching the thin line of foam in the wake of the ship, spreading left and right ; and, as it divided, veining the waters like marble. Now he awoke to the fact that for some time apparently there had been a slackening of speed. The waves no longer ran out to left and right from beneath the keel. He heard a sudden shout from the prow.

" Sorcerer ! "

Fursey's heart gave a jump ; and, glancing around, he saw Sigurd the Skull Splitter smiling affably as he directed Fursey's attention to the great raven-embroidered sail. It lay against the mast quite loose and relaxed.

" The wind has fallen," said Sigurd. " It's time for you to unloose one of your favourable winds. It's a good thing you brought them with you."

Fursey could see no way out of his predicament. He arose shakily and made his way to the mast. When he pulled the cords and four stones fell from their covering cloth on to the deck, the Vikings looked rather surprised. They said nothing, however, but sat back waiting to feel the brave breeze on their faces once more and to see the raven sail flap and swell. When five minutes had elapsed without anything happening, they began to whisper among themselves and cast dark glances in the sorcerer's direction. Fursey closed his eyes and began to regret that during her lifetime he hadn't been kinder to his mother. The discussion which followed was tumultuous and protracted. It centred

mostly around the manner in which Fursey should be ravaged
and maimed before he was flung overboard. The Vikings
had come speedily to appreciate that in the absence of a
favourable wind it would be incumbent on them to resort
to the back-breaking business of rowing until a wind should
once more spring up. It was obvious to Fursey that he
was a grievous disappointment to them, and he listened
with dismay to their talk of hamstringing and houghing.
The steersman, who seemed a man of particularly irritable
temper, impatiently drew a nine-inch knife from his belt
and, placing it between his teeth, began to scramble over
the benches towards Fursey.

"Drowning is too comfortable an end," he mumbled.
"Let us proceed at once to demolish him utterly, but by
small stages."

Sigurd took no part in the discussion, but stood by the
mast listening to the various expressions of opinion. It was
Snorro, who seemed to have taken a liking to Fursey, who
restrained the ardour of his shipmates.

"Even the best of wizards," he urged, "can make a
mistake. I've been watching Fursey, and I'm convinced
that he's the briskest of men, but is at present suffering
from a consolidated stomach. Under such conditions no
sorcerer can do himself justice. You have all seen him
producing wine and mead from the bare branches of a thorn
tree. Take care lest by laying violent hands upon him
you offend so powerful a sorcerer and he retaliate by starting
to beat the sea and thereby raise a storm. Remember, too,
his value to us as a guide to the opulent monastery of Clonmacnoise."

The Norsemen hesitated and stood in groups muttering
fiery Viking oaths. Snorro stepped up to Sigurd and began
to urge him to use his influence on Fursey's behalf. The
wretched Fursey sat alone on his bench shivering in every
limb. At last Sigurd spoke.

"Fursey," he said, "in this matter I fear that you have

fallen appreciably short of success. How has that come about ? "

" To tell you the truth," squeaked Fursey, " I'm not much of a sorcerer. I lack practice. I really don't know how to capture and imprison favourable winds."

Sigurd studied him thoughtfully. " Maybe it's just as well," he said at last, " that you know nought of the subject. A little knowledge might have been dangerous and productive of lamentable, and even fatal, consequences. You might have only succeeded in dealing out a hurricane. Go back to your places, men, and take to the oars."

" Maybe the men would like a drink," suggested Fursey weakly, " to make up for their disappointment."

This suggestion had a soothing effect on the crew, and for ten minutes Fursey busied himself producing satisfying beakers of the choicest ale, which he distributed to all. When everyone was carousing merrily, he pulled his rope from the mast and, coiling it over his shoulder, returned to his seat beside Snorro.

" Thank you," he said. " I owe it to you that I have escaped their desperate purposes."

There was a friendly light in Snorro's one eye. " That's all right," he whispered. " I have fortunately some influence with the Captain. My mother is promised to him in marriage. You can do something for me when we land," he added. " I would deem it a friendly act if you would so work magically on my coat of mail that through it no steel may bite."

" Certainly," agreed Fursey. " The moment we land I'll work on it with the mightiest charm I know."

So potent was the ale which Fursey had produced and distributed, that there was soon a gladsome change in the attitude of the crew towards him. His name was shouted from all corners of the ship, and when Fursey's eye was caught he was toasted in the foaming beakers. Before long willing hands grasped him and conveyed him once more over the well of the ship to the mast, where he was required to produce a second round of drinks. Fursey, who had a weak man's liking for being liked, worked with a will, producing further beakers, this time as big as buckets. Scenes of uproarious joviality followed. Fierce warriors rolled around in the scuppers, engaged in friendly throttling matches; while the ship's skald, who had been brought along so as to compose a poem on the adventure, began to recite at the top of his voice, with tears streaming down his face, an epic of his own composition on the life and deeds of the fabulous Ragnar Ironbreeks. At length Sigurd the Skull Splitter intervened and restored order with a blunted axe half overlaid with iron, which he kept for such occasions. Back in their places, the oarsmen flung their moustaches back over their shoulders so that they would not interfere with the rowing and set to work with a will. For some time the dragonship kept going around in circles to the immense amusement of its crew; but at last matters righted themselves, and the long, slim ship, impelled by its fifty oars, cut its way forward straight into the sunset. The skald, who had fallen asleep with his head in a beaker, was prodded awake with a spear and instructed to recite a heartening lay. To obviate the possibility of his falling overboard, he was placed seated with his back to the mast, to which he was lashed with a length of rope. His timpans, flageolets and whistles were placed in a basket beside him so that his recital might lose nothing in artistic effect. After some moments of gloomy meditation he set his fingers coursing up and down the few strings of the timpan and began the epic account so well known to Viking raiders, of the tyrant Charlemagne, who had decreed death for every Saxon who refused baptism. Some parts of the history he related, some he sang. Hour after hour the tale continued. It told of the banishment of an entire race from their native land to Denmark and the shores of the Baltic, because of their fidelity to the faith of their fathers. It told of Christian fire and sword, of martyrdom and massacre; and it asserted that the faith in the old gods was living still. The faces of the Vikings grew pale and grim, and they tugged harder at

their oars, as they listened to the relation of the wrongs of
centuries. Fursey, happy in his new popularity, sat in his
place amidships listening to the fierce, sad tones of the skald
as they filled the ship and then faded away across the evening
seas. The recital was in a language which he did not understand, but he thrilled at the emotion with which the passages
were charged, and he was charmed by the occasional instru-
mental accompaniment. He sat, his eyes wandering from
the rune-carved weapons and the grotesquely decorated
ornaments of his companions to the great carved dragons
rising high in the stern and prow. He gazed for a long
time into the blood-red glamour of the sunset and watched
the incredible play of pearl and copper green and every
other imaginable colour on the surface of the water. The
sun had disappeared into the shimmering carpet of the sea
by the time the skald had concluded his recital ; and, as he
was now quite sober, he was unlashed from the mast and
crept back to his place in the prow, where he sat motionless,
gazing with a face of unutterable sadness at the fast shrinking
colours in the west. Fursey watched his thin, delicate
features covertly, wondering, as every layman wonders, what
strange thoughts were gripping his poet's brain. The skald
could not have answered the question. His mind was a
tumult of faint echoes of all the race's memories of sunsets,
of partings and of broken armies. The delicate forehead
and intelligent eyes, brooding on the waste of darkening
waters, concealed no real activity. The brain beneath was
merely attuned to all that in human history had been dignified
and beautiful ; and because all beauty is permeated with
sadness, his mind and face were sad. Fursey's gaze wandered
to Sigurd erect in the prow, and thence to the fifty oarsmen,
moving rhythmically forward and backward as one man.
It was one of those blessed hours when everyone is at peace
with his companions, feeling himself to be in perfect union
with those near him and with his surroundings. Fursey
was indescribably happy. His troubles seemed to be
very far away and unimportant. He felt that he loved

these men and all mankind. The Vikings spoke little, and
that little in undertones. Some time later, when the stars
began to come out, Snorro raised to the heavens his one
melancholy eye to identify for Fursey the constellations which
he recognised, and Fursey in his turn named the few that
were known to him. It was an abbreviated conversation
though it lasted for hours, a conversation without strain, a
dialogue such as is usual between old friends, mostly brief
statement and affirmative grunt. When the moon came
into the sky, changing the entire ocean to a sheet of silver,
Sigurd arranged the relays of oarsmen, and a great part of
the crew stretched themselves on the floor of the ship to
sleep. Fursey bade Snorro good-night and, creeping beneath
his bench, was soon asleep too.

When Fursey awoke he climbed on to his seat again and
sat blinking at the misty splendour of the morning. As
far as his eye could see was a line of broken beaches and
green headlands, backed by forest.

" Where are we ? " he asked.

" South coast of Ireland," answered Snorro, " approaching
the Saltee Islands."

Of course. The little breeze that blew was laden with
pleasant odours and heavenly fragrance. It could not be
otherwise—it came to their nostrils across the holy land of
Ireland. They were rowing close inshore to obtain such
protection as they could from the breeze, which was unfavourable. Fursey could see at the edges of the woods droves
of pigs feeding on nuts and roots, while the herdsmen, clad
in goat's skins, sat blowing patiently through rustic pipes very
much out of tune. Here and there, where a woodland track
leading from settlement to settlement came for a little space
into the open, a traveller on horse or foot paused to stare
out to sea at the long oaken ship with its two great dragons
rearing themselves from the water fore and aft. By Sigurd's
orders all weapons had been concealed, and the banner that
was flown indicated trade ; but, as the morning wore on,
Fursey noticed that excitement was manifested in every

settlement which they passed. Horsemen would set out galloping along the roads and little bands of five or six men would run out to the end of a spit of land and even up to their waists into the sea, waving swords and defying the Norsemen to land and fight. The Vikings paid no attention, but continued to bow over their oars. Fursey's heart gave a mighty bound, however, when he witnessed the first of these challenges and watched half-a-dozen starveling natives capering madly in the surf as they brandished notched and rusty swords and howled opprobrious epithets at the disciplined Viking force of ten times their numbers. As the dragonship sped swiftly by there were tears in Fursey's eyes. It came to him that whatever else one could say about his countrymen, no one had ever been able to accuse them of cowardice.

The breeze had been leaning over for some time, and now it was found to have veered sufficiently to justify raising the great raven sail. While this was being done, breakfast was handed around, a hunk of badger flesh, garnished with garlic and kale. Fursey knew that Norsemen were vain of their appearance, but he was surprised to see that now that they were rid of the necessity for rowing they produced bronze razors and small mirrors made of polished steel. Hooking their moustaches carefully back behind their ears, they began to shave the rest of their faces. The older and more wrinkled sea rovers were even provided with large wooden spoons, which they placed in each side of their mouths in turn so as to stretch their corrugated cheeks and so have a smooth surface for the passage of the razor. Then they plaited their moustaches and set to polishing their bronze and amber armlets and necklaces. Only when these offices had been completed did they begin to manifest an interest in the strange shore along which they were travelling. Snorro knew the coast intimately and was able to name every headland and islet. The seaboard was strange to Fursey, though he remembered having heard the names of the larger landmarks and territories. He was able, however, to explain certain phenomena unfamiliar to the Norsemen, as, for instance, the meagre, half-naked creatures, more like some nondescript species of the animal order than human beings, who came to the mouths of their caves or suddenly popped up their heads from behind rocks to stare at the strange ship.

" They're undoubtedly maritime hermits, who live largely on shell fish," explained Fursey to the intrigued Vikings.

" But do they not live in community ? " he was asked.

" No," replied Fursey. " Their love of monastic seclusion is such that they cannot stand the sight of one another," and he made a feeble attempt to explain the nature of sanctity. But the Vikings only shook their heads and made the centuries-old joke common to every Germanic tongue, in which Ireland is called " Irre-land "—the Land of the Mad.

On the following morning they rounded the toe of Kerry and started to make their way up the west coast. As they passed under the Skellig and Blasket Islands, places efflorescent with sanctity, the Norsemen gazed with amazement at the headlands on which motionless figures knelt with arms outstretched in prayer. Fursey explained that these were saints, who had taken up this devout position many years before and were in a state of abstraction from the things of sense ever since. One reverend figure, his bald pate covered with a fine green moss, particularly took the sea rovers' fancy ; and they became turbulent until Sigurd, to quiet them, steered close inshore so that they could have a good look at him. He knelt on a small grassy plateau at the cliff's edge and was at least a hundred-and-twenty years old. His clothes had been worn off him and swept away many years before by the action of wind and rain, but Heaven had not suffered him to be ashamed, and accordingly a thick, white beard covered every part of his person. In his outstretched right hand a pair of squirrels were laboriously raising a family.

" Are you certain he's alive ? " asked Snorro suspiciously.

"Of course he's alive," retorted Fursey indignantly. "Even in my time in Clonmacnoise there was a Father Juniper, a man of such gentleness that ducks came without fear and roosted on every part of his person."

"Was he canonised?"

"No, he was expelled," replied Fursey. "His benign influence was such that he charmed the wolves, and he invariably came back from a walk accompanied by two or three of them. The abbot had to keep armed men permanently posted at the gate. It was an expense, and it was felt to be bad for discipline,"

As they sailed northwards towards the broad mouth of the River Shannon, Fursey sat silent in his place amidships, the prey of painful thoughts and imaginings. His conscience was nibbling him. He glanced furtively at the unattractive countenances of the evilly-disposed men with whom he was associated. It was all very well launching oneself into a life of iniquity, but surely there should be some pleasure or gain to be got from it. One had only to contemplate the fierce aspect of his companions to realise that they were men exposed to all the hurricanes of unbridled passions, and their very proximity was alarming to Fursey. Yet these were the men whom he was helping to lead against his own countrymen and, worse still, against his own kind. His conscience told him that he was on the wrong side. "Ill will come of it," he muttered to himself.

"We're passing Ballybunion," said Snorro suddenly.

Fursey roused himself to gaze with morbid horror at the little town which had the worst of all names.

"You know the settlement?" asked Snorro.

"No," responded Fursey, "but I've heard of it. I understand that the dissolute inhabitants are entirely given over to pleasure and vice. It's much frequented in the summer months by members of the lower clergy, who spend their time gaming and in the consumption of strong liquors. It's a notorious centre for cockfighting, dicing and other licentious pursuits."

Even though it was still only early afternoon, the night
life of Ballybunion was already under way, and one could
hear the wicked hum of the settlement, the barking of
depraved dogs, the incessant rattling of dice boxes and the
indignant howls of drunkards being ejected from taverns
because they had no more money. But the dragonship soon
left this modern Babylon behind and crept up the estuary
of the River Shannon.

It was almost dusk when they arrived at Limerick and,
rowing some hundred yards beyond the settlement, anchored
in mid-stream. There was much whispering among the crew,
and at length a boat was lowered, into which Sigurd and
Snorro scrambled.

"Come on," said Snorro to Fursey, "but leave your
weapons and helmet behind."

The surprised Fursey climbed into the boat and Snorro
quickly rowed ashore. There Sigurd gave his final instructions
to Snorro in undertones, and strode away by himself into the
town.

Fursey glanced around him and saw that the city consisted of an irregular patch of grass, around which were
dotted at intervals some fifty or sixty circular cabins, built
of wickerwork and thatched with straw. Beyond the houses
he could see in the gathering dusk fields of tillage and pasture
stretching away to the outskirts of the forest. The
inhabitants, who were mostly Danes, wore multi-coloured
cloaks chequered with spots and stripes. An occasional
Irishman was to be seen clad in a loose-sleeved mantle of
frieze. On the quay beside Fursey a local saint was solemnly
shaking hands with his friends before setting out on a perilous
journey into the wilds of North Kerry, where he was to make
his fourth attempt to convert the robber lord of that territory,
known far and wide as The Wolf of Ballybunion. In the
centre of the green an idle crowd was listening to a street
preacher, clad in a kilt of severe and uncompromising cut,
who was urging them to burn something or other of which
he didn't approve.

" Come, and I'll show you the city," said Snorro, touching Fursey's arm.

" Why have the others not landed ? " asked Fursey as they set out.

" Sigurd is afraid that they'll start drinking in some Mariners' Rest and betray the fact that we're not traders. So he has confined them on board ship until we start upstream before dawn."

" And where has he gone himself ? "

" He has gone to the King's House to fix things. That's it over there, the building with the three skeletons hanging from the tree outside the door."

" What do you mean by ' fix things ' ? "

" Well," explained Snorro, " when we sack Clonmacnoise and pass by here again to-morrow evening the King will expect a percentage in return for keeping his mouth shut and not impeding our passage. After all, he's a Christian, and would normally be expected to oppose a raid on a monastery."

" It's all very bewildering," said Fursey. " I always understood that although this is a Norse settlement it had been converted to Christianity and was notable for its piety."

" It is rather in process of conversion. The King is a Christian, but most of his subjects still cling to the older faith. He does not persecute them on that account, being a liberal and enlightened man. Most of the public institutions are still what you people call pagan. And certainly it is the case that Limerick has always been noted for its many religious institutions. There, for instance," said Snorro, pointing to a cluster of huts within a palisade, " is The Sick and Indigent Sea Rovers' Institution."

Fursey peered over the palisade and saw half-a-dozen ancients doddering round the enclosure.

" All hardy Vikings once," declared Snorro. " Now all they're any good for is eating porridge and yapping about their battles with their toes to the fire. Over there is The

Broken-Down Norsemen's Institute. It's necessary to have lost a minimum of two limbs to secure admittance."

" Let's have a drink," suggested Fursey suddenly.

" Certainly," agreed Snorro. " Have you any money ? "

" No," replied Fursey, " but I have a rope. All I want now is a tree."

Snorro searched the gathering darkness anxiously with his one eye. At last they detected a tree in a quiet place behind one of the cabins. Soon they were seated on the turf and provided with a flagon of ale apiece.

" Why did you bring your battleaxe with you," enquired Fursey, " if Sigurd doesn't want it to be known that we are an armed force ? "

" An odd battleaxe doesn't count," replied Snorro. " A Norseman would look naked without his battleaxe. Besides, in a strange town you have to have something to keep away the dogs."

They sat for some time in silence. If Fursey had hoped to make Snorro drunk and so effect his own escape, his plan was doomed to failure. Snorro continued to drink, but very temperately. At last Fursey spoke again.

" Why have you and I landed ? "

" We're to spend the night in the town to pick up any gossip that may be relevant. Before we go upstream to-morrow we must be certain that nothing untoward is happening in the neighbourhood of Clonmacnoise. If there's a war in progress, or any movement of armies, we'll hear it talked of in the place in which we're going to spend the night."

" I see," said Fursey. After a few moments he ventured another question. " I'm not much use to you as a spy. Why did you bring me with you ? "

Snorro emptied the beaker before he answered.

" Well," he said, " before an undertaking such as to-morrow's raid it's usual to take the omens. The crew are anxious that this should be done so that they may have some indication of what to expect to-morrow."

" It seems reasonable," remarked Fursey, " but what has that to do with me ? "

" Well," replied Snorro, " taking the omens involves the examination of entrails for the purposes of divination, and Sigurd was afraid that the crew might perform the ceremony while he and I were absent on shore. That's why he told me to take you along with me."

" I don't understand," said Fursey. " I'm sure it's an interesting ceremony, but I don't mind missing it."

" You won't miss it," said Snorro patiently. " It's your intestines that are to be consulted."

" *My* intestines ! " ejaculated Fursey. " But will I survive the ceremony ? "

" I never heard of anyone that did," replied Snorro gloomily. " But you needn't worry. Sigurd had got it adjourned for twenty-four hours. You see, we plan to anchor the ship to-morrow around the bend below Clonmacnoise, and you and I will land and creep to within sight of the monastery. You will point out to me the dispositions of the settlement ; and then we are to creep back and report to Sigurd, who will draw up his plan so as to take the place by surprise."

" I see," said Fursey impatiently, " but what's that you said about an adjournment for twenty-four hours ? "

" Sigurd explained to the men that your usefulness will not be exhausted until the attack has been launched. He pacified them by promising to divine from your entrails after the raid whether or not we shall have a smooth passage home. The men are inclined to grumble ; they say it's not quite the same thing. They'd rather learn about the prob- abilities of success beforehand."

" Naturally," was Fursey's feeble rejoinder. " Nevertheless, I trust that Sigurd prevailed."

" He did. Anyway," said Snorro soothingly, " I would not wish you to be put to death until you have worked magically on my coat of mail, as you promised, so that through it no steel may bite."

"That will take some time," responded Fursey hastily. "It will be necessary for me to collect certain powerful herbs and unguents."

"There's no hurry," Snorro assured him as they arose, "you have really until to-morrow afternoon. I wouldn't wish you on any account to botch the job on the coat of mail."

Fursey was very pensive as they walked back through the town. Although it was now quite dark, most of the inhabitants seemed to be out of doors, leaning against the walls of the houses gazing into nothingness.

"What do you think of Limerick?" asked Snorro.

"It seems to be a city of bewhiskered old women," replied Fursey.

"It is," replied Snorro, "both male and female."

They had come to a low, rambling building in the centre of the town.

"This is where we stay for the night," said Snorro, and he read for Fursey the inscription over the doorway. "'Night Shelter for Unemployed Vikings, under the patronage of Thor the Thunderer.' That's Thor," he added, pointing to where there stood over the doorway an immense statue of a very formidable character waving a hammer. They had to take their place in a queue of Norse down-and-outs in sordid and base attire. It was hard to believe of most of them that they had once ridden the seas in search of adventure, for they were in general low and obscure fellows with squalid beards and dangling hair. They all appeared to be suffering from malnutrition, and those that weren't either lame or halt had broken backs or lacked their full complement of eyes, ears and arms. When the queue moved forward sufficiently to bring Snorro and himself within the doorway, Fursey saw a broad-shouldered warrior seated behind a table in the entrance. He had a battleaxe swinging from his wrist by a leathern thong, and he was entering each man's name in a sheepskin register.

" That's the Superintendent," whispered Snorro.

As Fursey and his companion came alongside, the Superintendent glanced up at them and shot at them a series of questions.

" Newcomers ? "

" Yes," replied Snorro.

" Names ? "

" Snorro and Fursey."

" Occupation ? "

" Able-bodied seamen, at present unemployed."

" Race ? "

" Norse."

" Religion ? "

" Worshippers of Thor the Thunderer."

" Very well," said the Superintendent. " Battleaxes are to be surrendered at the Office. It will be returned to you in the morning," and he handed a small metal check to Snorro. Then he read aloud to them the regulations, a copy of which hung on the wall.

" 1. The Superintendent has the right to refuse admission to anyone who may reasonably be suspected of being in a rabid state.

" 2. Any attempt at stabbing or throat-slitting will render the offender liable to immediate expulsion.

" 3. Knives, spears, swords, battleaxes or hatchets smuggled into the Institution under circumstances giving rise to the reasonable suspicion that they have been brought in for an improper purpose are liable to confiscation."

Fursey and Snorro passed into the dormitory. About thirty inmates were huddled over a spark in the fireplace at the far end of the room. The hall was long and narrow, and a long bench ran its entire length. About three feet higher than the bench a rope also ran the length of the room. One slept sitting on the bench with one's hands on the rope. You then rested your chin on your hands like a dog resting its chin on its paws. At sunrise the Superintendent, after a warning shout, cut the rope with his battleaxe and all the

late sleepers fell on to the floor.   These things were explained
to Fursey by a thin, white-faced creature who sat down
beside him.   Snorro had gone out into the washroom which
adjoined the dormitory.   The stranger, who addressed Fursey
in nervous, intimate whispers, was barefooted and clad in
rags.   Indeed, the only entire garment he had was a battered
Viking helmet.   He seemed haunted by some fear, and his
eyes kept shifting up and down the room.   Fursey realised
suddenly that he was in an extreme state of terror and that
he had perforce to speak to someone.

"Do you know," he whispered suddenly, "whether they
make you say prayers to Thor?"

"I don't know," replied Fursey.   "I was never here before.
Ask someone."

"I was never here either," responded his companion,
"but I've been in similar places."

His eyes roved anxiously up and down and at last lighted
on another human wreck who was sitting a few feet away.
His elbow was resting on the rope and he looked more like a
corpse that had been dried in the sun, than anything else.
When questioned he answered in deep, sepulchral tones.

"Oh, yes, this is a very religious institution.   Only last
week there was an atheist in here, and he hid in the washroom
while the rest of us were committing our well-being to Thor.
The Superintendent dragged him out and nearly hacked
him to pieces before throwing him out.   Oh, the Superintendent is a very pious man."

The ragged creature began to tremble so as to set the
whole rope vibrating.

"What's wrong?" whispered Fursey.

"I'm a Christian," came out in a terrified whisper.   "I
got in here under false pretences.   But I can't join in public
prayers to Thor.   I'd be afraid that I'd be stricken dead."

"Well, you better get out quick," advised Fursey.

"But will they let me out?"

"What's to prevent you slipping down towards the door?

If you're asked any qustions, say you're sick and that you want to go outside for a few moments."

" I'll try it," said the little creature. " Thanks."

" Wait a minute," said Fursey, gripping him by the arm. " Look, do you want to do a pious act ? "

The miserable creature's teeth began to chatter. " What is it ? " he asked at length.

Fursey had taken a desperate resolution. " Listen," he whispered urgently, " did you see the dragonship ? "

" Yes, traders."

" No, raiders. They're going to sack Clonmacnoise to-morrow."

The little man uttered a pious ejaculation and looked at Fursey with horror.

" There's not a moment to lose," hissed Fursey. " When you get out of here make straight to Mulligan. He's the chieftain of the territory in which Clonmacnoise is situated, and his is the nearest military aid. Go at once. Don't waste a moment."

" Wouldn't it be better to warn Clonmacnoise ? " gasped the stranger.

" No. Time would be lost. The monastery in its turn would have to seek aid from Mulligan. I'll try to warn Clonmacnoise myself. Do you think you can do it ? I notice that you've no shoes."

" I'll do it," said the little man. " I'll do it somehow."

" Rouse the countryside anyway," urged Fursey. " But don't tell anyone until you're well clear of this territory. This place is all Norse."

Fursey watched the little man sidling down the hall and then make a sudden rush through the door. Then Fursey bowed his head on the rope with a full heart. He saw in his mind's eye the fluttering rags and the bare feet running through the night, across thorns and sharp rocks. How little the Christians had done for that frail, starving man, and yet he had not for a moment hesitated.

Snorro was standing at Fursey's elbow. " I'm just drifting around to pick up what information I can. I'll be back."

Fursey nodded, and Snorro disappeared once more into the washroom.

" Here's Thorkils," said the corpse who was sitting beside Fursey.

Fursey looked up and saw a huge, red-haired man shouldering his way down the room from the door. He seemed to be sodden with drink, and the other inmates got out of his way hastily. His features were grim and ill-favoured, and his ginger moustaches were uneven and ragged as if they had been bitten off in some struggle to the death. He was of powerful physique and had hands like two hams. He passed Fursey and, going to the fire, threw two aged Vikings into the corner so as to secure a place for himself. He sat for a few moments warming his knees, then he turned his great torso and let his glance travel up the middle of the room. His eyes fell upon Fursey. It was some moments before Fursey realised that he was being stared at. When he saw Thorkils' bloodshot eyes fixed upon him, he averted his own gaze. Thorkils immediately staggered to his feet and came uncertainly across to Fursey.

" Are you laughing at me by any chance ? " he enquired roughly.

Fursey assured him that he wasn't.

" Because if I thought you were I'd make the pieces of you fly this way and that."

Fursey again assured him that he was mistaken, and Thorkils returned to the fireplace.

" That's Thorkils," repeated the cadaverous creature seated beside Fursey. " I wouldn't argue with him if I were you. He has the name of being peevish when he's crossed."

" I've no wish to argue with him," responded Fursey nervously. He allowed his eyes to wander all over the room, and it was a long time before he ventured to throw a quick glance across at Thorkils. The big man was watching him from under beetling, ginger brows, and the moment he caught

Fursey's eye he heaved himself on to his feet once more and came staggering across.

" Are you quite certain that you're not laughing at me ? " he queried. " Because if you are, it's the last thing you'll ever do. By the time I'm finished with you I'll leave you totally bereft of warmth and animation."

" I'm not laughing at you," said Fursey faintly. " I assure you that I'm not laughing at anyone. You can take my word for it."

Thorkils hiccupped. " That's all right then," he said, " but I warn you that I'm not a man to be laughed at. I've formed the opinion that you're of an artful, gloomy and mischievous disposition. I'm well acquainted with your trickeries. So be careful."

Thorkils returned to his seat, and Fursey began to pray desperately for Snorro's return. A few moments later he noticed out of the corner of his eye that Thorkils was once more getting to his feet. All around Fursey the inmates seemed sunk in their own thoughts. Fursey himself arose and with shaky steps walked the length of the room. He took his stand near the door beside the Superintendent. When he looked back he saw that Thorkils was watching him with narrowed eyes. When a few minutes later the Superintendent was called from the room on some business, Fursey began to move idly in the direction of the washroom with the intention of attaching himself to Snorro, but on the way he was intercepted by Thorkils.

" I knew you were laughing at me," said the Viking, and raising his great fist he brought it down with all his strength on Fursey's pate. Fursey uttered a lamentable moan and crumpled on to the floor. It took the Superintendent and Snorro five minutes to remove Thorkils from the premises, and it is doubtful if they would even then have succeeded in doing so, only that the Superintendent lost his temper and rendered Thorkils unserviceable by a sudden blow on the skull with the flat of his battleaxe.

When Thorkils had been thrown out, they began to search among the debris on the floor for the remnants of Fursey. They found him under the bench quite unconscious, but with a languid smile on his face.

" I feared at first," said the Superintendent, " that the vital spark had fled."

They lifted Fursey and put him on the bench with his chin resting on the rope, and trusted that he would be all right in the morning.

CHAPTER IV

ON the summit of a small, green hill Fursey and Snorro lay on their stomachs on the grass and gazed down at the monastic settlement of Clonmacnoise. It lay half-a-mile away just above the high flood mark of the river, a cluster of beehive huts and small churches clearly visible in detail in the mild afternoon sunlight. One could even see the tiny, black figures of the monks moving like ants in the passages between the whitewashed cells, and dotted in the surrounding fields. Looking over his shoulder, Fursey could see the dragonship around the bend of the river, drawn in close against the bank. Snorro was grunting to himself as he strove to disentangle one of his moustaches from a bed of thistles. Fursey spoke rapidly in an attempt to hide his emotion.

" It's a most famous monastery," he said. " In the sixth century the blessed Kieran chose this spot for his foundation because it was lonely and remote from men. He knew that his monks could work and pray in this spot, their minds free from worldly imaginings. And so they have during four long centuries, even to the present day. They have lived in close converse with the saints, barricaded in from the world and from worldly follies."

"Are they happy?" grunted Snorro.

"Ah," replied Fursey, "who is happy?"

"We mustn't waste time," said Snorro. "Point out the geography of the place to me."

"The whole settlement is enclosed by a palisade of wooden posts and thorns," said Fursey, pointing. "That is to keep out the wild beasts which lurk in the forest. The gateway, which is of wickerwork, is on the northern side, opening on to the Pilgrims' Way."

"It will be easy to cut our way with battleaxes through the palisade," said Snorro.

"Yes," replied Fursey sorrowfully, "very easy. Do you see the great cross and what looks like a forest of stones?"

Snorro shaded his one eye with his hand. "Yes," he replied at last.

"That is the graveyard where the generations of princes of the neighbouring territories are buried. It's a very high-class graveyard. You have to be an abbot or a chieftain or a very great warrior to get into it."

"I observe that there are two very solid-looking round towers," remarked Snorro.

"Yes," answered Fursey, his eyes coming to rest on the conical caps of the two narrow, tapering buildings of stone which rose high above the surrounding huts like two upright pencils.

"I'm acquainted with round towers," growled Snorro. "That's why surprise is so important. If the monks once get up into those towers with their gold plate we'll never get them out."

"That's the object of round towers," said Fursey softly.

"I think we better attack from the river, having first sent a small landing party to cut off retreat in case some of the fleeter young monks try to escape into the woods with the valuables. What's wrong with you? You're crying."

Fursey passed his fist across his eyes.

"I was thinking of the twenty-four years that I spent in Clonmacnoise as a lay brother. It's the only real home I've ever known. I know every member of the community."

"Don't worry," said Snorro jocularly as he bared his two yellow fangs. "Your friends will all be with the saints to-night."

"I trust so," said Fursey mournfully. "The only one I'd have any doubt about is the cook. He's a man of hard temper. Many the time when I was working in the kitchen

he hit me over the head with the ladle ; but, then, I suppose
I wasn't much good."

"You're against them now ? " asked Snorro suspiciously.

"Yes, of course," replied Fursey. "Didn't they expel
me without adequate reason, and hasn't the abbot ever since
been intent on burning me ? "

"We better crawl back and report to Sigurd," said Snorro.

"Wait a minute," said Fursey desperately. "I perceive
over there some herbs that I shall require for the spell that
is to make your breastplate invulnerable. I won't be a
moment collecting them."

"Come back," hissed Snorro. "You'll be seen from the
monastery."

But Fursey didn't wait. He scrambled down the incline
to the shelter of a hedge about twenty yards away. When
he glanced back, Snorro was waving frantically to him to
return. Fursey crept along hurriedly until he found a hole
in the hedge. He forced his way through, and in a moment
was running as fast as his legs would carry him across the
fields towards the monastery.

Peace pervaded Clonmacnoise. Father Crustaceous, who
on account of his great age was allowed considerable licence
and freedom from the rule, was stumping about the settlement
with the aid of two sticks, poking his nose everywhere in the
firm conviction that unless he kept an eye on everything
chaos would inevitably result. He had stood in the doorway
of the poultry house sucking hard at his one remaining tooth
and finding fault with Father Killian's system of organising
the hens. Then he had looked into the bakeries and watched
from under his fierce eyebrows the laybrothers at the querns
grinding corn. He tested with a large, malformed thumb the
loaves of wheaten bread reserved for the use of the fathers,
and the bread of poorer quality made from barley, which was
for consumption by the laybrothers and for distribution to
the poor. In the dairy he dipped his finger into the churns
and tasted the butter, and he sniffed suspiciously at the
vessels of curds put aside for the manufacture of cheese.

He visited the forge and poked at the birch logs with his stick. He looked disapprovingly at the heaps of wood charcoal, which was used by the workers in metal; and asserted that the charcoal had been a different colour when he was a boy. He felt that it was very necessary for some responsible man to keep an eye to things, for the Abbot Marcus had not yet returned from Britain. He should, of course, have been back long ago, but somewhere or other on the way he had been stopped and persuaded to found a monastery, so it was unlikely that he would arrive for another few days. In the meantime it was up to an old watchdog like Father Crustaceous to ensure that nobody was slacking.

In the library six choice scribes were busy illuminating manuscripts. To the leg of each table a goose was tethered, so that each scribe could bend down, without interruption of his work, and secure himself a fresh quill as required. The Librarian himself sat apart sunk in melancholy abstraction. The reason for his ill-humour was not far to seek. In the previous year a Censor had been appointed by the Synod of Cashel to visit every monastery in Ireland and search the libraries for written matter offensive to morals. He was an active and conscientious man, and in each monastery which he had visited he had left behind him a heap of cinders where there had been previously treasured manuscripts of secular or pagan origin. He had been only three weeks in Clonmacnoise, but already he had committed to the flames most of the Greek and Latin manuscripts, as well as four copies of the Old Testament, which he had denounced as being in its general tendency indecent. He was a small, dark man with a sub-human cast of countenance. One of his principal qualifications for the post of Censor was that each of his eyes moved independently of the other, a quality most useful in the detection of double meanings. Sometimes one eye would stop at a word which might reasonably be suspected of being improper, while the other eye would read on through the whole paragraph before stopping and travelling backwards along the way it had come, until the battery of both eyes was brought to bear on the suspect word. Few words, unless their consciences were absolutely clear, could stand up to such scrutiny; and the end of it usually was that the whole volume went into the fire. When he had first arrived at Clonmacnoise he had explained his method to the heartbroken Librarian.

" I've an old mother," he said, " who lives in a cottage on the slopes of the Macgillicuddy Reeks. She is for me the type of the decent, clean-minded people of Ireland. I use her as a touchstone. Whenever I'm in doubt about a word or phrase, I ask myself would such word or phrase be used by her."

There came to the Librarian's mind an image of an incredibly old peasant woman with the wrinkles of her face caked with dirt.

" Can your mother read ? " he asked.

" No," replied the Censor indignantly, " she's illiterate. But I don't see what difference that makes."

" And I suppose she never heard of Rome or Greece ? " said the Librarian pathetically, as he watched the monastery's only copy of Ovid's Metamorphoses curling in the flames.

" No, of course she didn't," replied the Censor. " And isn't she just as well off ? "

The Censor had a permanent smile on his face. It didn't denote good humour; he was just born that way.

" What some of you people don't realise," he explained to the mournful Librarian, " is that in this country we don't want men of speculative genius or men of bold and enquiring mind. We must establish the rule of Aristotle's golden mean. We must rear a race of mediocrities, who will be neither a danger to themselves nor to anyone else."

Once a week it became necessary to wash out the filter of the Censor's mind, which otherwise would have become choked with the dirt through which he self-sacrificingly waded for the common good. This office was performed by four sturdy laybrothers, who held him under the pump and pumped water at high pressure through one of his ears.

A stream of filthy, black liquid was forced out through the far ear. The operation was painful, and the Censor screamed throughout ; but he didn't mind : he knew that it was all for the glory of God and the honour of his country. When the sieve of his mind had been thoroughly cleansed, it was once more in smooth working order to filter the literature of his people. The Librarian had made several ineffectual attempts to hide under the floor boards manuscripts noted for their antiquity or their beauty, but the Censor, who had a nose which was constantly in motion, sniffing and twitching like that of a ferret, had smelt them out. The Librarian now sat gloomily watching the sub-human face of the Censor as he read his way through one of these tomes, his eyes moving left and right and in all directions, and his nose a-quiver.

As it was not fitting that such a famous monastery should be without its wonders, a daily miracle was to be seen outside one of the cowsheds. There was a brindled cow, and every afternoon at milking time a bird came and perched on one of its horns. The bird sang to the cow during the milking, and the cow, previously reluctant to give milk, gave it freely when thus sung to. The monastery was fortunate also in having an exceptionally nimble-fingered milker, who had followed the profession of pickpocket before his reform and entry into the cloister.

On the little stretch of grass before the great church the Master of Novices walked up and down, giving his pupils the most excellent moral precepts. A final touch of innocence was added to the peaceful scene by three or four rabbits, who sported on the sward at the foot of one of the round towers.

Brother Patrick, the most diminutive laybrother in the settlement, had been sent to collect watercress in a moist ditch some distance from the monastery. He had nearly filled his bucket when the sound of running footsteps made him raise his head. To his great horror and affrightment he beheld a small man in armour and wearing the horned helmet of a Viking, scuttling down the hillside straight towards him. The stranger held a weighty battleaxe with both hands over one shoulder. Even as Brother Patrick stared at him, the long sword which the Viking wore caught between his legs and he pitched headlong. But he was on his feet again in a moment and burst through the hedge to where Brother Patrick was scrambling madly to escape.

"Don't you know me?" gasped the Norseman. "I'm Fursey."

Brother Patrick paused neither for thought nor for discussion, but, seizing his bucket, he brought it down with all his force on the Viking's head, driving the latter's helmet well down below his nose. Then he turned and bolted madly back towards the monastery, raising the echoes from the surrounding hills with cries of "The Danes! The Danes!"

The monks working in the fields heard his cries and looking up beheld an unmistakable Viking on the hillside running around in circles as he sought with both hands to wrench his helmet from over his eyes. With one accord they turned and fled towards the monastery. The Master of Novices at once assumed command. By his direction the gold plate and ornaments and the most precious manuscripts were conveyed into the stronger of the round towers. The monks were fortunate in having time to convey into this refuge nearly everything portable which was of value. The round towers were permanently equipped with the means of defence, so that nought remained to do but quieten the affrighted community and allot each one his task. From the narrow windows the monks watched with horror the long dragonship come creeping around the bend of the river and touch the grassy edge below the monastery. Immediately a horde of fierce warriors swarmed ashore and made uphill towards the settlement. Simultaneously a line of Vikings came into sight on the hillside to the south and ran towards the monastery brandishing battleaxes and emitting shrill and terrible cries. A sudden shout of anguish came from both round tower "Father Crustaceous!"

He came doddering around the corner of the farm buildings, where he had been inspecting the beehives. He paused and looked about him, evidently astonished at finding the settlement deserted. Then he heard fifty voices shouting his name, and, raising his head, he suddenly saw the Norsemen closing in on the settlement. Then started an amazing race for safety. Father Crustaceous, sucking hard at his naked gums, made what speed he could with his two sticks. He had not hobbled as quickly for twenty years, and the effort nearly killed him. His face was covered with sweat as he reached the nearest round tower, and willing hands dragged him up the ladder to safety. The ladder was withdrawn and the door slammed as the first Vikings hacked their way through the palisade.

Meanwhile the hapless Fursey had succeeded in wrenching his helmet from over his eyes. The first thing he beheld was a horde of savage warriors rushing by him with uplifted weapons and hideous cries. Fursey immediately joined them, as he thought that it was the safest thing to do. When he reached the settlement he ran around several buildings waving his battleaxe in the hope of convincing his companions that he was intent on the destruction of the entire community and would not be satisfied with less. At last he paused out of breath at the door of the poultry house. There was no sign of Snorro, but at that moment Sigurd the Skull Splitter came running around the corner. It was borne in powerfully upon Fursey that it was expedient for him to show himself a man of ferocious and bloodthirsty disposition, so he kicked in the door of the poultry house and started laying about him with his battleaxe in all directions. Sigurd dashed in after him. They were immediately involved in a chaos of flying wings and indignant screeching and cackling.

" Curse of Thor on you ! " snarled Sigurd as he strove to remove a desperately struggling cockerel from beneath his corselet. " I thought you were leading me into the treasury."

Fursey was too frightened to reply, but wielded his battleaxe

all the more formidably to demonstrate his courage. The
entire population of birds made their escape through the open
door except for one hen, who hadn't enough intelligence to
consult her own safety. The unhappy fowl thought that her
last hour had come, and fluttered from one corner to another
squawking desperately.

Meanwhile the ill-humour of the Norsemen was growing.
They were finding nothing of value in the churches or cells,
and they ran with torches hither and thither setting fire to
the thatched roofs of the settlement. From one of the round
towers Father Sampson hurled opprobrious epithets at them.
Sampson was a man of warm temper, who had been a professional wrestler before his entry into the cloister. His
muscles knotted and unknotted as he beheld the senseless
destruction on all sides of him. At last when he saw a torch
being applied to the roof of the monastery brewery, he
could contain himself no longer. He emitted a howl of
anguish and, tearing open the door of the round tower,
sprang down the fourteen feet to the ground. The high
cross over the grave of King Flann stood to hand. He
wrenched it from its foundations and rushing at the nearest
Viking, who happened to be Snorro, he discharged his ill-
humour upon him by hitting him with it over the head.
Sampson was a powerful man, and the high cross was a
formidable weapon. Snorro was immediately telescoped.
The upper half of his body disappeared from view altogether,
and the remarkable sight was witnessed of a pair of legs
running around by themselves for a few moments before
they collapsed. Several Vikings closed on Father Sampson,
seeking with their battleaxes to hew asunder his backbone,
but so politic was he in his defence, and he laid about their
shoulders, ribs and other appurtenances to such good effect
that the senses and vital spirits of many of them ceased to
perform their usual offices. At last Sampson heeded the
urgent commands of the Novice Master and returned to the
round tower. The ladder was quickly lowered and he was
dragged to safety.

Sigurd was more angry than he had ever been in his life ; and, rallying his men, he ordered an assault on the round tower. The Norsemen clambered on each other's shoulders so as to reach the door fourteen feet above the ground. No sooner had the two warriors on top begun to attack the wooden door with their battleaxes than thick streams of blazing fat and pitch descended from the narrow windows, followed by a shower of stones. The Vikings fled screaming. Father Crustaceous' head appeared in an upper window, his face wreathed in a beatific, if toothless, smile. Sigurd retreated black-browed and counted his casualties. Half-a-dozen of his hardiest warriors sat round on the grass suffering from scalp wounds and shock, while three others lay wallowing in their death agonies, imploring someone to take a last message home to their mothers. Six other forms lay prone and still. A pair of legs leaning against the wall was all that was left of Snorro. The skald was sitting upon a piece of timber sorrowfully composing a poem about the adventure. Father Sampson, who had an eye for strategy, now began to direct a fusilade of stones at the beehives beyond the farmyard wall. A few moments later an angry swarm descended upon the Norsemen and, before they knew what was happening, myriads were inside their corselets and greaves. But what finally broke their morale was the sudden appearance of a small, swarthy creature in the doorway of the library. The Censor, in the dark depths within, had been quite unaware of what was happening outside. He had been hot on the track of an improper innuendo and had been chasing it from page to page, never for a moment losing the scent, until he had finally trapped it at the end of the chapter disguised as a moral platitude. With a sigh of satisfaction he closed the tome and placed it carefully in the fire. Then he noticed that the library was empty, and that from outside came the acrid smell of smoke and the crackling of flames. He walked to the door and beheld with surprise that the greater part of the settlement was on fire.

The Vikings were already sufficiently shaken by their grim

experiences, but when a little, dark creature with a twitching nose and a permanent smile on its face suddenly manifested itself in the midst of the smoke they were gripped by a sudden fear. They knew that monks were powerful magicians in their own way, and when they beheld the sub-human visage and the two eyes rolling at them independently of one another, they did not for a moment doubt but that they were confronted by a hard-featured demon of the trickier sort. Sigurd, realising that his men were on the point of taking to flight, spoke first.

"It's been a dismal catastrophe," he said. "Our fortunes are confounded. Suspend your sorrows, my men, and return to the ship."

They picked up their wounded and their dead, and retired slowly to the river, pursued by catcalls and hoots from the defenders of the round towers. The Censor, being a man of quick understanding, only delayed to cast one glance at the raging fires which threatened the whole settlement; then he returned and set fire to the library. He emerged a few moments later, his permanent smile a little broader than usual as he prepared a speech of sympathy for delivery to the Librarian.

Meanwhile Fursey, peering round the door of the poultry house, watched the Norsemen slowly and sternly making their way towards the river. He told himself that it was high time that he too departed, but in the opposite direction. He knew that he would get short shrift if he fell into the hands of either party; so creeping from his refuge he quickly slipped through a gap in the burning palisade and was soon scampering up the hillside towards the shelter of the trees. At first he was of a mind to shed his incriminating armour and weapons, and proceed on his way in the homely russet which he wore underneath; but remembering that the countryside was greatly annoyed by wild beasts, he deemed it wiser to retain his fighting kit and only rid himself of the long sword, which was more of an encumbrance than anything else. He doubted his ability to wield the heavy battleaxe to any effect, but its possession gave him confidence. His objective, The Gap in the Knockmealdown Mountains, was twenty miles beyond Cashel; and he knew Cashel to be at least three days' journey on foot. He was afraid to take to the road, but as long as daylight lasted he kept it in sight, carefully skirting the scattered clumps of sally trees which grew along the edges of the swamps. As he made his way over the uneven ground, he reflected how difficult it was to live a life of iniquity. His first act on landing on his native soil had been a good one—he had saved Clonmacnoise from spoliation and its inhabitants from slaughter.

His reflections were interrupted by a sight which concerned him far more immediately. He had come upon a heap of gnawed bones, the souvenirs of some late lamented person. Fursey turned and made straight for the road. It was the hour of sunset, and he knew that with the onset of darkness there would be little danger of meeting individual wayfarers. He realised, of course, that he was not altogether safe on the road either. It was not unusual to espy by the roadside a speckled wolf gnawing the mangled joints of some traveller; still he felt it was safer to be on the road than in the vicinity of trees, from the overhanging branches of which a wildcat might at any moment spring and tear the scalp off him. With the imminent approach of night his fears increased. The countryside through which the thin road wound seemed to him to be of a very dubious character. It was littered with great rocks and occasional trees, and on each side there was the incessant trickling of water. He had no doubt but that the neighbourhood abounded fearfully in wolves, otters, badgers, kites and eagles. As the last glimmer faded from the sky in the west a lonely howling in the distance sounded dismally on his ears. He saw in his mind's eye some accursed spot in which stood a magician summoning the dead to converse with him, and he remembered, too, that the distress of dogs or wolves at nightfall indicated the proximity of vampires. He looked anxiously around for signs of local fog, which he knew to be a sure sign of their presence. He saw nothing however but the deepening shadows between the trees. As the distant howling rose to a most lamentable, mournful note, he tried to persuade himself that it was no more than the obscene caterwauling of some lonely cat avid for the company of its kind. When he came to a place where the trees overhung the road, creating an inky blackness ahead, he stopped, his heart hammering with fright. He knew that in such spots one might well encounter anything. He nerved himself to go on.   Beneath the trees the air was greasy. He fixed his eyes on the dark blue patch of sky in the far distance beyond the trees and began to run, fully expecting that before he reached it he would find a tomb in the bowels of some unfriendly beast. But he passed safely from beneath the trees and relaxed into a quick walk, breathing heavily as he stumbled over the loose stones on the uneven track. And so hour followed hour while he forced himself onwards, his way lit only by the indifferent stars.

When the moon came sidling into the sky from behind the far-off hills it shed its light fitfully, obscured from time to time by shredded cloud. With the increased light, Fursey's fear of wild beasts lessened, for he could see further in every direction. He made up his mind that if he saw a pair of yellow eyes looking at him, he would run for the nearest tree. He assured himself that if he could succeed in clambering up in time he would be able with his battleaxe to keep at bay any wildcats which he might encounter in the foliage. Every few minutes he glanced fearfully over his shoulder to assure himself that nothing was stalking him from behind. But if the opaque moonlight, softening the outlines of rock and tree, had lessened his fear of wolves, it served to increase his dread of the possible materialisation of some unsavoury citizen of the spirit world. He heard the bell of a distant church sorrowfully striking the hour of midnight, and he knew that between the hours of twelve and one in the night, in ghostly moonlight on a lonely road, one is apt to encounter presences that are dangerous. He distrusted the empty wind, which made no sound in the trees, but which he could feel from time to time against his face. He turned a corner and came to a stretch of vacant road along which the trees were spaced like soldiers. He experienced a sudden fright as he saw a few yards from him a raven perched on a gatepost. It cocked its glossy head and looked at him wickedly. Fursey passed by trembling and entered the avenue of trees. The shadows lay in grey bars across the road. He became conscious of a fluttering movement in the air above him. He stopped and glanced up. Innumerable bats were fluttering up and down between the trees. As Fursey watched, one of them, larger than the others, fluttered down and, alighting on the road ten paces ahead of him, resolved itself into a gentleman wrapped in a black cloak.

Fursey's heart stopped beating altogether, then it tried to jump out through his throat. He was conscious of a wave of dizziness ; but it passed at once, and he found himself clutching his battleaxe with trembling hands as he and the vampire gazed across at one another.

" It's really a beautiful night," said the vampire at last.

Fursey opened his mouth and with his tongue, which felt like a piece of wood, tried to moisten his parched lips.

" Is it ? " he gasped.

" You have nothing to fear from me," said the vampire persuasively. " Don't you know that my kind are only dangerous to humans in a state of insensibility, either through sleep or fright ? You never heard of a vampire so ill-bred as to seek to achieve his purpose by violence ? "

Fursey gathered together his quivering wits and told himself, as from a long way off, that this was true. Nevertheless he tightened his grip on the battleaxe. He knew well that, being unaccustomed to the use of the weapon, a sudden cut at the vampire if it approached him would probably only result in his hewing off one of his own legs, with no inconvenience to the phantom whatever. All the same, possession of the weapon seemed to give him courage.

" In any case," continued the stranger, "I am replete as

I have just come from visiting a plump archdeacon." The
vampire smiled slightly. "An estimable man. He is just
beginning to realise that he is suffering from anaemia, but
he will last another couple of weeks. I may add," he continued somewhat stiffly, "in case you still doubt me, that
I am not one who ravens promiscuously about the countryside.
I select good class clients, and I stick to them."

"I'm not doubting your word, sir," said Fursey.

"In that case," replied the vampire, "you will have no
objection to my joining you. Our ways seem to lie in the
same direction. I reside some miles from here in a churchyard adjacent to the road, and there is nothing I enjoy as
much as a walk on a fragrant night such as this with an
intelligent companion. Now that my night's work is done
I feel that I can allow myself that little relaxation."

Fursey could see no way out of his predicament. The last
thing that he wanted to do was to offend the sallow stranger.
While he found it hard to believe that a vampire's purposes
could be other than malevolent, the gentleman's account of
his call on the archdeacon seemed plausible enough ; and
while Fursey felt that he could not approve of such dissolute
conduct, he was glad that the vampire had already paid a
visit that night. His only alternative seemed to be to retrace
his steps along the road which he had come, and that was
out of the question. He threw a quick look at the visage,
gaunt, pale and bewrinkled, in the hope of reading there
whether or not the vampire had it in his mind to do him a
mischief. He observed that the stranger, for all his pale
looks, was very iron-visaged, a fact which impressed Fursey
very painfully. He felt that if the vampire had set his
mind on a walk with an intelligent companion, it would be
the height of unwisdom to deny him.

"Very well," said Fursey weakly, "but I should be greatly
obliged if you would keep some paces from me and slightly
ahead. You will readily understand that, not being accustomed to the company of the undead, it will take me a little

time to become used to your presence. No discourtesy is
intended."

The vampire bowed stiffly and fell into position as Fursey
desired, and together they began to walk along the moonlit
road. There was silence between them for a long time, and
Fursey had begun to reflect that in such an unlucky looking
countryside even such a companion was better than none.
He kept a nervous eye upon the vampire all the same lest the
latter should become sportful or indulge in trickery. At
last his companion vented a deep-fetched sigh.

" Human beings are very unkind to us forlorn denizens of
the spirit world," he said. " I suppose they don't always
mean to be, but they are nevertheless often unkind."

" How so ? " asked Fursey.

" Why do you think that spirits manifest themselves to
humans at all ? Loneliness. A spirit bound to some forlorn
spot experiences an intolerable boredom and a homesickness
for all that he has left behind him in the world of men."

" Humans are also lonely," said Fursey.

" It's different," replied the vampire shortly. He seemed
dissatisfied and changed the subject. He cast an appreciative
eye over Fursey's armour.

" I have been admiring your furniture," he said. " I
observe that you are a Viking gentleman."

" No," replied Fursey. " I was with them, but I'm not
one of them. I'm a Tipperary man, born and bred."

" That Clonmacnoise business has been a sad disappointment. I was speaking to-night to the banshee attached to
the Mulligan family and she's very sore about it."

Fursey pricked up his ears. " I'm interested in that.
What actually happened ? "

" Well, a large scale battle was expected between the
Norsemen and the Mulligan clan. A member of the lower
orders, a base and abject fellow, who had got a lift in a chariot
from Limerick, gave the alarm, notifying the Mulligans of an
impending Norse raid on Clonmacnoise. The banshee, who

is a lady of great charm and refinement, repaired last night to the residence of the young chieftain in order to give notice in the traditional manner of the impending slaughter. I must say that it was most impressive. I watched her myself from a vantage point in a neighbouring tree. She put up a very good show, if you'll pardon the colloquialism. She walked around the ramparts in her traditional garments of white gauze, wringing her hands and moaning most plaintively. It was interesting to see the tapers being lit in each bedroom of the prince's dwelling and the startled residents sitting up in bed. At every corner of the ramparts she seated herself languidly for a few moments while she combed her white, silken hair, continuing all the while to give tongue to the most lamentable complaint. It was unutterably sad and most touching and did not fail to bring tears to my eyes. But no sooner had she commenced the second movement of the Grand Wail under the prince's window than the craven died of fright. The lady is a very considerable artist, and she is very put out about it. She feels that her professional integrity is besmirched."

" Why ? " asked Fursey.

" Well, after all, she had given the traditional notice of impending battle and slaughter, and, as things transpired, there was no battle at all. On the following morning there was no chieftain to lead the doughty Mulligans against the Vikings."

" But at least the young prince died," objected Fursey.

" But he died for the wrong reason," snapped the vampire, " and he died in bed, which is disgraceful to a Mulligan. He was to have died honourably on the following day, his back-bone hewn in twain by a giant Norseman."

They proceeded for some time in silence while the vampire conquered his momentary ill-humour. When he spoke again it was with affability.

" I judge," he said, " from your alarming furniture that you are walking the high roads seeking adventure."

" Not exactly," answered Fursey.

" When seeking adventure," continued the vampire, " the principal thing is to avoid deep wells, hollow trees and such obscure places. One must always keep in mind that while one's entry therein may be easy, one's coming forth may well be miraculous. When I was of the world of men my mind thirsted after honourable adventures. My name was George, and you can picture me setting out along the crooked roads every springtime in search of adventure, mounted upon a Kerry jennet. The winding roads of this land had an unfailing attraction for me. I loved above all the sight of the road rising and disappearing over a little hill. One never knew what lay beyond the rise. Turns in the road are attractive too, because one can never be quite certain of what one may encounter round the bend. Of course, in point of fact, there is never anything round the bend ; but when a man ceases to believe that there may be, it is time for him to die."

Fursey glanced almost with affection at the silent, sad creature who walked a few paces distant from him. He quickened his pace so as to bring himself alongside the vampire and fell into step with his companion.

" Did you never have any adventures ? " enquired Fursey.

" One only in a whole lifetime," replied George sadly ; " that is to say, only one before my final one."

" Tell me about it," requested Fursey. " I have grown footsore, and it will haply enable me to forget for an hour my manifold pains and aches."

The vampire stared gloomily at the road before him for a while before he began.

" All your life," he said at length, " avoid one thing as you would avoid the very plague itself. Never have dealings with a rowan tree."

" A rowan tree ? " queried Fursey.

" Yes, a rowan tree, the tree with small, red berries, which

some people call the mountain ash. It's a tree with properties
of a magical character, only too often productive of dolour
and annoyance. It was in the month of May—the spring
had been late and the bushes and trees were as yet only
covered with a fine web of green, when one pale, sunny
evening I came cantering down a country road on my Kerry
jennet, seeking as ever some honourable adventure. In the
centre of a patch of grass stood a single rowan tree. The
evening air was balmy, and I dismounted so as to rest myself
and my steed. It was a pleasant place neighbouring on a
small lake, on which, as I lay idly on the grass, I counted
twenty sleek ducks and one bedraggled drake who, even as
I looked at him, made his way up on to the bank, cocked a
knowing eye at me, and staggered away in search of refreshment. In short, it was a pretty, sylvan scene. Suddenly
I became aware of a series of strained sighs proceeding from
the tree against which my head was resting. Imagine my
astonishment a moment later on hearing from the woody
depths a voice, which addressed me as follows :

" ' Noble sir, within this tree are bound by wicked enchantment the one-and-twenty daughters with which bounteous
Nature graced Mulligan, Prince of this territory. So singular
was the beauty with which we were endowed, that it awakened
the base desires of a roving magician, as unattractive as he
was spiteful. When we each and every one of us had spurned
with ignominious words his repeated offers of marriage, he
wrought with deadly malice a potent spell, which had the
deplorable effect of binding us in this tree in enchanted
sleep for a period of five hundred years. The five centuries
are now at an end. Do you, good sir, cut down this tree and
effect for us our release from our leafy prison.'

" On hearing this eloquent discourse breathed in dulcet
tones like to the sound of harps, I was at first deprived of
speech. Then I realised my good fortune. It's the dearest
wish of every gentleman who wanders the roads in search
of adventure, to come upon a distressed lady whom he can

free from enchantment or from the foul machinations of a giant or similar depraved character, but to be presented with the opportunity of liberating in the one operation no less than twenty-one distressed virgins exceeded my wildest dreams. This, I told myself, will make me famous throughout the land. I had no axe with which to fell the tree, but I set about the operation with my sword. The bole of the rowan tree is slender, but my sword was correspondingly blunt, and the task was a tedious one. From time to time I paused to rest, but not for long. The other twenty distressed ladies joined in their sister's plaint and, in accents mild but urgent, exhorted me to persevere. I had happy visions of a well-deserved rest when their liberation should be accomplished, my head pillowed in the lap of the statelist of the virgins, while her twenty beautiful sisters sat couched among the wild flowers, singing melodious songs for my delight. At last, when I had all but cut through the bole, I exercised the strength of my arms and, breaking off the trunk, overthrew the tree. The one-and-twenty virgins issued forth."

"That must have been a memorable moment," interjected Fursey enthusiastically.

"It was indeed," said the vampire sadly. "I had forgotten that the distressed virgins were over five hundred years old. There issued from the stump of the tree the most incredible procession of aged crones, the ugliest creatures that ever Nature formed."

"Bewhiskered, I suppose?" said Fursey.

"Bewhiskered to the knees," said the vampire dramatically. "You never saw their like for decrepitude. Each held one hand at the back of her hip to prevent her framework caving in, as they doddered around me, overwhelming me with their thanks. I all but took to my heels, not leaving behind me as much as a kind look."

"Remarkable," said Fursey.

The vampire shook his head dolefully. "Their visages were so time-shattered that one marvelled that one could look on them and live. They were veritable night hags, yet so strong was their feminine spirit that they immediately hobbled over to a nearby elder tree and began to pluck the sprigs and berries for colouring matter to make rouge for their cheeks. My gallant Kerry jennet shied when she saw them and, breaking her halter, made off in a frantic canter, her hooves beating sparks out of the road. The last I saw of her was crossing the skyline still in full gallop."

" It was very awkward for you," said Fursey.

" Awkward ! " exclaimed the vampire. " I can tell you that it was more than awkward when they began to remind me of the respect and honour owed to poor, distressed gentle-women by their saviour. They adjured me to choose one of their number for spouse, insisting that it was customary. They admitted a slight discrepancy in age, but reminded me that their hearts were young."

" It was a choice that I should not care to have to make," remarked Fursey.

" I didn't make it," replied the vampire, " though to all my protestations of my unworthiness of such an honour the reply of the eldest sister was ever the same. ' Nay, proud George,' she said, ' you are our saviour, and you must have the reward hallowed by tradition and immemorial custom. Make your choice. There is not one of us but will rejoice to be your bride.' "

" A ticklish situation for a man of honour," commented Fursey.

" Very ticklish," agreed the vampire, " yet so ardent was their spirit that they followed me around for three weeks to the great scandal of the countryside. The clergy took a poor view of it and spoke very ill of me. Eventually there was nothing for it but to make my escape under cover of darkness."

" Adventure is not all that the writers of romance would have us believe," remarked Fursey sagely.

" It's not," said George, " but my thirst for adventure was not quenched. I sought it afterwards for many years, but only found it once again."

" What were the circumstances ? " enquired Fursey.

" I prefer not to speak of it," replied George solemnly. " Suffice to say that I undertook to lay a master vampire. He won."

" So that's how——," said Fursey gently.

" Yes," was the reply. " I am now the father and grand-father of many vampires, both male and female. It's not a bad life if only human beings would leave us alone. But they're always messing round with pointed stakes, fresh garlic and wild dog roses, so that you're never quite certain when it'll all end."

They had come to the low wall of a churchyard. The vampire stopped.

" Here our ways part," he said. " I reside over there in the building inscribed ' Family Vault.' Would you care to come in for a few moments to meet the girls ? "

" No, thank you," said Fursey hastily. " I have to be on my way."

" Goodbye then," said the vampire with a wave of his pale hand. " And don't think so badly in future of us who belong properly to your world, but have lost our places in it."

CHAPTER V

THE day was ebbing. The entire arc of the sky was curtained with cloud. A grey, monotonous light occupied the countryside. The wind had pressed against Fursey all the morning and afternoon while he toiled along the crazy track which wound up the hillside, and he

was conscious now of a wintry chill in the air ; so that when
he came to a grassy bank crowned with a tangle of thorn, he
crept gratefully into its shelter. He seated himself with a
sigh of thankfulness and, resting his elbows on his knees,

stared down at the Tipperary plain, which lay beneath him
like a vast carpet, patterned in varying shades of green and
criss-crossed by lines of hedges and boundary ditches running
in all directions. He could just discern in the green distance
a fluffy ball of smoke, which hung in the air, marking as with

a dot the site of the city of Cashel It was three days since Fursey had parted from the vampire beside the broken wall of the churchyard, and ever since then he had been travelling in a wide circuit so as to avoid the road which crept across the plain, and to avoid above all the settlement of Cashel, which was the seat of the ecclesiastical and civil government. It was scarcely three months since the authorities at Cashel had sought to cure Fursey of his sorcery by the simple expedient of tying him to a strong stake of faggots and burning him, and he knew that in the neighbourhood of the settlement he would be readily recognised. Although he was tired he was reasonably content : he had circumambulated the danger zone successfully and was near his objective. Two days previously he had rid himself of his armour and his battleaxe, realising that by now news of the Norse raid on Clonmacnoise must have spread far and wide, and consequently that as long as he wore the incriminating Viking dress he was in far greater danger from his countrymen than from a wild beast which might come strolling out of the forest. He knew that if he were seen by one of those lank shepherds clad in sacking, who were to be met with mooching about in the most unexpected places, the hue and cry would be raised ; so he had shed his martial furnishings and had proceeded on his way clad in his homely cloak and pigskin trousers.

Fursey was tired and very lonely. Indeed, as he rested his chin on his cupped hands, it was his extreme loneliness that occupied his thoughts. All his adult life he had lived in community, and he now found his own company in the highest degree burdensome. It was a terrible thing to have no one to talk to. He shook his head despondently and began to reflect on his melancholy situation. He knew of no one in the entire world who had his interest at heart or even cared what became of him. He doubted if even Maeve cared. Did her thoughts ever stray back to those days when they had first known one another ? It had been in her father's cottage at the edge of a mountain lake not very far from the spot where he now sat. For three glittering weeks they had walked and chatted, scrambling over the boulders at the lake's edge, until Fursey had been caught in the web of her kindness and had lost his heart utterly. But had she ever loved him ? He doubted it. He knew little of women and less of the emotions that inform their actions, but he suspected that what had been a glorious companionship for him had been for her no more than humdrum daily existence. It was true that at a moment's notice she had run away with him from the very steps of the altar ; but, he asked himself bitterly, was it not the case that in so acting her motive had been to avoid an unwelcome marriage ? He could not believe that she had ever really cared for a boastful bully like Magnus. Her father had forced the marriage upon her ; and, acting on a sudden impulse, she had seized the opportunity of escaping from it. It was not love for Fursey that had motivated her actions at any time. On her own admission to the Abbot Marcus her only feeling for Fursey had been pity because he was helpless and without friends. Fursey's spirit twisted and turned inside his frame under the torture of those remembered words. He found himself grinding his teeth angrily. He was rather surprised at the sudden vision he had of himself sitting crouched at the edge of the track, grating his teeth horribly in anger at the thought of his wrongs. The picture pleased him. It made him see himself in an unaccustomed light—as a very formidable fellow, intent on the satisfaction of his injuries, so he crunched his teeth again with greater vehemence.

" I'll get even with them both," he said darkly. " First I'll quench Magnus, and then I'll brew Maeve such a powerful love potion that she must needs worship me for evermore."

But instead of being ravished with delectable visions of the future, Fursey began to brood gloomily on his imminent apprenticing to the master sorcerer Cuthbert, a man with whom he was already acquainted and whose proximity had always filled him with fear. The prospect of spending some weeks, or even months, in the company of such a formidable wizard caused Fursey the liveliest apprehension.

" It will be a dark and dirty business," he muttered, and began to think bitterly of the forlornness of his situation. His thoughts wandered back to his lack of someone in whom to confide. He thought of Albert, but he hesitated a long time before summoning his lugubrious familiar. At last he sighed despondently and whispered the name.

" Albert ! "

The two bear's paws came slowly into being, followed by the rest of Albert's unlovely anatomy. The familiar was squatting on his hunkers on the path, his head bent forward as he contemplated his master balefully.

" You don't seem very pleased to see me," said Fursey. " Your face is a veritable map of sorrow."

Albert's smoky red eyes flashed fire. He bared his teeth.

" Just look," he ejaculated. He gripped the ground firmly with his front paws and shook himself like a dog. He was immediately enveloped in a cloud of white dust.

" What's that ? " asked Fursey in surprise.

" Dandruff," snarled Albert. " My coat is falling out in chunks."

Fursey ran his eye over the rusty black hair which covered his familiar.

" How is that ? " he asked innocently.

" How is that ! " howled Albert indignantly. " Because you're deliberately starving me. I'm almost completely dehydrated."

" Oh," said Fursey with distaste. " I suppose you're looking for more of my blood."

" More ! " screeched Albert. " What did I ever get out of you except a thimbleful ? Didn't I tell you the last time you summoned me that I needed feeding at least every second day ? God be with the days when I had a master with some sense of his responsibilities ! I didn't know how lucky I was. You'd never think to look at me now that I was once a nimble and lively elemental. Your meanness and neglect has me completely destroyed and punctured."

"See here," said Fursey. "I'm not going to stand impertinent backchat from you. I've enough troubles of my own without, every time that I see you, having to concede to your selfish demands."

"Selfish demands!" Further words failed Albert. He rose and padded back and forward on the road for a few moments, throwing his snout despairingly to the sky as if to call all creation to witness that never had an elemental been so tortured. At last he came to rest opposite Fursey, and bent his gaze upon his master with hatred flickering in his eyes.

"I only wish," he choked, "that in your recent several perambulations a brace of lusty wolves had fastened on you with their paws."

"To feed you constantly with my blood," said Fursey coldly, "would seem to me curious and dreadful conduct."

"You're a man of perverse intelligence," yelped Albert. "Who better than I can advise you as to what things will tend to your profit and welfare? But you are determined to maltreat me and make an enemy of me."

"I'm tired of your company and your bad temper," replied Fursey. "Kindly vanish."

"I'll thwart you in your designs," screeched Albert as he began to disappear in spite of himself. "I'll frustrate you. I'll tell every spirit and demon I know that you're nothing but a hard-fisted curmudgeon."

As he faded into nothingness Fursey shook his head sorrowfully. He sat for a time in gloomy meditation, then he rose with a sigh and continued his way along the mountain track He had not travelled very far when he came to the edge of a small moorland lake. A man in grey stood on the brink. He held a fishing rod in his hand and was carefully coiling up his line. When he saw Fursey, he walked over to join him.

"Any luck?" asked Fursey, nervously wondering who the stranger was.

"No luck," replied the angler, "though I tumbled one or two."

Fursey recognised in the stranger's eye the mad glint of the fanatical fisherman.

"Is the fishing any good around here?" he asked soothingly.

"No," said the stranger. "Limestone bottoms."

"I beg your pardon," said Fursey.

"It's a very serious thing for an angler to have a limestone bottom," explained the man in grey.

"I suppose so," said Fursey, looking at his companion curiously.

"Ground feeding," said the angler.

"I see," said Fursey.

"Maybe you're going my way," said the man in grey. "Up the hill? My name is Turko."

Fursey bowed his head politely, but did not otherwise reply, as he deemed it unwise to tell in turn his name to the stranger. The omission did not pass unnoticed by Turko, and he eyed Fursey suspiciously as they mounted the track. They had not walked very far when he suddenly stopped and turned about.

"I trust that you're not a spy from Cashel," he said menacingly, "because if you are, it would be better for you that you had never been born."

Fursey hastily assured him that nothing was further from his thoughts than to spy on anyone.

"What are you doing then in this gloomy and inhospitable region? I warn you not to attempt to dissemble. You're in a very sorcerous neighbourhood, and we refugees in the hills are men of irritable temper."

Fursey did not like the turn the conversation had taken, bnt he thought it wiser to speak the truth.

"My name is Fursey," he replied. "I'm seeking an old acquaintance named Cuthbert, who, I have been told, has taken up residence in these hills."

"Oh," said Turko, "so you know Cuthbert. He lives in a cavern some distance from this spot."

"Being in the neighbourhood," volunteered Fursey cautiously, "I thought it would be but courteous to call on him and pay my respects."

Turko shot a quick glance at him and then began to lead the way up the hillside in silence. They had progressed a considerable distance before he again stopped and spoke.

"You know that Cuthbert is a sorcerer?" he asked, looking Fursey straight in the face.

Fursey hesitated. "Yes," he replied at last; "in fact, I have some slight acquaintance with sorcery myself, but I'm in a very small way of business."

Turko seemed at last convinced of Fursey's *bona fides*. His face cleared, and he took Fursey by the arm. When he again spoke, his voice was shot through with friendliness.

"I see by your dress," he said, "that you are a stranger in these parts, but if you are a displaced person like ourselves you are heartily welcome to our community. A couple of months ago the Bishop of Cashel launched a pogrom against the men of intellect resident in his diocese. Many of us met our end at the stake, which is an unlucky way to die and very inconvenient. Others did not even get that far, but died uncomfortably during the preliminary examination, in which racks, thumbscrews, knotted cords and ingenious wheels were brought to bear in order to drive home the authorities' point of view. Fortunately, some of us escaped by timely flight to the hills, and we now dwell in rather loose community in sundry caves and foxholes which we have rented from Festus Wisenuts, who is the landlord and sole owner of this area of mountain. You will find us an interesting and distinguished company. I myself am a crystallomancer—I read the future in a crystal. I possess

a very potent stone, which I brought with me in my flight.
Our community does not lack scryers and astrologers ; we
have an abundance of sorcerers, a couple of mathematicians,
a ventriloquist, two conjurers, three clairvoyants and one
reciter of poetry."

"One cannot but be at home," murmured Fursey courteously, "among such polite society."

"We are fortunate in having an enlightened and sympathetic landlord," explained Turko. "He's a man of
ineffable ambitions, who for many years devoted himself to
the mysteries of occult mathematics, a subject which is
enveloped in a chaos of cloud and darkness. To tell you the
truth, I doubt if Festus Wisenuts came out any wiser than
he went in. But he is a man with a raging thirst for knowledge, and for some years past he has been treading the
crooked paths of sorcery. He began his studies by taking
up residence among the tombs, but I don't think he learnt
much there either. He now lives a little distance from here
in a dreary cavern and does magic all day long. He rarely
emerges except to climb the mountain to a plateau of
abominable repute, where he spends a couple of hours trying
to coax the demons from their marshy haunts."

"He must be a man of interesting and elegant mind,"
said Fursey nervously. "It will be a great pleasure to make
his acquaintance."

"Yes," said the crystallomancer slowly, seeming to weigh
his words. "I have no doubt but that you will find him
interesting. He is a man of most distinguished appearance,
tall, grave and handsome. His face is ornamented with a
narrow, silvery beard, which is the envy of many. He affects
a black cloak covered with the signs of the zodiac, which
imparts to him a priestly appearance. But I'll let you in
on a secret," added Turko confidentially. "He's not any
good as a wizard. A man like Cuthbert could make rings
round him. But naturally none of us ever dares to let
him suspect our opinion of his efforts and achievements.
After all, he's our landlord ; and if he took it into his head,

he could turn us all out of our caves with a notice to quit. Of course, he's not likely to do so. I suspect that he's secretly glad of the proximity of so many wizards. You see, he's not at all above picking up magical tricks from his tenants and pretending that they were always part of his own repertoire. But I'll say this for him, he's a man devoted to his profession. He works hard. As I passed his cave on my way down here, he was standing in the entrance essaying some magical sleight-of-hand with the remnants of a goat."

" Is it not the case," enquired Fursey, " that these interesting experiments are not always performed with complete immunity from danger to those who undertake them ? "

Turko lowered his voice. " I'll be quite frank with you," he said. " I'm glad that I'm not a wizard. The gift of sorcery is frequently an embarrassing profession ; in fact, it's apt to prove in the highest degree perilous."

" There's no need to tell me that," replied Fursey with conviction. " I know from my own experience that a sorcerer needs the utmost subtlety to continue alive at all."

" That is so," conceded Turko ; " but I wasn't referring to outside interference by busybodies, who can only think in terms of flaming pyres and torture chambers. I was referring rather to the perils to which even a cunning wizard exposes himself when actuated by an insatiable and base curiosity. Too frequently he will essay untravelled fields of experiment and will unloose potent forces which he lacks the knowledge to control. The end is disaster."

" Crystal gazing seems a much safer profession," remarked Fursey sadly.

" It is," agreed the crystallomancer, " though the authorities burn you for that, too ; but there's no use worrying about such things, as they'll burn you for almost anything. In the eyes of established authority the one unforgivable sin is to have an original and enquiring mind. Ideas—that's what they're afraid of."

" Life is very peculiar," commented Fursey.

" But to come back to what I was saying," continued

Turko, " Festus Wisenuts as a wizard labours under a feeling
of inferiority. He knows in his heart that he's a negligible
sorcerer, but he daren't admit it to himself or to anyone else.
The result is that to convince himself and others of his great
abilities he's always attempting the most extravagant experiments. At one time he had a young cockatrice chained in
the depths of his cave, and he spent a fortnight trying by
magic to teach it to play the bagpipes. As you may well
imagine, the cockatrice didn't like it ; and it strained at its
chain and behaved in a most formidable manner, menacing
destruction to all who approached. We were all of us afraid
to enter the cave to pay the rent, and Festus Wisenuts became
quite nasty about it. Then, unlike other sorcerers, he will
not rest content with a dun dog or a speckled cat as his
familiar, but must needs have nothing less than a tawny
Moor. Well, tawny Moors are hard to come by, and for a
long time past he's been trying to conjure one into existence.
He spent a week going around in circles with his face awry,
breathing to left and right, and sprinkling powdered loadstone ; but all he succeeded in conjuring up was a young hippo-
griff suckling its supernatural children."

" Was there no sign of the tawny Moor ? " asked Fursey,
interested in spite of himself.

" Not a sign," answered Turko shortly. " He tried it
again, lost his head in the middle of the spell, forgot the
words, and all but turned himself into a frog."

Before Fursey could comment there was a sudden clap of
thunder overhead and a comet shot across the sky. Turko
flung himself on his face and Fursey immediately followed
suit.

" There he is again," said Turko savagely. " Another
experiment gone wrong."

When the crystallomancer was satisfied that the danger
was past, he got slowly to his feet and brushed the dust
from his clothing.

" I have little sympathy with such apish antics," he com-

mented bitterly. " I don't mind a man becoming learned
in runes or spending his time compounding salves. I don't
deny that magic may be useful sometimes ; for instance,
in enabling one to tie up an enemy's guts. But there should
be a law against a man releasing infernal powers when he
doesn't know how to control them. What are you standing
there for ? Why don't you come on ? "

" Do you not think," enquired Fursey, " that it might be
wiser to retrace our steps ? "

" Nonsense," replied Turko shortly. " You'll have to get
used to the perils inherent in close residence to Festus Wisenuts. Not," he muttered, " that there isn't a certain amount
of wisdom in what you suggest. I've told the others again
and again that Festus is a danger to us all ; but what can
we do ? If we descend into the plain the Bishop will have
us burnt."

Turko continued along the track for some time with set
brows, while Fursey trailed along behind him. When the
crystallomancer spoke again, he prefaced his remarks with a
gloomy shake of the head.

" The experiments of Festus," he said, " have been playing
havoc with the weather, too, during the past week. If you
come out of your cave for a breath of air, and go for a ramble,
you're lucky if you succeed in covering a hundred paces
without hearing an explosion, and before you can race back
and gain the shelter of your cave you're deluged by a shower
of rain. God knows our caves are damp enough without
the addition of artificially induced thunder showers. To
tell you the honest truth, I'm sick and tired of living in this
locality. Apart from the danger of having as neighbours a
bunch of short-tempered wizards, my digestion is ruined by
witch's broth."

" If does not appear to be a suitable locality in which to
set up residence," commented Fursey ; " at least not for a
man who hopes for quiet and longevity."

Turko turned his head and stared at Fursey earnestly.

" Life here," he said, " is in the highest degree a hazardous business. I strongly advise you as long as you're here to keep on the best of terms with everyone. That's what I do, and in addition, just for safety, I keep in my cave a heated ploughshare, which is well-known to be a powerful antidote against the spells of wizards."

" You don't happen to have a second one to spare ? " enquired Fursey.

" I'm sorry, I haven't. If I had, you'd be welcome to it."

They breasted the rise and paused for a moment to regain their breath. A narrow area of moorland stretched from where they stood to the base of a high cliff.

" You have uttered your mind to me very openly," said Fursey with feeling, " and I want you to know that I'm grateful, and that I'll respect your confidence. I hope that during my stay here we'll be friends."

The crystallomancer's face softened suddenly and he flashed a smile at his companion.

" Of course we will," he answered. " I've taken quite a fancy to you."

They made their way across the broken ground towards the cliff. Fursey noted with a sinking heart the awful desolation of the place. The bracken through which they had to pass was nearly waist-high and the ground underfoot so broken and treacherous that he stumbled several times over rocks hidden in the waste of fern. When they emerged from the bracken and began to skirt the base of the cliff, Fursey glanced up at the soaring wall of fissured stone overhanging their path and hoped earnestly that nothing would fall on him. As they made their way around a giant boulder they came suddenly on an old man of venerable appearance sitting cross-legged on the ground in the lips of a narrow cleft. His nose was sunk in his extensive white beard, and he sat so motionless that at first Fursey thought that he was either asleep or dead.

" He's a mathematician," whispered Turko. " We mustn't

disturb him. He sits there all day, his daring spirit essaying untravelled realms of speculation."

Fursey tiptoed past. A few moments later they passed the opening of a vast cavern.

" That's where Festus Wisenuts lives," said Turko. " It's too late in the evening to bring you in to introduce you. In any case he's probably busy doing magic."

Fursey was not sorry to defer his visit to the erratic Festus, especially as he noticed that there was a corporal's guard of moles standing at the entrance to the cavern. Of the landlord himself he could see nothing : no doubt he was busy pondering magic in the dark depths within. As he hurried past, Fursey's gaze made a quick circuit of the cave mouth, from the row of sentinel moles, over the jagged sides and ceiling. He shuddered : the opening was like a giant mouth yawning wide to snap and swallow him. He was glad when they left the cave behind. He was grateful, too, for Turko's comforting presence.

" I'll tell you what we'll do," said the crystallomancer suddenly. " My cave is close at hand. We'll go there, and I'll let you search the future in my crystal. This is the very best hour for using the crystal, the hour of sunset."

This suggestion was very agreeable to Fursey, who was by no means averse to deferring his visit to the sorcerer Cuthbert as long as possible. He quickened his pace instinctively, and Turko fell into step beside him, so that before long they arrived at the hollow cavity in which the crystallomancer dwelt. It was a pleasant, open place, with a neat bed of mugwort growing at the entrance. At the rear of the cave stood a small table. The crystallomancer lifted it and, bringing it towards the entrance, placed it before a low rock, on which he told Fursey to sit. Fursey seated himself and watched Turko's further preparations with considerable interest. First, Turko covered the table with a white linen cloth. Then he took a black, ebony wand and traced on the ground a circle seven feet in diameter so as to include in its circumference the table and the rock on which

Fursey was sitting. He placed a small brazier in the vicinity
and drawing some handfuls of grains from a series of silken
bags which hung on the wall, he cast them on to the glowing
coals. A fine smoke arose, struck the rugged ceiling and
spread throughout the cave. Fursey sneezed once or twice
as the aromatic perfumes crept up his nostrils.

"You will soon accustom yourself to the vision-inducing
incense," said Turko, appearing suddenly through the smoke.

Fursey wiped his streaming eyes and nodded his head
bleakly.

Turko disappeared once more into the depths of the cave
and emerged a moment later loaded down with the paraphernalia of his profession. Carefully he drew from its black
cloth a crystal of pale, water-green beryl and placed it on
the table. Then he added a sword, a length of twine, a new
knife, a pair of scissors and a piece of stick.

"What's that?" asked Fursey, alarmed at the production
of lethal weapons.

"It's a wand of hazelwood of twelve months' growth and
three feet in length," explained Turko, "and this is a magic
sword."

"I see," said Fursey. "What do we do next?"

Turko placed two tapers on the floor on either side of the
circle. He lit the tapers before he replied.

"You mustn't move," he said. "You must keep your
face towards the east and your eyes fixed upon the crystal.
I am now about to charge the potent stone. When you
observe a mist gathering in its depths, the interior faculties
of your being will expand like a flower. Then when you
are thoroughly entranced, the globe itself will vanish from
your sight, the mist in its depths will part and you will be
ravished by a vision of the radiant being who is the abiding
spirit of the stone."

"I see," said Fursey nervously.

"I must warn you," continued the crystallomancer, "that
if your purpose is evil the crystal will avenge itself on you
sooner or later with awful effect."

" I have no purpose," said Fursey hastily, " other than to learn what the future may hold for me."

" That's all right," said Turko soothingly. " For your information, you may as well know that the basis of this operation is magnetism, which accumulates in the crystal by reason of the iron with which its constitution is infused. In the cerebellum," he said, tapping Fursey on the back of the head, " there is a reservoir of magnetism, which streams forth from the eyes when the gaze is concentrated on the crystal. We must establish contact between the magnetism projected from your skull and the magnetism trembling in the stone. Now," he added briskly, " do you wish to observe events taking place at a great distance in time or space, or do you prefer rather to be made aware of events which will occur in the near vicinity and before very long ? "

Fursey thought of Maeve, who was no doubt resident at no great distance.

" Events near at hand," he replied, " and which will happen soon."

" Very good," said Turko, and he began to make passes with his hands back and forward over the crystal.

" What are you doing ? " asked Fursey.

" I'm magnetising the stone," replied Turko shortly. " Don't talk. Concentrate."

Fursey found it hard to concentrate with the crystallomancer's hands waving back and forward within two feet of his nose, but he continued to stare at the globe. At long last Turko, with a final languid wave of his hand, withdrew on tiptoe and cast another few handfuls of grains into the brazier. A cloud of white smoke billowed up and obliterated everything.

" What do you see ? " hissed the crystallomancer in Fursey's ear.

" Nothing," said Fursey.

" It's a good sign," came the answer. " If the crystal at first is hazy, it means that one is likely to see an image."

"But I can't see the crystal," said Fursey. "I can't see anything with the smoke."

"Keep looking at it," came the angry reply. "The smoke will clear in a moment."

As the smoke thinned, the crystal swam slowly into Fursey's view.

"Do you see black clouds?" enquired the crystallomancer anxiously.

"No," replied Fursey.

"Good thing," muttered Turko. "Black clouds are inauspicious. By the way, I should have told you that anything you see on the right-hand side is merely symbolical. Keep concentrating."

Fursey was becoming dizzy, but he continued to stare at the crystal for a seemingly interminable length of time. The veins stood out on his forehead.

"What do you see?" came the sibilant voice of the crystallomancer.

"Nothing," gasped Fursey.

"Keep concentrating," said Turko savagely.

Fursey's two eyes protruded like bullets. Turko was making frantic passes over the crystal.

"The crystal is darkening," cried Fursey suddenly.

"Good," exulted the crystallomancer. The sweat ran down his forehead as his hands waved wildly back and forward over the stone.

"The crystal is becoming blindingly bright," shouted Fursey. "It dazzles me."

"The effulgence proceeds from its interior," replied Turko. "Keep staring at it. Don't mind your eyesight. Is a form or vision becoming manifest?"

"Something is becoming manifest," said Fursey, lowering his voice suddenly.

"Do you see a radiant being, the abiding spirit of the stone?"

"No. I see a cow."

"A what?"

" A cow's head."

" What's she doing ? "

" She's looking at me."

" What do you mean ' looking at you ' ? "

" Just looking at me."

" Well, you keep looking at her. Don't let your gaze waver "

Fursey and the cow continued to stare at one another for a long time without either party making a move.

" What's happening now ? " came the crystallomancer's voice.

" She's waggling her ears at me."

" Remarkable," muttered Turko.

" There are shadows beginning to move across the crystal from right to left," announced Fursey. " The cow is fading."

" The operation is at an end," declared Turko. " You will see no more."

Fursey rose to his feet and felt suddenly very tired. They walked together into the fresh air outside the cave.

" Remarkable," repeated Turko. " Have you ever had dealings with a cow ? "

Fursey thought for a moment. " No," he answered.

" Then there's a cow coming into your life," declared Turko with finality. " We will try the experiment again before the moon becomes full. In the meantime you would be well advised to take an infusion of the herb mugwort from time to time during the moon's increase. It has valuable anti-bilious properties and will aid your power of vision. I shall not charge you my usual fee for to-day's session."

" That's very generous of you," responded Fursey, " but you must at least let me stand you a drink. I'm sorely in need of one myself."

Turko watched suspiciously as Fursey manipulated his rope and produced two flagons of ale.

" I had forgotten that you are something of a wizard,"he muttered as he took the proffered flagon gingerly. " I trust that I did not offend you earlier in the evening by my remarks about the profession."

" Not at all," replied Fursey. " You have earned my gratitude by being so frank. I'm glad to know the nature of the people amongst whom I must dwell."

" Do you intend prolonged residence ? " enquired the crystallomancer politely.

Fursey stirred uncomfortably. " Some weeks at least. I shall probably stay with Cuthbert or in his neighbourhood."

" Is it long since you have seen Cuthbert ? " asked Turko.

" About three months."

" I'm afraid that you will find him sadly changed. The poor fellow has become a martyr to drink."

" Indeed," commented Fursey.

" He made his way here in a tattered and deplorable state. His cottage had been burnt by a furious mob during the witch hunt inspired by the Bishop, and Cuthbert barely escaped with his life. His sorrows are many, but most of all he deplores the loss of his store of magical books and his collection of horrible rarities, moles' feet, murderers' knucklebones and the like."

" Yes," said Fursey, " he had a considerable collection. I saw it once."

" When he came here first," continued Turko, " there was no consoling him. ' What use is a sorcerer to anyone without his stock-in-trade ? ' was the burden of his complaint. Poor fellow, he's scarcely to be blamed that he took to smothering his sorrows in alcohol. Like you, he has a rope, so that the means to intoxication are unfortunately always ready to hand. However, he keeps a plenteous board, due to that same rope, and he is able to produce the most delectable dishes, a fact which renders him highly popular in the community. I'm sure that you will be happy with him."

" I hope so," replied Fursey, without conviction.

" It grows late," said Turko. " It is time for us to go. At least a mile of rough mountain country lies between us and the cave in which Cuthbert dwells."

Fursey rose unwillingly to his feet and they set out across the soggy moorland.

" I'm still exercised about that cow," remarked Turko.
" Are you certain that your vision was not due to the delusions
of a bewildered fancy ? "

" I saw a cow," replied Fursey obstinately.

Turko shook his head, and they continued the rest of their
way in silence. From time to time Fursey glanced apprehensively at the black shadows oozing from the crevices of
the awful heights which reared themselves above the stretch
of bogland. In the twilight the outline of the hills was harsh
and threatening, and their mass overwhelmed whatever little
spirit he possessed. He felt against his face the small, damp
wind which came across the moors. It stroked his face
mockingly and slid away, smoothing a path for itself across
the tips of the heather. In the failing light the entire upland
had assumed an ominous character. The familiar material
things, rock, bogland, shimmering pool and hill, seemed
charged with malice. They seemed to Fursey to be watching
him closely, waiting for the appropriate moment to rise up
and destroy him. His fears were by no means diminished
when there suddenly came to his ears from the heights above
the lonely howling of some distant wizard chanting his way
carefully through the intricacies of a conjuration. Fursey
gasped and quickened his pace so as to keep abreast of his
companion. At last they came to a tumble of great rocks
sprawled in the shadow of the hill.

" This is the place," whispered Turko. " I'll leave you
now. Unless I regain my cave before nightfall I'm likely
to break a limb in crossing this unfriendly stretch of country."

Without another word he turned and hurried back along
the way they had come. It came into Fursey's mind that
the crystallomancer also was afraid of Cuthbert ; then he
forgot Turko and looked anxiously about him. He was at
the entrance to a slender cleft in the rocks from which emerged
a negligible trickle of water, formed probably by the continual
gathering of moisture on the roof of the cave into which the
crevice opened. As Fursey peered nervously into the orifice
he became aware of a dim light in the interior. All at once

it was obliterated.   Someone had come between it and Fursey.
He could see the outline of a human being standing before him.

" Who's there ? " asked a hollow voice.

Fursey mastered a sudden impulse to turn and take to his
heels.

" Fursey," he quavered, " your old friend, Fursey."

A tall man with stooping shoulders emerged from the cave.
He was clad in a tight-fitting suit of black, sadly dilapidated.
He bent his wan face on his visitor and examined him with
sharp, glittering eyes.   He had a puckered, rabbit's mouth
and a long lock of black hair hung down over his forehead.
His appearance was far from prepossessing.   He was the
sort of creature one might reasonably expect to meet about
midnight on a lonely country road in the neighbourhood of a
graveyard.   Fursey shuddered under the steady gaze.

" I'm Fursey," he squeaked. " Don't you remember me ? "

Cuthbert raised a meagre hand and rubbed his cheek.   A
sly and furtive look came into his eyes, but he said nothing.

" I met you last spring when you were sexton of Kilcock
Churchyard," continued Fursey.   " I enjoyed for one night
the hospitality of your cottage."

" Yes," answered Cuthbert at last, " I remember you.
You're the little laybrother whom they expelled from the
monastery because the demons began to play tricks on him.
I remember you well.   Come in."

He turned and re-entered the cave.   Fursey with a
quaking heart stumbled in after him.   Inside it was more
light.   From a flat rock, which evidently served as a table,
a long taper flickered oddly, casting shadows that advanced
and retreated up and down the walls.   On the floor at the
back of the cave was spread a heap of rushes.   There was a
large number of empty flagons scattered here and there, but
there were no furnishings.   Cuthbert seated himself on a stone
and motioned Fursey to a similar one where the taper light
would play on his face.   They looked across at one another
in silence.   In the half-light Cuthbert's visage seemed
demoniacal.

" Will you have a drink ? " he asked suddenly.

Fursey was conscious of a sudden relaxation of tension.

" No, thank you," he gasped, remembering even in his frightened state that he would be wise to keep his mind clear so as to be able to grapple with whatever might ensue.

Cuthbert raised a flagon from the ground at his feet and took a deep draught. Fursey realised suddenly that he was half drunk.

" You see before you," declared Cuthbert, " the ruins of a great sorcerer."

With a grandiose gesture he replaced the flagon on the floor at his feet. Fursey murmured deprecatingly, but Cuthbert raised a silencing hand.

" Yes," he said, " I have lost everything. I have lost my magic books. I have lost my store of insidious poisons, powders and philtres, my menagerie of toads, moles, bats and vipers, my beautiful garden of noxious herbs and plants— the collection and care of a lifetime, all gone ! Not even the marrows of a murderer or the thumb of a suicide is left."

As he sank back, resting his spare frame against the wall of the cave, he presented a most rueful spectacle, a living example of the condition to which sorcery and alcohol can bring a respectable sexton.

" A man of your abilities——" began Fursey soothingly.

Cuthbert shook his head despondently. " How can I start again ? " he asked. " A sorcerer without the tools of his trade is lamed and helpless. It would have been better if they had apprehended me and immolated me in the fire which consumed my possessions."

" We must never lose heart," muttered Fursey.

" Such an affliction as I have undergone," answered Cuthbert, " undermines the spirit. There is no medicine for a cankered heart. I am an outlaw who may never abide for long in the one place. Soon the authorities will search out this refuge, and I shall have to take to the roads. I may make an ignoble living amongst sportsmen and peasants, charming cocks for cock fighting or the like. I have no other future."

Listening to this dolorous discourse, Fursey began to wonder whether his long journey and the manifold dangers which he had encountered had all been to no purpose.

" But you still retain your knowledge," he argued anxiously. " You know how to manufacture love philtres, for instance?"

Cuthbert appeared to observe the note of anxiety in Fursey's voice. He raised his head suddenly. " What do you want of me ? " he asked.

" I was advised by Satan to seek you out," began Fursey.

" A very upstanding gentleman," commented Cuthbert with a respectful bow of his head, " but one with whom I have only a slight acquaintance. How is His Highness keeping ?"

" When I last saw him," replied Fursey, " I regret to say that he was not in the best condition."

" Indeed," replied Cuthbert solicitously.

" He presented a very battered appearance," replied Fursey. " He was generally soiled and seemed very rickety as to his legs. Moreover, he had lost the tip of an ear."

" I'm sorry to hear that," commented Cuthbert. " Did he have the misfortune to meet with an accident ? "

" He had the misfortune to meet with a gentleman of the anchorite class," explained Fursey, " and the affair had an unfavourable outcome."

" These religious have the country ruined," remarked Cuthbert acidly. " Things have come to a nice pass when the Prince of Darkness himself is not safe from their depredations."

" He advised me to apprentice myself to you."

" With what object ? "

" Well, chiefly so as to learn the manufacture and use of love philtres."

Cuthbert turned on Fursey a disapproving eye.

" I'm surprised at you," he said. " I would never have suspected you of gallantry. I hope that your ultimate intentions in the matter are honourable."

" Most honourable," Fursey hastened to assure him. " I merely wish to deprive an unpleasant fellow of his life and contract a union with his spouse."

Cuthbert's brow cleared. " That's all right," he said. " I feared at first that more than one female was involved and that the matter wasn't respectable."

He sat for some time in silent thought, staring at the floor of the cave. When he raised his head to look at Fursey once more there was a brittle glint in his eye.

" Am I to understand that you are fully resolved in your purpose ? "

" Yes," replied Fursey stoutly. " I'm ensnared in the love of a woman whose natural perfections are such that I'm determined to stop at nought to gain her regard. To begin with, I want to learn how best to murder an audacious villain named Magnus, against whom I am implacably incensed. My hatred of mankind is such that I shall stop at nothing. Already I have become a man of the most pernicious principles. I've sold my soul to the Devil, and my rogueries are being spoken of far and near. I've led a band of Viking pirates against Clonmacnoise and burnt the holy settlement to the ground. I'm determined to become a menace to humanity, and I beg of you to take me as your apprentice and use your utmost endeavour to instil into me all the wickedness you know."

Fursey paused from lack of breath and anxiously studied Cuthbert's face to ascertain if he could whether or not the sorcerer believed him. Cuthbert was leaning forward with his elbows on the table watching him closely. As Fursey finished his peroration, Cuthbert slapped one hand into the other enthusiastically.

" There's a catching oratory in your words," he declared. " I'm glad you came to me. Maybe your companionship will serve to free me from my present morbid melancholy. We'll begin your instruction to-morrow. We'll go down to the graveyard and raise a wraith or two, for there's much to be learnt from the souls of the lost."

Fursey heard this speech with considerable trepidation, but he smiled bravely and assured the sorcerer that there was nothing he would like better. Cuthbert rose smiling and laid a skinny hand on the shoulder of his apprentice.

" Take some of the heather," he said, " and make yourself a comfortable couch. The taper is flickering out. It's time for all good people to be in bed."

CHAPTER VI

NOTWITHSTANDING Cuthbert's apparent enthusiasm on the night or Fursey's arrival, he manifested no inclination on the morrow to commence the instruction of his apprentice in the sinuous mysteries of witchcraft. A great lethargy possessed him, and during the ensuing weeks he lazed about the cave, sometimes drinking moodily, at other times sitting for long hours with a twisted smile on his face as if his mind was busy with curious and serpentine designs. He roused himself from time to time to deal with customers, besotted peasants who came with offerings of rough wooden bowls or ill-made pottery, requesting him to cure warts or whooping cough. Except for these folk cures he did no magic ; and Fursey, secretly glad of the respite, performed the menial tasks of the cave, drew water from a nearby brook and brought in sticks and gorse to burn, for it was already winter. The only other duty laid upon him was the collection of herbs and venomous plants, which he soon learnt to identify. Besides their use in the making of drugs and medicines, Cuthbert spoke constantly of the necessity for building up a large stock of magical armament in keeping with his position as a major sorcerer. Fursey was a docile and assiduous servant, and came back from each excursion bowed beneath a load of poisonous fungi, foxgloves, hemlock

or the dreaded deadly nightshade. He even went beyond his instructions and brought in plants that looked to him tolerably venomous. Some of these Cuthbert discarded, other he put aside to try by way of experiment on the next

peasant who should call seeking his assistance. Fursey was
kept busy. Some herbs had to be gathered at certain phases
of the moon, and he spent a week hunting for a stone which
it was indispensable to find in a peewit's nest. A brisk
trade developed with the other warlocks scattered throughout
the hills. On Cuthbert's instructions, Fursey carried loads
of dogwood, hawkweed and henbane to their caverns and
bargained with them for elf-shots, murderers' knucklebones
and the fingers of unbaptised babes. Cuthbert spoke vaguely
of making magic brews and performing ritual but his lassitude
was such that he never made a start.

At first Fursey was nigh overcome by the demoniacal
character of his surroundings. The weather was of a very
irregular character. Patches of druidical fog floated against
the wind, and the neighbourhood was subject to sudden
storms and hail. One heard strange voices on the breeze,
and at times the air would be filled with a kind of twittering
or chirping, which Fursey knew to be the voices of spirits.
It was not unusual to meet some initiate toiling up the track
with a load of assorted stones collected from four parishes,
or to see a wizard coursing back and forward on the hillside
in the form of a greyhound. The night was often hideous
with tumults and strange bawlings, and from the mouth of
the cave wandering fires were visible. At first Fursey could
not sleep at night through fear of being suddenly embraced
by the spectral arms of some visitant. He felt that if he
were to experience such a foul caress he would surely breathe
forth the vital spark. But soon the fatigues of the day, his
journeyings hither and thither, guaranteed his night's rest,
and he was asleep as soon as he laid his head on its rustling
pillow. He accustomed himself also to the less alarming of
the magical manifestations. He could look on a griffin
rampant in a green field without feeling an overmastering
desire to take to his heels. He came to appreciate that
these projections and appearances, not being directed at
himself, were in nowise likely to injure him. He knew that
no one on the mountain had reason to bear him malice, so

that he no longer took cover if he saw a pale young gentleman
floating by him on the wind or beheld high overhead in the
grey cloud drift of the sky a boat of shining crystal rowed
by a faery on his way to The Land of Youth. He even
accustomed himself to the scratching and mewing of enchanted cats at night and their hideous caterwauling. There
was, however, one mountain slope which he avoided, a place
where chimeras, spoorns, calcars and sylens slouched among
the rocks leering at the passers-by. Turko the Crystallomancer had told him that on the summit of the mountain
itself dwelt belated worshippers of Ogma and Segomos and
the other weird, cruel and bloody divinities of the Gael.
Their devotees adored holy wells and the elements, and their
crude shrines were tended by loathsome and malignant witch-
hags. They were the last worshippers of the old native
faith, which had been supplanted everywhere else by the
foreign religion that the blessed Patrick had brought from
Britain. Fursey knew that wherever there was strong
religious conviction there was blood-letting and oppression,
so he avoided the hill where the pillar stones of paganism still
stood. Once when he was on his way to a piece of soggy
ground well known to him as a place where all classes of
vegetable wickedness grew in hideous luxuriance, he essayed
a short cut, which brought him within the shadow of the
mountain of ill-repute. All at once he found himself on the
edge of a crevasse across which a bridge had been flung. A
woman stood on the bridge and, as Fursey stopped to stare
at her, she held out her hand, offering him a cluster of nuts.
He immediately turned and retraced his steps, and as he
glanced fearfully over his shoulder he saw that both bridge
and woman had vanished. In this neighbourhood on All
Hallows Eve the nature spirits of paganism fore-gathered,
lingering for a while as if in sadness by the cairn on the
mountain top and beside the dolmen which Christian icono-
clasts had overthrown. Fursey saw their great shadows
against the sky at sunset and fled to the safety of the sorcerer's
cave.

Before a couple of months had run, Fursey had come to know, at least by sight, most of the mountain dwellers who lived nearby. The mathematicians rarely spoke to anyone and had no interest in Fursey's bundles of herbs or venomous plants. All day they sat in the openings of their caves working out problems far exceeding all numbers in arithmetic. The sorcerers were in general cross-grained and snappy, and were always asking Fursey to undertake little jobs for them, such as the kidnapping and murdering of small boys, from whose boiled bones a powerful ointment could be made. Fursey invariably declined with his best regrets, pleading that he was articled to Cuthbert and was precluded from performing such tasks for others, however anxious he might be to accommodate them. The wizards would mutter in their beards and become very testy in their subsequent conversation, so that Fursey as soon as courtesy permitted would bid them good day, hoist his wares on his back and proceed on his way.

Some fifty paces from Cuthbert's cave dwelt an alchemist, a person of the human species, but lame and crooked, squat and bandy-legged. As one might expect of a man whose only desire was to assemble wealth, he was in the highest degree hard-visaged. His efforts to turn into gold the flint arrowheads and horseshoes with which his cave was littered, appeared to meet with little success. Clad in base and servile weeds, he seemed an impoverished and benighted creature. From time to time, when he wearied of treating his flints and horseshoes with balm of mercury and putting them through the various methods of alchemical confection, he would revert for a week or so to a search for the Elixir of Life. He would sit for days almost completely immersed in a herbal stew over a slow fire, striving to renew his youth by saturating his body with certain potent juices, of which sugar of mercury and celestial slime were important ingredients. The preparation of this bath was a slow affair, a lengthy process of congealation and distillation was necessary before the advent of a divine sparkle in the mixture indicated to the alchemist that it was time for him to peel off his clothes and get in. He was an unfriendly fellow, who held intercourse with no one. He was suspicious of all who approached his cave, imagining that they were intent on prying into his alchemical secrets.

Fursey met the cow while he was on one of his excursions collecting sowthistle, nipplewort and buckbean and similar herbs of a soothing nature. Although the snow had fallen in thousands during the preceding night, he found the constant bending and tugging at obstinate roots very warming, so he had taken off his cloak and flung it on a nearby hedge. When his basket was full, and he turned to resume the garment, he saw the last shred of it disappearing down a cow's gullet. Fursey's first thought was that the cow was apparently hungry. There was snow on the ground and the poor beast's bones were apparent through its hide. Then it was borne in on him that he had seen that particular cow somewhere before. When she slowly stirred her ears, he remembered Turko's crystal. For a long time he stood staring at the cow, while she returned his gaze with impassive melancholy. It was apparent that no thoughts were stirring in her brain, she was just looking at Fursey because she couldn't think of anything better to look at.

" She's lost her way," he thought, " and she's suffering grievously from malnutrition."

He put down his basket and scraped away a square yard of snow from the ground. Then he directed her attention to the grass growing underneath. The cow seemed unimpressed.

" I don't wonder that you're dejected," said Fursey. " You look as if you hadn't eaten anything for a month. If only I had my rope with me I'd produce some body-building food for you. The best thing you can do is to come along with me and we'll find you something to eat."

He walked round the cow and gave her a smart slap on the buttock. As she did not seem to have anywhere in particular to go, she permitted Fursey to drive her before him up the track to the cavern. Cuthbert, who was sitting inside drinking a flagon of mead, sprang to his feet when the cow walked into the cave and stood staring at him, flicking her tail.

" Where did you get her ? " he demanded hoarsely. " Did you steal her ? "

" Certainly not," replied Fursey primly. " I just brought her along for a square meal."

Cuthbert muffled a curse, and began hastily to move his most cherished possessions out of the cow's reach.

" You'd better get her out," he said meaningly.

" You surely wouldn't begrudge her a bite to eat," retorted Fursey. " The poor thing is almost hollow."

Taking up his rope he cast it over a projecting ledge of rock and pulled. Immediately a load of hay fell from the ceiling. The cow bowed her head and began to munch contentedly. There was a string of blasphemy from the back of the cave, and a moment later Cuthbert came clambering across the hay.

" If you haven't that animal and the haystack out of this cave by the time I come back," he snarled, " I'll have your life."

He stamped out into the open air and disappeared from view. When the cow had eaten her fill, watched by the admiring Fursey, he led her out and tethered her in a hollow in the cliff, where she would be assured of some protection from the elements. Then he started to carry out the hay in armfuls and pile it about her. The cow watched him contentedly. Then she brought up Fursey's cloak from her stomach by way of cud and started to chew it reflectively. Fursey shook his head at her in smiling disapproval, and returned to the cave to sweep out the last traces of the hay. As he finished the task, Cuthbert re-appeared and stood in the cavern mouth watching him approvingly.

" I'm glad this happened," declared Cuthbert. " The incident has thrown a flood of light into the recesses of your soul. As it happens, I am a profound psychologist as well as a considerable sorcerer. When I saw the care you bestowed upon that ruminant I read your spirit like an open book. Your soul stood naked before me."

"What did you see?" asked Fursey, leaning on the broom.

Cuthbert nodded his head sagely. "Your affections have welled over the dam of your resolution. Your brimming heart craves an object to love and cherish. We must win the woman Maeve for you at once. We have delayed too long."

"Oh, thank you," said Fursey delightedly.

"Don't thank me," replied the sorcerer in businesslike tones. "To a considerable degree I am consulting my own convenience and comfort in the matter. Unless we provide you with a proper object for your affections, I don't doubt but that before long you will have the cave so full of feathered and four-legged pets that there will be no living here at all. Not that I blame you," he added kindly. "It's your nature, and no man can slip away from his nature. Now, what was it I undertook to do for you?"

"First we have to rid the world of an objectionable oaf called Magnus," prompted Fursey; "a man who has done grievous wrong to me and mine."

"Exactly," said Cuthbert. "I clearly remember the circumstances. We shall slay him to-night."

"How?" asked Fursey breathlessly.

"Such a matter is a mere bagatelle to a man like me," replied Cuthbert. "I'll riddle him with magic. Let me see." He seated himself on his favourite rock and absently conjured up a flagon of black ale to help him in his cogitations.

"How would you like him to die?" he asked at length.

"Roaring," replied Fursey without hesitation. "Roaring and wallowing in a horrible manner."

"Let me see," repeated Cuthbert. "We could overthrow him by cold and heat, but that would require a spot free from observation, a napkin of unblemished whiteness and a chafing dish. We have the first named, but we lack the other two ; so we'll have to think of something else."

He took a long pull at the flagon of ale and ruminated.

"Will you be satisfied," he said at last, "if I afflict him with a lingering and painful disease, so that his speech and hearing become benumbed, his toes and fingers fall off, and he finally be bereft of every sense ? "

"No," declared Fursey fiercely. "I will not be talked into a persuasion that anything less than his total demise will suffice."

"But it's a lovely spell," said Cuthbert coaxingly. "Its first effect would be to afflict him with a baldness ; and all we would need for it would be the toenails of an unbaptised male child, the entrails of a sacrificed cock and the molars of a glutton."

"I respect your artistic instincts," said Fursey firmly, "but I will not be satisfied unless you pierce the fluidic envelope of his soul."

"Very well," sighed Cuthbert, "have it your own way. We shall drown all his faculties at once if you so desire. We could waste him by burying a taper, but that's a slow and tedious business. The surest and speediest method of inducing death is to get your familiar to wear a pair of the victim's drawers while a certain potent spell is woven. The drawers are then dipped in boiling water mixed with blood, and buried. Death follows within an hour."

Fursey's fancy was for a moment beguiled at the thought of Albert in the unaccustomed garment, but he shook his head sadly.

"I haven't got a pair of his drawers," he admitted reluctantly.

"You're not much help to me," muttered Cuthbert. "There's only one thing for it. We must have a parricide's skull. Go over to Festus Wisenuts and borrow the one he has. Tell him I sent you and he won't hesitate to lend it."

"Is it essential ? " asked Fursey in dismay.

Cuthbert turned on him a glittering eye. " Yes," he answered, " if you want the job done to-night. In the meantime I'll prepare the ingredients, and we can start the spell the moment you return."

Fursey set out reluctantly. Although he had been more than four months resident in the cave in the Knockmealdown Mountains he had not yet seen the erratic landlord whose sub-tenant he was. He dreaded, however, that unless Magnus was quenched to-night, long months might elapse before Cuthbert would again be in the mood to weave the necessary spell. He knew the exact location fo Festus' dwelling and began to hurry his steps, remembering that he had left Cuthbert with almost a full flagon of ale in his fist. It would be a heartbreaking disappointment if on his return he were to find the sorcerer, as was so frequently his wont, lying on the floor of the cave snoring.

As Fursey approached the rocky place where Festus lived, there was a crack of thunder overhead and there fell from the sky suddenly an abundance of white pullets. On striking the ground they shook their tails and scampered away in all directions, watched by Fursey with eyes as round as saucers. He halted in miserable indecision, and it was a long time before he succeeded in forcing himself to go on. As he dragged his feet after him towards the yawning mouth of the cave he saw with relief that there were no sentinel moles. A single green cat sat in the entrance washing her face. She looked up as Fursey approached and contemplated him inquisitively, with one green forepaw suspended in mid-air. Fursey eyed her suspiciously and walked in a wide circle round her. As he did so, he came suddenly on Festus Wisenuts himself in the opening of the cave.

Festus was exactly as Fursey had heard him described, a tall, grim-visaged man with a long, slender, silvery beard, clad in an imposing black gown ornamented with the signs of the zodiac. He did not observe Fursey's approach, being apparently intent on the spell which he was weaving. Fursey watched with horror as the old man in hideous ecstasy

capered round a copper tripod, sprinkling ground glass and
powdered spurge. Beyond the tripod stood a virgin kid
crowned with vervain. Suddenly Festus began whirling himself round in a magical manner. Faster and faster he
whirled, while the air became full of a sound like the plaining
of damned souls. All at once, Festus stopped and tearing
a stone of red enamel from the folds of his flowing black
gown, flung it into the tripod. An inky cloud billowed
forth and enveloped Fursey. Half-blinded, Fursey retreated
backwards until he bumped into the wall of the cave, where
he stood with coal-black hands and face, coughing and rubbing
his smarting eyes.

"Success at last!" came an exultant voice. "I have
created a tawny Moor."

Fursey, his eyes still streaming, stood gaping at Festus.

"Approach," commanded the magician, "and henceforth
do my bidding."

"I assure you, sir, that you're making a mistake," choked
Fursey.

"What?" thundered the magician. "Can it be that,
like the others, you are nought but a false seeming and that
my suffumigation has once more gone awry? That is soon
proved."

He picked up a blade and tested the point with his thumb
while Fursey looked desperately to left and right.

"You have nought to fear," declared Festus. "This is
a new and unused knife. It cannot hurt an elemental essence,
as I judge you to be; but if you are a mere figment, your
natural antagonism to new steel will cause you to disappear,
probably in a thin smoke."

"Such action as you contemplate can only have tragic
consequences," said Fursey faintly. "I'm human. I beg
you to believe me, sir."

"Human! Nonsense!" snapped the magician. "I've
just conjured you into existence. I admit that you're not
my idea of a sooty Moor, but in these hard times we have

to be content with what we can get. Approach until I test your quality."

"Honest to God, sir, I'm human. To stab me would be a great mistake."

"How can you be human?" cried Festus in a sharp, shrieking voice. "You're standing within a circle fortified with mysterious characters of which the import is known to me alone. There was no one within the circle when I began the spell. If you are human and have since crossed it you would have received a shock which would have killed you."

Fursey desperately rubbed some of the black from his face with his sleeve.

"Can't you see I'm not a tawny Moor?" he said imploringly. "I'm Cuthbert's apprentice, and I came to you to borrow a parricide's skull."

Festus stood in the centre of the cave breathing angrily through his nostrils.

"If you're deceiving me," he declared menacingly, "I'll inflict you with violent fits."

"I never deceived anyone in my life," said Fursey pitifully. "I haven't it in my nature. I'm only a simple country boy. I beg you to believe me, sir."

Festus flung his knife suddenly on the ground and turned aside with a gesture of angry impatience. Fursey saw his chance and, darting from the cave, fled down the hillside as if all the powers of darkness were in close pursuit. He did not slacken in his flight until he was once more climbing the rise to Cuthbert's cave. Even then he was afraid to stop to recover his breath, but continued to stagger forward with one hand pressed hard over his heart in an attempt to stay its frenzied beating. As he re-entered the cavern, Cuthbert cocked a lively eye in his direction. Fursey sank on to a stone and breathlessly told his story.

"Never mind," grinned Cuthbert, putting down the empty flagon. "We'll do without the parricide's skull. I've since thought of another way of annihilating your enemy Magnus. We'll damp him out by the antagonism of fire and water."

" I wish you had thought of that before you sent me near Festus," complained Fursey.

"Never mind," said Cuthbert soothingly. "At least it was an experience for you, and your life is the richer for it."

It was fully half-an-hour later before Fursey felt himself capable of rising to his feet preparatory to taking his part in the black ceremony which was trembling in Cuthbert's well-stocked mind. Even then he only dragged himself to his feet because he noticed that his companion was advancing steadily in inebriation, and he feared that if the weaving of the spell were any longer delayed, Cuthbert would become completely incapacitated. As it was, the master sorcerer was rather unsteady on his legs and very talkative. He began by making Fursey kneel down while he crowned him with a wreath of wild parsley and vervain. Then he spent some time rooting in a corner amongst a heap of elf-shots, rowan twigs and holed stones. At last he found what he was looking for, a flint pebble, which he handed to Fursey, instructing him to go outside into the open air and cast it over his left shoulder. When Fursey had done as he was bid, he returned and found Cuthbert standing in the centre of the cave with one hand resting on the rock table. The sorcerer's pallid countenance was overcast by a film of thought.

" It won't work," he said. " I forgot completely that four black cats are required and a bat who has been killed by lightning, as well as the nails from a murderer's coffin ; and that all must be set up at a crossroads on a suicide's grave. Moreover, the proper time is during the waning of the moon. The still hours of the night are best, and it doesn't do at all to select a spot where spectres are addicted to appearing."

" It seems to me," said Fursey impatiently, " that we won't get anything at all done to-night."

" Trust me," said Cuthbert with a drunken hiccup. He

disappeared once more into the recesses of the cave and re-
appeared with a fresh wax taper.

" Over there on the shelf of rock," he said, " you will find
a box containing sticks which I have gathered at midnight
from four points equidistant from a suicide's grave. Yes,
that's it. Now we must kindle a fire."

The sorcerer chatted amiably while Fursey wearily heaped
the sticks in the cave mouth and struck fire from a flint.
Soon the sticks were crackling merrily.

" The fire must be periodically renewed in proportion to
the length of the business," declared Cuthbert. " That will
be your duty. In addition you must cast on the flames
from time to time a handful from this bag of calcined bones,
but not so much as to put out the fire. And above all, don't
let that vervain crown fall off your head."

Fursey re-adjusted his wreath and took the bag which
Cuthbert handed him. Then he squatted on the floor beside
the fire. Cuthbert held the wax taper towards the flames
until it slowly softened in his hands and he was able to knead
it into the rough image of a man.

" Does that look like Magnus ? " he asked.

" Not very," admitted Fursey.

" Not a bad likeness all the same," remarked Cuthbert
blithely, " when one takes into consideration the fact that
I have never seen him. Well, we'll trace his name on it so
that there'll be no mistake." He produced a needle and with
its point carefully lettered the image. " Now," he continued,
" you must concentrate your will power on Magnus. Concentrate on him with every faculty of your being."

Fursey's countenance assumed a dogged, far-away expression as he strove to carry out the sorcerer's instruction.
Cuthbert, in the meantime, retired to the back of the cave
and began to chant an incantation. It was a lonely sound,
and Fursey was glad to see him re-appearing from the shadows
with the image still held in his hand. He advanced slowly
towards the fire, mouthing foul and baleful jargon. Then

he knelt and traced a circle round the fire with his finger. Further muttering and mumbling followed until Fursey began to feel the air thickening and becoming greasy with wickedness.   At last Cuthbert stopped.   He made a few mysterious passes in the air as if he were milking an imaginary cow, then he turned his face to his apprentice.

" Now," he whispered, " I have charged the element. Hand me that needle and keep concentrating on your enemy."

He took the needle from Fursey's trembling hand and, heating it in the fire until it was red-hot, he jabbed it viciously into the stomach of the waxen image.   There was a sudden screech from outside the cave. Fursey and Cuthbert straightened and looked at one another.

" What was that ? " enquired Cuthbert.

" I don't know," replied Fursey.

They listened for a few moments, but the uncouth sound was not repeated.

" An animal I suppose," remarked Cuthbert, and, bending forward once more, he heated the needle in the flame.   When the steel had again reddened he withdrew it and carefully stabbed the image a few times, finally drawing the needle out at its back.   There immediately burst upon their ears a series of the most fearful howlings.   Cuthbert paused and once more looked at Fursey.

" There it is again.   It seems to proceed from the alchemist's cave.   Maybe you ought to go and see what it is. Perchance there is something amiss."

Fursey scrambled to his feet and trotted the intervening fifty paces to their neighbour's dwelling.   When he peered in he was astonished to see the alchemist, his face ashen, lying doubled up on the floor, with his two hands pressed against his stomach.

" What's wrong ? " enquired Fursey.

The alchemist turned on him a pair of bloodshot eyes.

" Sudden, strange, unheralded pains," he gasped.

" Oh, is that all ? " said Fursey, and he turned and trotted back, anxious not to miss any part of the quenching of

Magnus. Cuthbert was busy turning a poker in the fire, bringing it to a red-hot condition.

" Indigestion," he commented when Fursey told him what he had seen. " If it were a mental malady, we could perhaps cure it with soft music ; but there's nothing to be done about indigestion."

He withdrew the glowing poker from the flames, blew on it once, and thrust it into the stomach of the image. From the direction of the alchemist's cave the most pitiful lamenta· tion smote the air. Cuthbert paid no attention ; but, uttering a baleful verse, cast a handful of calcined bone dust on the now mangled image and worked the dust into its stomach with the poker. Suddenly there appeared at the mouth of the cave a distraught figure raving and cursing in a most fearful manner. It was the alchemist, and as Fursey and Cuthbert rose to their feet in astonishment, he fell on his back and rolled about on the ground.

" He appears to be in great sweat and agony," remarked Cuthbert. " Go and see what's wrong with him."

" He's ill all right," replied Fursey, trying to hold the alchemist in the one place by pressing his shoulders against the ground.

" Great nuisance," commented Cuthbert. " Just when we were getting on so well too."

" He won't stay still," shouted Fursey as he struggled with the wallowing alchemist, " and he's vomiting a mar- vellous diversity of objects. Already he has brought up four pieces of coal, a brass mirror and two hilted knives."

" Indeed? " replied Cuthbert admiringly, and he approached to view the phenomenon. The alchemist seemed in evil case : he had broken out in so great a sweat that the very fat seemed to be running off his body. Cuthbert glanced at the wretched man and his face at once fell. He rushed back to the cave and grabbed the waxen image, which he laid down before the fire and which was slowly melting away.

" I shall try to disenchant him," he shouted. " Keep a tight hold on him."

Fursey wrestled manfully, one knee on the alchemist's chest and the other on his forehead.

"He's retching in a most formidable manner," he cried. "He has just brought up a handful of human bones varying greatly in size and character. Do you think they're his ribs?" he added anxiously.

"Keep holding him," shouted Cuthbert. "I'll try to turn off the magic, but I fear that I may be unable to prevent the spell taking its ordained course."

The alchemist's struggles grew less violent as Cuthbert hastily kneaded the wax image into shape again, stamped out the fire and started enunciating the spell backwards. When the disenchanting formulary was at last completed and he emerged again from the cave, his unfortunate victim had ceased to struggle altogether and lay on the ground looking up at the sky with glassy eyes.

"Poor fellow," commented the sorcerer. "You'd better help him to his feet and bring him in for a drink. It's the least we can do for him."

The alchemist allowed Fursey to assist him to rise and seemed to be glad to have someone to hold on to, as he was hardly able to keep his legs under him; but when he realised that he was being led towards Cuthbert's cave his eyes became round with horror. He was incapable of speech, but he resisted Fursey desperately. He broke away at last and made off staggering across country with only one apparent wish, to put as great a distance as possible between himself and the cave of the master sorcerer.

"A strange affair," remarked Fursey; "but to return to matters of greater moment, do you think that we have successfully annihilated Magnus?"

Cuthbert had sobered considerably. "I do not," he replied solemnly, "and I'm not going to try it again."

It was some hours later, when he was turning restlessly on his heather bed, that Fursey realised what had happened. He lay still for a while listening bitterly to Cuthbert's alcoholic snoring; then he turned and buried his face in the pillow.

On the following day the alchemist was found in an exhausted condition in a distant boghole. He was conveyed back to his cave by some of his acquaintance and carefully put to bed. Cuthbert did not fail to do the gentlemanly thing. He made a formal call and offered his apologies. The alchemist listened to his explanation with a wan smile.

During the ensuing weeks Cuthbert avoided the subject of Magnus, and when Fursey at last summoned up courage to ask him to make another attempt, he replied coldly :

"You must learn to do these things for yourself and cease relying on me for everything. When you are a fully qualified sorcerer you can set the matter in train yourself."

"But when will I be fully qualified ? " asked Fursey despairingly. " I seem to be learning nothing."

"You're too impatient," answered Cuthbert. " Why, as yet you're merely a novice. I'll see about having you initiated at the Sabbath on May Eve. In the meantime you should devote yourself to a life of wickedness. As far as I can see, you don't seem to be doing any wickedness at all. A man in your position should perform at least one evil deed every day."

While Fursey was most anxious to do everything proper to a novice in the Black Art, his difficulty was that he couldn't think of anything wicked to do. Such things as uncharitable conversation about his fellow sorcerers or theft of their goods were out of the question, for he was in mortal terror of the possible reaction of his victims. He had a wholesome fear of exciting their malice, having no wish to find himself suddenly transfixed by a spell and perhaps turned into a toad or something equally loathsome. The mathematicians seemed the least dangerous, and he spent a whole day making a circuit of their caves, searching for the smallest and weakest of their number so as to pick a quarrel with him, and then suddenly fall upon, kick and otherwise belabour him. But they all looked so grandfatherly with their flowing white beards that he hadn't the heart to interrupt their calculations ; and so ended by doing nothing. He experienced a certain satisfaction from the fact that he was slowly starving the lugubrious Albert, but he was very much in doubt as to whether or not this would be in his favour when he had to make confession of his wickedness at the forthcoming Sabbath. He had not summoned Albert for many months, and he often wondered whether his familiar had by this time faded away altogether through inanition. He doubted it ; after all, Albert was pure elemental spirit ; and Fursey had a shrewd suspicion that he couldn't fade away, however shadowy and intangible he might become.

One of Fursey's regrets was that he very rarely saw Turko the crystallomancer, who spent all his spare time on angling expeditions. The promised second sitting before the crystal had never materialised. When Fursey met the cow, he had gone over on the following day to tell Turko all about it, but the crystallomancer had manifested no interest whatsoever. Fursey had left the cave very hurt and had not sought his company since. He realised that Turko's was a mercurial disposition, sometimes he was glad to see a visitor, but at other times, especially if he was working, he greeted with a scowl anyone who approached him. A man as shy and tender-hearted as Fursey was grievously hurt by an unfriendly reception, and after experiencing Turko's uncertain temper once or twice, he was unwilling to seek the crystallomancer's company again without positive invitation.

Fursey's main pleasure now was feeding the cow, who had grown so fat that she could hardly walk. She didn't want to walk anyway. She seemed content to spend her life eating the wall of hay with which Fursey kept her provided and reflecting about it afterwards. She even slept standing up with her chin resting on the rampart of hay, while she contentedly inhaled its aromatic sweetness.

Spring came late to the mountains, but padding rains and fitful sunshine brought it at last. The flaming yellow gorse ran in thin columns up and across the hillsides, and birds made their appearance, fluttering from bush to tree. The air was dry and sweet, and the constant breeze heady like new wine. The exiles in the hills emerged from their caves rubbing and scratching their beards, and perambulated blinking in the sunshine and smiling affably at everyone they met.

"It wants but a week until the Witches' Sabbath on May Eve, when you will be formally initiated as a sorcerer and become a recognised member of a coven," said Cuthbert to Fursey. "It would be a good thing for you to become socially acquainted with the more influential members of our community before that date, therefore I have decided to give a party."

Fursey was deeply moved by this evidence of his master's kind interest in his welfare and, as he was himself very fond of human society, he lent a willing hand in the preparations. First the invitations had to be issued. Cuthbert, after careful thought, decided on twenty guests, and writing the invitations on small pieces of sheepskin, he despatched Fursey with them to various caves and holes in the mountain. The invitations indicated that Cuthbert would be "At Home" at sunset on the following Saturday night and that formal dress should be worn. Then master and apprentice hung up their ropes in the cave and set to with a will producing delectable food-stuffs and an adequate supply of drink.

"We have no pottery," said Fursey suddenly. "What will they drink out of?"

"My dear Fursey," smiled Cuthbert, "we are going to do this thing in style. We shall borrow from an old warlock friend of mine his much-prized set of robbers' skulls."

On the morning of the party Fursey took a besom and swept the cave, while Cuthbert nailed a forked branch of wild hazel over the entrance. Then the master sorcerer tastefully arranged a few feathers from the wing of a black cock and some belladonna in a small bowl, which he placed in the centre of the rock table.

"What do you think of that?" he asked, stepping back to admire his handiwork

Fursey, with his head on one side, contemplated the bowl in its circle of robbers' skulls.

" It's very genteel," he replied.

Cuthbert rubbed his meagre hands with satisfaction and allowed his eyes to travel back and forward through the cave.

" All in the best of taste," he remarked. " Now all we have to do is to place the brazier where it won't be knocked over and leave beside it an adequate supply of soothing perfumes for burning."

As the sun shot its last beams from the distant horizon, the first of the guests arrived, a small, swarthy warlock from a cave near at hand.

" An ill-bred fellow," muttered Cuthbert to Fursey ; " he would be the first to arrive. His father was a tradesman, so I suppose we can't expect anything else."

The warlock shook hands with his hosts in a perfunctory manner and, not noticing Cuthbert's slight hauteur, immediately began to talk shop. He drew from his capacious pocket a rope plaited the wrong way and a handful of weasel's teeth, and began to extol their magical properties. Cuthbert escaped from him as the other guests began to arrive and took his stand in the opening of the cave, shaking hands with each newcomer and introducing Fursey to those who did not already know him. Although most of the guests had perforce left their wardrobes behind in their flight from the authorities, they each had made an attempt at formal or festive attire. There was a considerable display of black gowns ornamented with stars, pentagrams and crescents, and many wore wreaths of wild parsley around their necks. Fursey had never seen so many long beards assembled together before, and he blushed when affable notice was taken of him. Most of the guests were wizards, but Turko the crystallomancer had also been invited, as well as a mathematician, a scryer and a clairvoyant. The reciter of poetry was not amongst those asked, as he was not considered good class. There was one gate-crasher, the alchemist, who came wandering in, pretending that he did not know that a party was in progress. He was loud in his offers to retire, but Cuthbert, very tight-lipped, insisted that he should remain. The guests stood around in genteel conversation, wondering when the eating and drinking was going to begin. At last the atmosphere became so charged with impatience that Cuthbert turned to apologise, saying that he was waiting for the arrival of the last guest, Festus Wisenuts.

" I know that no one would wish to sit down to table," he said smilingly, " without our revered landlord."

The company hastily deprecated the very idea of starting supper without Festus, but their eyes continued to wander longingly towards the row of flagons in the corner. At last Festus arrived in a cloak flashing silver and golden stars, the very latest thing in sorcerer's dress. As he paused to speak a few rich man's words to Cuthbert, complaining of his worries and the present state of the bullock market, Fursey withdrew towards the back of the cave and hoped that he would not be seen ; but as they all seated themselves at the table and addressed themselves to the first course, a porridge of eel's meat and winkles, Festus fixed Fursey with a terrible eye. Fursey rose nervously and busied himself in helping to fill the robbers' skulls with ale, mead or metheglin according to each consumer's taste.

" Who's that fellow ? " Festus asked Turko, who was sitting beside him.

" Which fellow ? "

" That small, tubby man with the shock of white hair and the round, moonlike face ? "

" Oh, that's Fursey, Cuthbert's apprentice. A nice fellow, but somewhat thin-minded. Why do you ask ? "

Festus blew hard through his nostrils. " I am doubtful and suspicious of his origin. I don't know that I didn't create him."

The small, swarthy warlock, whose father was a tradesman, was talking loudly with his elbows on the table. To the disgust of everyone present he was spearing his food with the point of a hunting knife and so conveying it to his mouth, instead of eating it in a genteel fashion with his fingers like everyone else.

" I do think Cuthbert should be more selective in whom he invites," muttered the scryer to the mathematician. The mathematician nodded rapidly. He had never seen so much food on a table in his life and he hadn't time to reply in words. Turko raised his skull of ale and bowed smilingly to Fursey, who experienced a rush of happiness at this renewal of their friendship. At the head of the table, Festus Wisenuts was denouncing the government of King Cormac.

" We're taxed out of existence," he complained. " I had to surrender twenty head of cattle this year to meet the cost of the war with Thomond. Politicians are all the same. They hate the rich. They crush us with taxes, but they never think of taxing the poor."

The four of his tenants who were within earshot, nodded their heads sympathetically and waited in respectful silence for his next utterance.

It was a most successful banquet. Cuthbert knew that the secret of a successful party is a never-empty beaker and a judicious mixing of the drinks of those who tend to be abstemious. The good humour increased as course followed course of the most delectable viands, smelts, lampreys, mussels, fowl, edible roots, mountain berries, honeycomb and acorn pie. As the black, yellow and golden liquor flowed in an unending stream, Festus Wisenuts sat back on his lump of rock and tolerantly allowed those near him to speak as well as himself. Esoteric jests with a strong Black Art flavour were bandied from one bearded mouth to another, and even the mathematician was heard to emit a hoarse laugh. The small, swarthy warlock started an intense argument with the scryer about divination from the flight of birds, a subject about which he knew nothing ; but the company's good humour was by now such that they regarded his ill-breeding with greater tolerance. Fursey spent most

of his time swilling mead and laughing at nothing in particular.
He laughed at every sentence addressed to him, thinking it
was a joke ; and he even began to laugh whenever he caught
anyone's eye. Cuthbert, who knew his responsibilities as a
host, drank moderately and unobtrusively watched everything
and everyone. When he judged that his guests were replete
and in sufficiently good humour, he gave the signal to rise.
He then drew everyone's attention to himself by a slight
but penetrating cough. When all eyes were focussed on
him, he gently enunciated a few unrecognised words and
waved his right hand. Immediately all traces of the meal
vanished from the table, leaving the rock bare. Even a
piece of acorn pie which Fursey was stuffing into his mouth
disappeared from between his fingers. After a moment's
initial surprise, there was a burst of polite applause from the
company. Very neat, was the comment, a great labour-
saving device which must ultimately do away altogether
with the necessity for domestic help. The only one who
looked at all anxious was the wizard, who had lent Cuthbert
his unique and valuable set of robbers' skulls ; but Cuthbert
allayed his anxiety a moment later by producing them un-
damaged from the rock shelf and re-filling them for his
guests. The company then disposed itself in comfortable
positions on rocks and boulders, and waited for the next part
of the entertainment.

Cuthbert constituted himself master of ceremonies in virtue
of his position as host, and began by inviting a sprightly,
young wizard to perform a piece of magic. The young man
came forward, blushing shyly. He was a trifle nervous, but
the benevolent interest apparent on every face seemed to
give him courage. He began to speak in cultured tones,
carefully enunciating a spell which he had apparently learnt
by heart for the occasion. Then he made some circles in the
air over the rock table. A water dog came slowly into being,
squatting on its hunkers. It looked around the circle of
approving faces with its wise dog's eyes and carefully wagged
its tail. The young wizard reversed the circles in the air,

spoke some further magical words, and successfully re-conducted the animal into nothingness. There was a round of polite applause and he retired, bowing gracefully.

" Encore ! " shouted the swarthy warlock, who was by this time half drunk.

The nostrils of the assembled wizards quivered slightly in disdain of the vulgarian. Those in his vicinity turned their backs and engaged in learned conversation. Cuthbert's eye had fallen on the alchemist, who had spoken to no one since his arrival uninvited, but had guzzled everything within his reach during supper. He was now sitting in the front row, leering delightedly at the free entertainment.

" Maybe our friend the alchemist will oblige," suggested Cuthbert. " I'm sure we should be all interested to see him manufacturing a few bars of gold."

Every face lit expectantly, but faded again as the alchemist began to protest that most unfortunately he had left all his machinery at home. Cuthbert turned from him, the shadow of a supercilious smile playing about his mouth, and imme-diately fixed his gaze on a tall sorcerer, who, notwithstanding his flowing white beard, retained still the lively and audacious eyes of youth. Cuthbert nodded slightly.

" Our friend Gustavo ? " he queried.

Gustavo came forward at once and laying a phial of mercury on the table, began to conjure by air, fire, water and earth. Then he withdrew a mouse from his sleeve and tossed it into the air. Some weird gestures followed and the enunciation of rugged verses. Then with elaborate ceremony he poured a few drops of mercury from the phial. A cool breeze brushed the faces of those present, there was a sensation of throbbing in the cave, and seven young eagles fell from the ceiling into the alchemist's lap. There was a titter from the wizards as they saw the alchemist's face. The moment that the manifestation was over, the disconcerted alchemist rose and pleaded to be excused. He explained that he had just remem-bered a valuable herbal stew left simmering on the fire in his cave, and that he would really have to return and attend to it. He shook Cuthbert hastily by the hand and thanked him for a very pleasant evening.

When the gate-crasher was gone, Cuthbert called upon the mathematician. The old man explained that his subject was excessively curious ; and spreading some sand on the table, he traced a triangle with his forefinger. Then he prolonged two of the sides and proceeded to demonstrate that the angles at the base of an isosceles triangle are equal. The company listened intently ; and when the demonstration was over, sat back somewhat exhausted by the mental wrestlings involved. Then a mild-featured wizard advanced and laying himself on the ground, called on the spirit of darkness. As the spirit troubled him, he tore and wallowed, and his howls and yells was truly terrific. At length there appeared a weird form which emitted a curious kind of light. It seemed to be some class of serpent with a cock's head, but it vanished again before its nature could be properly studied. As the wizard rose to his feet and dusted himself down, the company applauded politely, but there was a general feeling that the demonstration was not altogether in good taste.

Then the scryer delivered a short discourse on divination by observation of the heavens and the planetary courses, by the interpretation of dreams, from sneezing or from the voices of birds. Having burnt some laurel, he produced a raven from beneath his cloak, and from its croaking divined that there would be an increase in taxation in the ensuing year.

Cuthbert, observing that interest was flagging, sent Fursey around the cave to renew the drinks. The guests brightened somewhat, and Cuthbert called on Turko the Crystallomancer to give a demonstration of his art. The swarthy warlock volunteered himself as subject, and Turko went through the ceremony already familiar to Fursey. But when the clouds in the crystal divided, the warlock became suddenly wan. He announced in trembling tones that all he could see was the leaping flames of a pyre and a circle of grim-visaged clerics standing around it, apparently chanting a requiem. When the vision faded he rose with a white face and made his way unsteadily back to his corner where he remained for a long time taking no apparent interest in the subsequent proceedings and seemingly plunged in gloomy foreboding. The other guests too seemed affected and became very silent. Turko explained in an apologetic whisper to his host that the phenomena in the crystal were altogether outside his control. Cuthbert reassured him in kindly tones that no one would think of blaming him, and with his hand on his shoulder conducted him back to his seat.

Many other interesting demonstrations followed. Severed hands phenomenized, a banshee came into being screaming and sobbing, and a swarm of flies as big as nuts flew in circles about the cave. Each won its meed of applause, and the company had begun to tell one another that this was one of the best parties they had ever attended, when Cuthbert turned to Festus Wisenuts and asked him would he deign to give a demonstration of his magical skill. The landlord signified his willingness and rose rather importantly. He took his stand by the table in the centre and bending down to the floor, drew a circle, which he examined carefully to satisfy himself that there was no break however small in its circumference. From his pompous bearing it was borne in on everyone present that a magical operation of a major character was imminent. With one accord the guests moved in closer to the circle so as to miss nothing.

"Gentlemen," began Festus, "after much labour I have perfected a conjuration for the creation of a tawny Moor. I am now about to bring him into existence."

The wizards shifted in their seats and looked at one another doubtfully, but no one said anything. Festus planted the brazier in the centre of the circle and began to feed the flames with bruised herbs. Then he made a circuit of the circumference breathing to left and right. In spite of their doubts as to his ability, the interest of the onlookers increased as he produced a mole from a bag and immolated it. They watched with bated breath as he began to sway gently from side to side and chant an incantation in a low melodious voice. Before long the air became brittle. The assembled magicians manifested a certain uneasiness when they found themselves suddenly involved in a hollow cloud, but it was not until a thick darkness supervened that they began to whisper to one another nervously. The atmosphere had become foul, portending that something extraordinary was about to happen. Their confidence returned somewhat as the darkness cleared, and Festus was seen to be standing calmly by the brazier heaping on odiferous herbs. As they bent forward so as to watch his every gesture, there was a sudden blinding flash of flame, which burnt the beards off everyone present. So intent, however, were the wizards on not missing any part of the experiment, that at first few noticed their loss.

" That Festus is a real hard ticket," commented Turko to Fursey as he picked up a handful of singed hair from his lap.

" 'Twill be well if nothing worse ensues," replied Fursey nervously.

He had no sooner spoken that it was observed that a hare had appeared from nowhere and was coursing in circles round the interior of the cave. It sprang and tumbled over rocks and other obstacles, its antics watched with the greatest interest by all present.

" There can be no doubt," whispered Turko admiringly as the hare ran along the ceiling, " but that Festus Wisenuts is a remarkable man. Nothing could be more beautiful than his ideas, but I cannot acquit him of being a trifle precious. . ."

Before he could finish his sentence, the hare sprang from the ceiling on to the table in the centre, and there vanished before their eyes. A sickly green light illuminated the cavern, there was a crackle of thunder overhead, and the rafters of the sky began to shake. Outside the rain fell in torrents. All at once there appeared suspended in the air over the heads of the company, two-thirds of an horrific monster vomiting flames. A shower of fire and blood descended. The assembled magicians retreated precipitately to the back of the cave.

It was obvious to everyone that something had gone amiss. One had but to look at the hideous and appalling specimen overhead struggling furiously to bring its missing one-third into existence, while Festus Wisenuts sweated as he strove with magical gesture and conjuration to wipe out the two-thirds which he didn't want.

" It's a kraken," muttered Cuthbert in awe stricken tones.

" I adjure thee, thou old serpent," Festus was shouting, while outside a terrible tempest raged, with lightnings, thunder and fireballs.   The magicians cowered against the back wall, while Festus who to gain greater freedom of movement had stripped off his cloak and stood in a star-spangled singlet and drawers, waved his arms frantically, doing all the magic he knew.   At last he succeeded, and the kraken faded slowly out of existence snorting sparks and bellowing indignantly.   But it was apparent that things had been upset in the world of shadows.   A series of ghastly illusions followed one another with great rapidity, evil-favoured spectra in divers and horrible forms and with much din.   The crouching magicians saw Festus struggling manfully to explode these painful phenomena, but no sooner had he banished one than there was another gnashing its teeth in its predecessor's place.   They followed one another with bewildering rapidity while the quaking sorcerers at the back of the cave shouted frenzied advice.   At length the succession of manifestations slackened. They appeared and vanished more slowly, and began to present an increasingly watery appearance.   The last of them was little more than a shadow, and when Festus banished him, he went with a querulous croak which was scarcely audible. Festus stood leaning against the table completely exhausted, but with the light of victory deep down in his eyes.   He did not enjoy his triumph long ; for as the guests rose from their haunches and ventured a wary return to the centre of the cave, there was a flash of blue light, and when the pungent smoke had cleared, there was nothing left of Festus Wisenuts but a small circle of grease on the floor.   The company stood for a moment staring at the circular patch, then those of them who were wearing hats, removed them reverently. Cuthbert did his best to reanimate the party, but a general gloom prevailed ; and one by one his guests took their leave with silent hand-shaking.

CHAPTER VII

WHEN Fursey awoke on the ensuing morning he found the cave cluttered with magical stores, horrible rarities and incantatory equipment of every description. Cuthbert was standing in the midst haggard but satisfied.

"I have not slept," he explained. "I spent the night travelling back and forward to the cave of our late, lamented friend, Festus Wisenuts. Poor Festus ! He had a great regard for me, and I know that he would have wished me to have his personal effects. Moreover there was much in his cave that was exquisite and dangerous, and it would not do at all if it were to fall into unskilled or unworthy hands. Many of our acquaintance, I regret to say, are of an acquisitive disposition ; and I'm afraid that when they awake this morning and shuffle their thoughts together, there will be a most indecent rush towards the cave of the deceased. How do you feel yourself ? Every time that I looked at you last night, you had a flagon of mead balanced on your nose."

"I feel as if countless men were hitting me on the head with hammers," replied Fursey dolefully. "They strike with extraordinary regularity, and never miss a stroke. In addition, I feel as if there was a forest growing on my tongue."

"Go out and dip your head in the stream, while I snatch a few hours' slumber. We have now an excellent and varied stock of magical armament at our disposal. When you come

back, we'll talk about that love philtre which you have set
your heart on.   You've been a good boy, and it's only fitting
that I should reward you."

Fursey wandered out into the lazy morning sunshine.   Still
only half awake, he made no attempt to assemble his scattered

wits. " Drink is a curse," he kept telling himself as he stumped with loosened knee-joints through the rocks and heather to where a small stream fell like a sheet of shivering glass into the excited pool below. He paused uncertainly on the brink ; then he lay on his stomach and immersed his head in the pool. Oh, the pleasure of cold water on heated, throbbing temples ! He scooped a handful of water on to the back of his neck, and raising himself slightly, let it run down the length of his spine. He shivered deliciously and immersed his head again. Then he lay for a long time on his stomach unwilling to move. It seemed to him that nothing was so excellent as the neighbourhood of water. He listened delightedly to the never-ceasing tinnient roar of the cascade and marvelled at the beauty of the silver drops which oozed from the peaty bank and fell to be lost in the mad, scintillant rush of waters below. " If only man were absent," he said to himself, " how beautiful the world would be ! " When he had drunk his fill, he rolled over on his back letting the points of the rushes tickle and prick his ears and cheeks. Slowly his wayward wits came home to roost.

He had been painfully impressed on the preceding evening by the unexpected dissolution of Festus Wisenuts. It had been perturbing to see a well set-up, haughty gentleman, apparently the master of his fate, suddenly taking his departure without leaving as much as a souvenir ; and as Fursey had crept on his hands and knees into bed, he had drunkenly resolved to abandon the profession of witchcraft before something equally deplorable happened to himself. But now, lying beside the stream in the timid morning sunlight, with an early bird on a nearby bush warbling for his delight, he was inclined to take a less pessimistic view of his situation. For one thing, he had been strangely pleased by Cuthbert's reference to him as ' a boy.' Although it had never occurred to Fursey to worry about the shame of middle-age, there is no man of forty but is gratified at being reminded that he is still only a young fellow. Then, Cuthbert had practically promised to compound a love philtre for him at last. This had been tidings

most grateful to his ear.   He closed his eyes and smiled at the
sky, his thoughts straying away to fasten on the image which
was so frequently in the forefront of his mind, an image, not
of the Maeve who stood in front of the fire stirring something,
or looking worried because she could not lay her hand on the
right pot at the right time, but of a Maeve who turned on him a
gaze that was sweet, kind and understanding, a woman who
spoke but little (and then only when spoken to), but who stood
slender and graceful, her face demurely aglow with love for
her lord and master.

The bird, trilling on the bush, nearly burst himself in a final
bravura *crescendo*, and deciding that he had had enough of it,
fluttered off in search of worms.   Fursey rolled over, gathered
himself together, and getting to his feet, sauntered off among
the rocks and the gorse, whistling blithely to himself. He did
not return to the cave until it was early afternoon.

" So you've untethered the cow," remarked Cuthbert.
" About an hour ago she had her head around the corner
looking in at me."

" Yes," replied Fursey, " I thought that on such a nice
morning she might care to take a walk.   I don't imagine that
there's any danger of her getting herself lost : she'll stay in
the neighbourhood of the food supply."

The master sorcerer was busy at the back of the cave packing
away the last of his new acquisitions.

" Sit down, Fursey," he said, " and give your best attention
to what I have to say."

Fursey seated himself on a lump of rock and fixed his eyes
expectantly on the pallid countenance of his master. Cuthbert
paced for a few moments back and forward, his hands clasped
behind his back and the black lock of hair nodding on his
forehead.   He paused at last and faced his apprentice.

" Are you still desirous of magically influencing this woman
so that she will love you ? "

Fursey nodded vigorously.

" Very well.   I now possess the ingredients for the composition of a most powerful philtre. The process is very concealed and recondite, and the manufacture of the potion will take three days. It is necessary that a man for whom a love philtre is made, should spend three days fasting, fed only on an occasional hair from the magician's head. You must partake of no food other than one of my hairs, which I shall deliver to you on a plate of unblemished whiteness three times a day, at sunrise, at midday and at sunset. Are you prepared to do as I say and abstain from solid food ? "

Fursey nodded again, but with less enthusiasm.

" There are vulgar methods of inducing love in a woman," continued Cuthbert, " such as the placing under her pillow of a few flocks of wool soaked in bat's blood, but such a method would scarcely be appropriate to the case."

" It would not," said Fursey decidedly. " If Magnus saw me approaching her pillow, he'd have my life."

" Exactly," replied the master sorcerer, " therefore a love philtre is best. I shall proceed at once to the manufacture of a bucketful ; and when the process is complete, we shall bottle the mixture. You may take a bottle with you, and you must find some means of introducing the contents into her food. All that will then be necessary, is that you should be the first person on whom her eyes alight, after she has consumed the potion. I shall keep the remaining bottles myself for disposal at a fair price to possible customers harrowed by the pangs of unrequited love."

Fursey arose very satisfied, while Cuthbert placed a bucket in the corner and got immediately to work. During the three days which followed, Fursey lay outside in the open air or on his bed striving not to let his mind dwell on his emptiness. Three times a day Cuthbert plucked a hair from his head in a businesslike manner and laid it on a plate, which he presented to his apprentice. Fursey experienced considerable difficulty in swallowing the hair until he hit on the expedient of washing it down with a flagon of mead. Meanwhile, the cave was murmurous with soft-spoken incantations and perfumed with healthful herbs and incense. The sorcerer had begun by placing, by way of sympathetic magic, two twisted straws at the bottom of the bucket. To these he added an apple shot through and through with magic, and the hearts of two pigeons. He sat by the bucket for hours on end stirring the mixture while he invoked Venus and other beings of loose reputation. Each morning a fresh confection of powders was added, and the resultant paste subjected to heat and reinforced by another atmosphere. On the third afternoon Cuthbert announced that the philtre was ready, and the joyful Fursey sat down to a gargantuan meal while Cuthbert stood alongside in friendly chat.

" We shall leave it to settle for a few days," he said, " and then we shall proceed to bottle it. I advise you to give it to the lady in small doses. It is an exceptionally potent philtre, and it seems to me that your state of love is such that you are likely to succumb to anything in the nature of an impassioned embrace."

" Could we not bottle it now ? " asked Fursey looking longingly at the bucket.

" No," replied Cuthbert shortly. " It must remain exposed to the airs for a few days so that it may acquire a certain consistency. As it is at present, it's too watery. Its only effect would be to make the lady giggly and flirtatious. When we come back from the Sabbath it will be almost ready for use."

" The Sabbath ! " exclaimed Fursey in sudden dismay.

" Yes," replied his master sternly. " To-morrow is May Eve. Surely you haven't forgotten the Witches' Sabbath at which you are to be initiated as a fully-fledged sorcerer."

Fursey had indeed forgotten about the Sabbath, his mind in the previous few days had been so occupied with thoughts of love. He knew nothing of what happened at a Sabbath : he only knew that it was an orgy of wickedness at which no honest man would care to find himself. When he remembered that he was no longer an honest man, but one sworn to wickedness, he groaned aloud.

" Where is it to be held ? " he asked.

"On the enchanted mountain of Slieve Daeane in the territory of Sligo."

"Is that far from here?"

"About a hundred miles from here, in the north."

"And how do we get there, on horseback?"

"No," snapped Cuthbert, "we fly. Here is a box of magical ointment. You will find a broomstick at the back of the cave. You'd better start anointing it."

There was considerable bustle on the hillside the following morning as the wizards made their preparations. Some sat in the sun outside their caves anointing besoms and staves, while others indulged in short trial flights to and fro. Every now and then some elderly sorcerer who was stiff in the joints and out of practice, had to be extricated from a tree. Familiars had been summoned to assist in the preparations, and they ran back and forward between the rocks shouting encouragement and directing their masters to suitable landing grounds. They were a motley crew, foals, toads, rats and giant fowl; and there was one horse-faced creature whom Fursey didn't fancy at all. Cuthbert's own familiar, a monstrous cat called Tibbikins, sidled in and out of the cave leering obscenely at Fursey as he sat in the entrance putting an extra thick coating of ointment on the flimsy broom allotted to him, which seemed to him totally inadequate to bear his weight. The younger wizards gambolled and capered through the air at great speed, essaying every type of dangerous trick, looping the loop, victory rolls and even flying upside down. One fell off in mid-air, but his cloak spread wide as he fell, and he made a successful parachute landing. Fursey, sitting outside the cave, viewed the whole proceedings with misgiving.

The wizards did not begin to take off until dusk. The date of the great quarterly assemblies of witches, Candlemas, May Day, Lammas and Hallowtide, were widely known; and at these times it was usual for the sturdier members of the clergy to prowl about the roads armed with slings and with their pockets full of stones. It was accounted a considerable feat to bring down a flying wizard; and many a cleric, otherwise

undistinguished, owed his advancement to his good marks-
manship. The wilier wizards, therefore, never began their
airy journey until nightfall, and they sought to attain altitude
as soon as possible. Cuthbert stood outside the cave watching
admiringly as his fellows one after another took off and shot
into the air.

" Hurry up," he said impatiently as the wretched Fursey
emerged trailing his broom behind him.

" Supposing I fall off ? " said Fursey miserably.

" If you fall off, it'll serve you right," snapped Cuthbert.
" Throw your leg across and come on."

" The handle is very slippery," complained Fursey, " and
it's not at all broad enough to support my person."

" I'll leave you behind," hissed Cuthbert, " unless you start
at once. It's only a matter of balance. You know what to
do. You have only to wish the broom to take you to Slieve
Daeane."

Fursey threw his leg tremblingly across the broomstick. As
he did so, Cuthbert left the earth and shot into the sky.
Fursey closed his eyes, mentally enunciated the direction, and
was immediately precipitated into the aether. Fursey had
made one long flight before, when he had carried off the
comely Maeve to Britain, but night flying was quite new to
him. It was by no means dark for there was an expansive
moon overhead, and there was little danger of collision with
other sorcerers as there was plenty of room in the sky. He
could see them to left and right of him at varying altitudes,
their black cloaks flapping in the breeze and their faces intent
as they leaned over their broomhandles. Not all rode on
broomsticks ; some favoured stout polished staves, and there
were a couple of warlocks of distinguished appearance on buck
goats. The riding of goats was accounted a difficult art,
because when travelling at high speed one's face was subjected
to the constant whipping of their beards, with consequent
reduction of visibility and increased danger of accident.
Moreover, while they provided a more comfortable seat than
a broomhandle, they were far less manoeuvrable in the air, and

being of an obstinate and wanton disposition, they were quite
capable, if annoyed, of turning their heads and trying to
unseat their masters with their horns.

Fursey had no time to watch the other members of the black
armada, all his thoughts being devoted to the importance of
not falling off. But gradually he acquired confidence. He
had some moments' anxiety when a wild goose joined him and
flew alongside, turning her head from time to time to look at
him and emit a squawk as if challenging him to race her. He
was relieved when she fell behind, as he had feared that she
might either collide with him or attempt to alight on his
broom and so upset his balance. He increased his speed and
soon caught up with Cuthbert, who was flying in a most
peculiar fashion leaning over sideways so as not to miss the
scenery below.

" A lovely night," shouted the master sorcerer above the
rushing of the wind. " Do you see the River Shannon
unwinding like a silver ribbon ? "

Fursey glanced down at the countryside far below. Dimly
he discerned field, forest and lake beneath a blue moonlight
web.

" Isn't it lovely ? " shouted Cuthbert.

" Wonderful," gasped Fursey, " I wish I was down there."

" We must strive to gain altitude," cried Cuthbert. " We
have soon to hop our first line of mountains."

He rose steeply, and the terrified Fursey saw him disappearing into the blue. He followed suit wondering would he ever
feel the kindly earth beneath his feet again. For three long
hours they travelled until Fursey became so stiff with the cold
that even his brain became benumbed. Mountain chain and
lake uncurled themselves below. Again and again Cuthbert
was lost in the darkness ahead when the moon gathered the
straying clouds over her face. Fursey ceased to care whether
Cuthbert was in sight or not. He knew that the broomstick,
throbbing like a live thing between his knees, would bring him
inevitably to his destination. He clung tightly with his
knees and with his benumbed hands, and ceased to think. The

intense cold induced drowsiness, and he must have fallen asleep ; for he was startled suddenly by a hubbub of screams and shouts.   When he opened his eyes he found that he was mounting a hillside at a height of about ten feet from the ground while four lank shepherds and a flock of sheep fled hell-for-leather before him.   The sheep scattered, and the shepherds precipitated themselves over hedges and into bog-holes.   Fursey reared the handle of the broom sharply and rose again into the sky.

" That was a near one," he muttered to himself.   " I very nearly crashed."

He remained awake after that and soon was flying across the stone-studded pass between the Ox and Curlew Mountains. In the half-light he discerned ahead a great lake littered with wooded islands.   The broomstick banked sharply and began to circle slowly as if seeking a landing place.   Fursey peered down and saw below him a sprawling mountain of naked rock. It crept back from the lakeside into the darkness, a tumbled mass of low, rounded heights, glittering grey-blue as the bare schist caught the straggling moonlight.   If ever a mountain looked enchanted, this one did.   Fursey's heart began to hammer as he beheld the great, hungry clefts, bespattered with patches of tawny grass, which ran hither and thither into the interior.   As the broom circled lower and lower his eye caught the flash of water, and beside the water a wide circle of flaming torches.   It was the landing ground.   His broomstick drifted gracefully down into the shadow of the bare cliffs, and he found himself on the earth once more.

" Broomsticks to be parked by the lakeside on the left," shouted a tall man in black.

Fursey's legs were so stiff that he could scarcely stand, but he succeeded in staggering painfully in the direction indicated, and left his broom against a great crag by the water's edge. He gazed fearfully over the small, black lake.   It was a forlorn and isolated spot.   The tarn lay still and dead.   There was none of the usual small movement of wind or water amongst the reeds or grasses at the edge. Fursey turned a white, frightened face and looked up at the bare, blue-grey cliff.

" This way," cried the man in black. " Familiars to be summoned, and stabled under the blasted oak fifty paces to the right."

Fursey moved as in a nightmare. The circle of torches shed little light where he now stood, but he was vaguely aware of shadowy figures moving and tumbling in the background beyond the fatal oaktree. Slowly he wound his way between the rocks. The word ' familiar ' was still vibrating in his mind, and he suddenly realised that he would have to summon Albert. The thought afforded him a moment's relief from his fright. It would be good to see someone he knew, even if it was only Albert. He stopped and whispered the name. The bear's paws appeared resting on a boulder. They were followed slowly by the rusty hair of Albert's person until finally the jaws and smoky red eyes of the familiar came into view.

" Hullo," said Albert.

Fursey gazed at his familiar with amazement. He had expected to see a shadowy figure more like a wisp of smoke than a lusty elemental spirit, but here was a broad, plump Albert with an impertinent smile upon his snout. There was no evidence whatever of many months' starvation.

" You've been up to something," said Fursey indignantly.

Albert did not reply, but looked at his master roguishly.

" I know what you've been doing," said Fursey with a sudden flash of inspiration. " You've been knocking round with vampires. That's what you've been at."

Albert shifted on to one fat ham, raised a leisurely paw and began to scratch his ear, still looking at Fursey over his shoulder with a self-satisfied smile. Before Fursey could express himself as to this seemingly insubordinate conduct, a thin hand was laid on his shoulder.

" Why are you loitering here ? " asked the black-clad attendant. " I said that familiars were to be stabled under the tree."

" Yes, sir," said Fursey hurriedly. " Come on, Albert."

Albert clambered off the rock and ambled up the incline in Fursey's wake. There was a curious collection of freaks sitting in a circle under the oaktree. Monstrous cats were washing their faces, or spreading their formidable claws and smiling at them. There were moles, hares, rats in great abundance, ferrets and greyhounds. The horse-faced familiar was there, and there were several imps with ears like elephants, and a brace of dwarfs. Albert walked into the circle and sat down demurely. Fursey observed Cuthbert's familiar Tibbikins leering at him from a branch overhead. So Cuthbert had arrived. Fursey wondered where he was.

" This way," said the man in black. Fursey followed him with foreboding. They had not far to go, and as they approached the place where the torches threw a fitful glare, Fursey beheld with trepidation a man clothed so as to resemble a giant goat, sitting on a solitary rock in the centre of the circle. He wore a headdress ornamented with curling horns and to his hands were affixed a pair of alarming claws. Around him circled in a wild dance a horde of the most hideous witches and wizards, each one whirling a cat by the tail.

" Why do you hang back ? " asked the attendant suspiciously.

" I'm not hanging back," squeaked Fursey. " What do I have to do ? "

The man in black produced a sack from which there proceeded the most uncouth squawking. He drew out a cat by the tail and handed it to Fursey.

" Join the circle and dance."

A moment later Fursey was on the ground wrestling with the cat.

" What are you doing ? " asked the attendant impatiently. He recaptured the animal and deposited her in the sack once more while Fursey mopped the blood from his face.

" You saw it yourself," he answered indignantly. " She nearly tore the clothes off me. I'm lucky she didn't take out one of my eyes."

" You should hold her taut and keep her at arm's length,"
explained the black attendant. " Thus you will escape
injury. Try it now."

Fursey took the cat's tail gingerly, tightened his grip,
pulled her suddenly from the bag and swung her round his
head.

" That's right," said the attendant, " keep her taut. Go
on now, join the circle."

Fursey capered across the sward trying to imitate the weird
cavorting and prancing of an aged witch-hag in front of him.
Around and around the central figure they danced, while the
goatman looked down on them from his rock throne. Fursey,
as he capered past, desperately whirling the cat over his head,
threw one terrified glance at the sneering mask which covered
the goatman's face. It was an awe-inspiring scene, hideous
with evil and contorted faces appearing and vanishing in the
glare of the torches as the dancers twisted and twirled this way
and that in the ungainly measure. The air was full of a horrid
hubbub, the wild cries of the dancers grating on the screeching
of the cats, who seemed to be all of one mind in disliking the
part which they were called upon to play in the business.
Before Fursey had completed the circle once, he was quite
convinced that he had lost the greater part of his scalp ; but
when on completion of the second circuit, the attendant deftly
took the cat from him, he was amazed to see that there were
only a few handfuls of his hair adhering to her claws. The
sable attendant dropped her quickly back into the sack among
the other cats, where, to judge from the sounds proceeding
therefrom, she continued to express her indignation.

" Supper is served one hundred and fifty paces to the left,"
said the man in black, and Fursey stumbled in the direction
indicated wondering miserably what fresh horror awaited
him. As he approached the table he recognised some of the
wizards from the mountain, but with difficulty. Men whom he
had known as courteous, dapper sorcerers were guzzling
food with an air of frenzy, their beards and hair awry, their
faces scratched and their clothes torn to shreds. Horrific

witches sat at the table screeching stupid feminine jests across at one another, hags whose ugliness was of such a revolting character that one glance at their visages was enough to convince the most passionate man that, when all was said and done, celibacy was best. Fursey had never before found himself in such alarming company. On his arrival at the table a one-eyed wizard whose hair hung about his shoulders like a wreath of snakes, raised a shout : " The meat course has arrived ! " It would not have surprised Fursey to have found himself suddenly seized and dragged on to the table, but his momentary panic was allayed when an incredible hag made room for him beside her with a kindly " Don't be frightened, lovey ". He seated himself smiling wanly.

Fursey was a man who enjoyed food, and his eyes nearly fell from his head when he saw what he was expected to eat. There were huge dishes on the table loaded with strings of entrails, carrion and putrid garbage. The black-clad attendant had set up a brazier beside the table, and when anyone seemed diffident about consumption of the food placed before him, he was immediately threatened with red-hot iron plates. To convince the delinquent that he was in earnest, the attendant directed attention to a leg-crushing machine in the background. Fursey ate with difficulty as the hag beside him had apparently taken a fancy to him and retained one of his hands in her lank claw all during the meal. Between courses she made love to him cackling girlishly. Fursey wished earnestly that he was elsewhere, as smiling politely, he gently repulsed her advances with an affectation of boyish shyness. He could see no sign of Cuthbert anywhere.

When at long last the unappetising meal was over, he managed to slip away from the amorous witch. She followed him a little way cooing seductively, but her chase of him was considerably slowed down by the necessity she was under of proceeding with the aid of two sticks on account of a fallen hip. No sooner had he removed himself to a safe distance than he found the ubiquitous black attendant standing at his elbow.

" You do not act wisely in rejecting the advances of Arabella," he said meaningly. " She is a most powerful witch, and she could easily deprive you of your life by shooting a flint arrowhead from the nail of her thumb."

Fursey took one look at the appalling specimen of womanhood in his rear.

" I prefer death," he said simply.

The attendant shrugged his shoulders and turned away.

" Take your places for the homage," he announced.

They lined up, and one by one paid homage to the great goatman, still sitting seemingly indifferent and immovable on his great stone seat. Fursey, when his turn came, did as the others : he went on his knees, bowed his head to the earth and swore allegiance. When this ceremony was over, there seemed to be a pause in the proceedings, and Fursey had time to look about him. There appeared to be about a hundred people present. It was hard to estimate the number as there was an incessant scurrying to and fro of shadowy figures in and out of the wavering light shed by the torches. He knew that a coven consisted ordinarily of thirteen persons, and he guessed that there were nine or ten covens present, perhaps not all in full force. Covens were rarely complete on such occasions, due to illness, some untoward accident such as had befallen Festus Wisenuts, or the activity of the authorities in sending the less agile wizards up in smoke. If the sorcerers and witches would only have remained still for a few moments, Fursey would have essayed a count, if only to keep his mind from occupying itself wholly with his fears, but the lakeside was a veritable bedlam : men and women skipped and tumbled with no apparent object, distorted faces emerged suddenly from the darkness and as quickly disappeared, witches sprang from rock to rock their faces intent, while others rolled in the heather, and a coven from the County Cork paraded back and forward walking on their hands. The screaming and the shouting united into a clamorous din, as if a hundred cats were being trodden on simultaneously. Several sorcerers, their eyes wide with excitement, spoke loudly to Fursey, boasting of their malice and the extent of their wickedness. Before he could answer they had run off to find other listeners. A torch in his vicinity spat a shower of sparks, and in the sudden glare he detected a small man leaning dejectedly against a rock. He looked reasonably harmless, so Fursey moved over in his direction.

"Very fine Sabbath," remarked Fursey ingratiatingly.

The stranger raised a pair of melancholy eyes.

"Yes, but I'm in no mood to enjoy it."

"Dear me," said Fursey, "that's too bad."

"Domestic trouble," sighed the little man. "In the course of an experiment this afternoon I accidently exploded the wife. She was a very good cook."

"This world is a vale of tears," said Fursey shaking his head sympathetically. "I've a little worry on my mind myself."

"Is that so? Maybe I could be of help."

"Well, as yet I'm merely an apprentice, but to-night I'm to be initiated as a fully-fledged sorcerer. I'm completely in the dark about the ceremony of initiation. Could you tell me whether it involves much pain or discomfort?"

"Not much," answered his companion. "You will be required to take your stand before the goat-man and place one hand upon your pate and the other on the sole of your left foot, and you must vow all between, that is your whole person, to his service. You will be required to swear complete obedience to the master of your coven and renounce the Christian and all other faiths. He will initiate you by baptising you with a new name, perhaps your own name spelt backwards, and by pricking you twice with a needle on the wrist. It is usual for him also to place his seal on the candidate by giving him a sharp nip on some part of his body. The resultant bruise will never disappear, and the spot will ever afterwards be insensitive to pain. The ceremony will probably conclude with a sermon by the goat-man on Evil's age-long struggle for empire."

" It could be worse," said Fursey with a sigh of relief.

" I beg your pardon," replied the wizard suspiciously.

" What I mean," said Fursey hastily, " is that while I'm quite prepared to surrender life or limb in the service of Evil, I'm naturally glad that neither is yet demanded of me."

" Hm ! You know, of course, that if the candidate is adjudged unworthy of the honour to which he aspires, he is simply thrown into the lake."

" Thrown into the lake ? "

" Yes, it removes all traces, and there are no embarrassing questions afterwards. The lake by which we are standing, is the terrible Lough Dagea. Anything which breaks its waters, is never seen again."

Fursey smiled nervously and moved nonchalantly a pace or two, so as to place his companion between himself and the brink.

" Why has this long pause occurred in the ceremonies of the night ? " he asked by way of changing the subject.

" A pause has not occurred. The goat-man is making a circuit of the revellers requiring of each a recital of his wicked deeds. In any case in which the amount of evil done since the last Sabbath, is not satisfactory, he scourges the delinquent with a wire whip. I observe that he's coming in your direction now."

Fursey started and moved back against a crag as he saw the great horned figure striding towards him. The melancholy wizard slipped away unobtrusively and was lost in the darkness. Fursey shook in every limb as one part of his mind remembered the proximity of the fatal lake, and the other part strove to assemble his little share of wit so as to confront the danger. The goat-man had taken his stand some paces distant. He was of normal height, but his goat mask and formidable horns conferred on him a terrible majesty. He held in his hand a most efficient-looking whip of woven wire, with which he carelessly flicked the tips off the heather. Fursey was dimly aware of a semi-circle of white faces, as other sorcerers and witches pressed around watching breathlessly.

" State your name and rank."

" Fursey, apprentice sorcerer."

" Your address ? "

" Knockmealdown Mountains."

" To what extent have you established your claim to be one of this noble company ? "

" I'm a man given to all manner of wickedness, sir."

" For example ? "

" Church burning, calumny, detraction, uncharitable conversation, envy of my betters, sloth, gluttony, drunkenness and the telling of lies."

" What churches have you burnt ? "

" The whole monastery of Clonmacnoise."

" You're a liar," said the goat-man coldly. " It was Vikings who burnt Clonmacnoise. All you did was to run round making a fool of yourself."

" That just goes to prove," gasped Fursey, " that as a teller of lies I'm at the top of the profession. I can't myself believe a single word I say."

The goat-man raised his whip alarmingly and cut a gorse bush in two with a sudden flick of his wrist.

" Why have you so scandalously denied your familiar his proper meed of blood from your person ? "

Fursey's limbs had turned to water, and he would certainly have fallen only for the rock against which his back was pressed. The sweat coursed down his face as he strove desperately to think of an answer, but relief came from an unexpected quarter. The dark-robed attendant stepped suddenly into the circle.

" I have viewed the familiar in question," he said. " He's certainly not suffering from malnutrition. In fact, he presents every appearance of being not only well-fed, but even pampered. Our information on that point must have been unreliable, my lord."

The goat-man paused uncertainly. Fursey passed his tongue over his lips and strove desperately to bring his knocking knees under control. When the goat-man had first spoken, Fursey had recognised the voice of Cuthbert, but with the goat mask Cuthbert seemed to have assumed another personality. Fursey felt that he had no reason to expect mercy on account of mere acquaintance.

" What's that I see on your face ? " demanded the horned figure. " Brackish tears ? "

There was a gasp of horror from the onlookers.

" Yes," squeaked Fursey with a break in his voice.

" What has caused them ? " thundered the goat-man.

" Fright," whimpered Fursey.

" It's a well-authenticated fact," announced the goat-man in a terrible voice, " that no witch or wizard can weep. You're not all that you would have us believe," and raising his whip he cut at Fursey. Fursey yelled and tried to escape, but there was no getting out of the circle. He capered madly as the whip was dexterously wielded, inflicting on him many a sore stroke. His howls were truly terrific, and when the goat-man desisted, it was not through any sympathy for his victim, but because of a sudden counter-clamour which attracted general attention. All hell seemed to have broken loose under the blasted oaktree. One could see, even in the dim light, fur and feathers flying in all directions, while yelping and gruff barks pierced the night. With one accord the company, led by the goat-man, hurried towards the tree, while Fursey aching in every limb scrambled after them, making a circuit however, so as to lose himself somewhere in the crowd. When he reached the vicinity of the oaktree, a remarkable sight met his eyes. The monstrous cat stood against the bole, her back arched, spitting fire. Albert was tumbling on the ground fighting with the horse-faced familiar, while the two dwarfs clung to his back kicking him wherever they could. Smaller familiars scurried back and forward barking shrilly. A hare and a mole were up on their hind-legs squaring up to one another, while rats ran in and out of the fighting, nipping everyone they encountered.

" This is unprecedented," shouted the goat-man. " Stop it at once, the whole of you."

There was an immediate lull in the fighting. Albert made use of the unexpected armistice to turn suddenly and aim a swipe at one of the dwarfs, knocking him sideways. In a moment they were all at it again. Various witches and wizards now intervened, ordering their respective familiars to vanish according as they became involved, until at length only Albert remained, squatting on a carpet of fur and broken claws. He swung his eyes intently left and right watching for the possible re-appearance of an enemy.

" Whose is this ungainly monster ? " demanded the goat-man, choking with rage.

" Fursey's," cried a dozen voices.

" Where's Fursey ? "

For a few moments there was silence. Then a thin voice came quavering from the fringe of the crowd.

" I'm here, sir."

" Come forward and take possession of this wild beast of yours."

The crowd parted, and Fursey crept halteringly through the passage.

" Someone will pay for this sacrilegious disturbance of our Sabbath," said the goat-man grimly.

" Yes, sir," said Fursey.

By the goat-man's directions the other familiars were summoned by their masters. The air trembled and condensed as they came one by one into existence. Albert, his head leaning forward from his bull-neck, fixed his red, smoky eyes threateningly on one of the dwarfs, who after the manner of small men, had his tongue out and was making faces at him.

" Keep them separated," commanded the goat-man. " Now, who began it ? "

" He did," squalled the brindled cat glaring balefully at Albert.

" Yes, it was Albert," cried a dozen of the familiars.

" What did he do ? "

" Making nasty remarks about everyone," shrilled the cat.
" Putting on superior airs ; looking for fight, that's what he
was. He trod on one of the dwarfs."

There was a chorus of assent. Albert had assumed a hang-
dog look. " It was an accident," he said sheepishly .

" No accident," screamed the horse-faced familiar. " He's
been elbowing us all and goading us ever since he arrived."

" He said his bear's claws were superior to mine,"snarled the
cat.

" Feminine envy," muttered Albert.

" Hold your tongue," snapped the goat-man. " Fursey,
order this monster of yours to disappear."

Fursey did as he was bid.

" Now," proclaimed the goat-man, " you may get your
broomstick and take yourself home. You're expelled from
the Sabbath. A man who cannot keep his familiar under
control, cannot hope to be initiated as a fully-fledged sorcerer."

There was a murmur of approval. Fursey went without a
word. He found his broom beside the lake where he had left
it, and in a few minutes he was winging his way across the mountain. As he flew southwards his emotions were of a very
mixed character. He was relieved to be away from such an
abominable spot, and he was strangely pleased that he had
escaped initiation. It left him as he was before, a sort of
half-sorcerer. He did not doubt but that Albert's behaviour
had been deliberate, and that its object had been to embarrass
him. Had not his familiar threatened to thwart and annoy
him ? But it might well be that Albert had unsuspectingly
done him a very good service. Fursey was sick of the company
of magicians, which seemed to him to be not only unpleasant,
but in the highest degree dangerous. He was tempted to
burn the broom handle in another direction and wing his way
to some territory where he was unknown, but he remembered
the love philtre now ready for use. At all costs he must secure
possession of it. Then, if Cuthbert permitted him to do so,
he would take his departure. " I must really get rid of Albert,"
he told himself, " if I don't, he'll get me into serious trouble."

When he alighted on the hillside before the cave, the light was creeping into the sky in the east, and in their nests the birds were stirring their wings. As he entered the cave the first thing he saw was the broad buttocks and twitching tail of the cow.

" What are you doing here ? " he asked, giving her an affectionate slap on the flank.

The cow raised her head and swung it around to look at him. Then she turned away and buried her muzzle once more in the bucket which contained the love potion. There was a loud, sucking noise.

" Come away," shouted Fursey, realising suddenly what was happening ; but by the time he had dashed to her head and snatched away the bucket, it was empty. For a moment he felt like striking her, but a wave of misery swept away his anger, and walking to a rock in the cave mouth, he sat down in bitter despondency. He was recalled to present events by a gentle nuzzling on the shoulder. He looked up. The cow was beside him. She extended her broad, rough tongue and licked his ear. He sprang to his feet. There could be no doubt about it : the light in her eye was an amorous one.

Two hours later, as the returning sorcerers circled the hillside on their broomsticks, they marvelled exceedingly to see Fursey scuttling in and out among the rocks with a cow loping close behind him. From time to time he turned and beat her about the head with an empty bucket ; but when he resumed his flight, she followed once more at a steady trot, mooing pathetically.

When Cuthbert returned to the cave he had shed altogether his character as goat-man. He was once more the friendly, though sometimes snappish, master whom Fursey had previously known. When he was told of the loss of the philtre, he gave vent to a sudden outburst of rage, but he recovered quickly and acted towards Fursey much as he had acted before. Fursey noticed however that the line of his mouth was more tightly drawn, as if his patience was almost exhausted. He helped to secure the cow and tie her once more in her stall, but her heartbroken mooing got on his nerves to such an extent that after two days he obtained Fursey's consent to destroy her.

A deep depression settled on Fursey. He was unwilling to leave the hillside as he still nourished a hope that Cuthbert might yet consent to help him either in the matter of removing Magnus or by preparing another philtre, but he felt himself to be in such disgrace that he did not dare to raise either matter with his master. He knew too that his stock stood very low on the mountain. The other wizards when they passed him on the hillside, averted their heads and plainly indicated that they were not on speaking terms with him. It was a week before Cuthbert summoned him to the back of the cave and spoke to him about his affairs.

" I hear," began the sorcerer smoothly, " that you did not show up at all well at the Sabbath. It's evident that you will never graduate as a wizard."

Fursey nodded his head in sorrowful assent.

" You will really have to go away," declared Cuthbert with a sudden burst of impatience. " You were useful to me as a servant, but the sight of your doleful countenance is having a most depressing effect upon me ; and if I have to endure it much longer, it will certainly drive me back to drink. Nor can I risk the spoiling of important experiments through your incompetence. That love philtre would still be here only for that cow you had mooching around the place."

" I'll go," replied Fursey, " but first I have three requests to make."

" Three ! " shouted Cuthbert. " I must say that I admire your audacity."

" Yes," replied Fursey determinedly, " first I want you to help me to rid myself of Albert."

Cuthbert had looked as if he was going to fly into an uncontrollable rage, but when Albert was mentioned, his countenance underwent a sudden change.

" That's the first wise thing I've ever heard you say," he
conceded. " It's high time that a stop was put to that
fellow's proceedings. We'll auction him off this evening."

" I give you a present of him," replied Fursey. " It will be
a little acknowledgement of my debt to you. You auction
him and keep the proceeds."

Cuthbert looked pleased. " Thank you," he said with a
courteous bow. " I've no doubt but that we shall find a
purchaser. A spare familiar is always useful."

" All I want," said Fursey heavily, " is to be assured that I
shall never see his ugly face again. I want to be entirely rid
of him."

" You're right," said the sorcerer. " It's obvious that you
don't know how to control a familiar, and a desperate character
like Albert is apt to get a man into trouble."

" I have two other requests."

" What are they ? " asked Cuthbert shortly.

" I want you to annihilate Magnus and win for me the love
of his beautiful spouse."

Cuthbert sprang from his seat and raged up and down the
cavern.

" We're back where we were when you came here last
October," he stormed. " Why I have neglected to turn you
into a toad long since, is something which I shall never be
able to explain to myself."

" Satan would have wished you to help me," replied Fursey
quietly.

Cuthbert paused at the sound of that great name.

" The fact that you are well-connected," he said acidly,
" doesn't justify you in imposing on everyone you meet. I
refuse absolutely to do any more magic on your behalf. I
shall not manufacture one drop of love potion while you are
still within the territory. As for Magnus—well, I'll do this
much for you : I'll give you some advice before you depart
from here to-morrow."

Albert was auctioned that evening. Fursey summoned him,
and he squatted on the central table, his snout wreathed in a

self-satisfied smile. There was a good attendance, and the wizards whispered to one another and nodded their heads gravely as they felt his hocks and his haunches, and examined his teeth. The bidding was brisk and rose quickly from a set of moles' paws to a wraith in an enchanted bottle. There the bidding ceased, and Albert was knocked down to an earnest, young wizard who was known to be a coming man. Fursey made a declaration solemnly handing over the familiar; and at his new master's bidding, Albert gracefully disappeared with a smug smile upon his face.

On the following morning Fursey coiled his rope and slung it over his shoulder. As he stood in the mouth of the cave ready to depart, he looked down sorrowfully at his tattered clothes and broken shoes.

"Will you not even give me a small phial of water," he asked, "to pour on Magnus' doorstep, so that by its latent magic, he may fall grievously and haply kill himself?"

"I'm determined to give you nothing of a magical nature," replied Cuthbert firmly. "I'm convinced that if I did, you would inevitably misuse it and injure yourself. Your wit is too thin. I advise you strongly never to attempt to practise the fatal arts. You're a man whose brain moves round and rattles in his head. I'm persuaded that dire effects will attend any magical operation in which you have a hand."

Fursey looked at him glumly. "You promised me advice. How will I proceed to destroy my enemy and win the affections of Maeve?"

"You must overcome Magnus by natural means."

"How?"

"You must challenge him to fight."

"But," protested Fursey, "he's a very considerable muscle-man."

"I'm not sending you away empty-handed. I've composed a letter for you. When you come within sight of Magnus' dwelling, pause in your travels and take up your abode in some convenient thicket. Then send this letter to him by trusty messenger."

" What's written in the letter ? "

Cuthbert unrolled a small parchment and read :

" Deliver up at once, perverse monster, the woman of whom you have robbed me, before my just rage brings about your deserved destruction.

Your implacable enemy,
Fursey.

If he has any manhood at all, he will react violently to such a challenge, and will come forth at once to meet you."

" And suppose he kills me ? "

" Why will you always insist on looking on the dark side of things ? " asked Cuthbert impatiently. " Even if he does, your troubles will then be over. But there's no need for you to let yourself be killed. All you have to do is exchange a few lusty knocks with him, and then when he's not looking, stab him with a bodkin."

Fursey looked gloomily at the piece of parchment and stowed it away in his pocket.

" Here is a poisoned bodkin. It's in a sheath, so that you won't kill yourself with it. A single scratch will encompass Magnus' death. Now are you satisfied ? "

" It's all very fine to talk," whimpered Fursey as he took the bodkin, " but this Magnus is a man of the most unexampled fierceness. He's a most savage character as well as being a regular Hercules. It's in the highest degree unlikely that I'll survive his initial blow."

" Then why let him have the first blow ? " said the exasperated Cuthbert. " All you have to do is get in the first buffet yourself ; and when he's on the ground, you can finish him off with the poisoned bodkin."

" I see," said Fursey.

" When he's slain," continued Cuthbert, " keep your head about you : don't fall into a swoon through exceeding joy. Remember you still have to win the woman."

" Could you not give me a small bit of magic," pleaded Fursey, " just enough to take away his bodily strength before I fight him."

" No," snapped Cuthbert, " it concerns my honour. If I gave you anything magical, you would surely transfix yourself. Goodbye now, and don't come back."

" Goodbye," said Fursey, and he turned and made his way slowly down the hillside towards the plains and the world of men.

CHAPTER VIII

FURSEY made his way along the shoulder of the mountain, knowing that on the windswept ridge the ground would be dry and firm underfoot. He continued as far as he could on the higher levels, descending slowly in a sweeping curve towards the plain. When at last a direct descent of the mountain flank became necessary, he picked his way carefully round the patches of soggy grassland, often turning to retrace his steps so as to avoid the treacherous peat swamps which lay across his path. He had a wholesome fear of the sodden bogs, so deceptively covered with fine grass. He knew that a single false step in those areas would result in a sucking sound and his total disappearance. But he made his way down the hillside without mishap, and in the early afternoon came to a long line of hedge, bright with hawthorn blossoms. He soon found a gap and clambered through into a bed of nettles. A moment later he was on the road. He seated himself on the bank amid the daisies and the buttercups, and sighed with satisfaction. It was good to have left the mystery-riddled mountains behind and to feel one's feet on the solid highway once more. He sat for a long time in quiet contentment. It was a still, bright afternoon. The air was soaked through and through with sunshine. It oozed like honey from a comb, spreading itself on the thick, green tangle of the hedgerows, and slipping down to surround and

embrace the dandelions and the primroses and all the other white and yellow flowers which brightened the borders of the road.   He glanced down the highway and over the plain.   As

far as his eye could see, the countryside was alight with the
graceful gaiety of May. Some trees sported buds which
resembled brussels sprouts, the chestnuts were laden with
their usual white pyramids : indeed, every tree had something
fresh to show, for over all lay the delicate, green web of spring.
He smiled, rubbed his chin and began to plot his course.

It was not difficult. He did not know the exact site of
Magnus' dwelling, but he believed it to be in the vicinity of
The Gap, the great pass separating the Knockmealdown
Mountains from the neighbouring range. All that he had to
do, was to follow the road until he had made a half-circuit of
the mountains : probably a day's travelling would bring him
to his objective. He was so pleased at having escaped
unscathed from sorcerers' territory that he did not worry as to
how he should encompass Magnus' dissolution and win the
affection of Maeve. The sheathed bodkin in his pocket gave
him confidence, and he determined not to occupy his mind
with future events until it was necessary for him to do so. He
sat for a long time in dreamy vacancy, dimly aware of the
minute sounds about him, the careful stirring of a bird in the
hedge and the slight rustle of the long grasses as they captured
a straying wind, held it for a moment and let it go. He lacked
the will to proceed further, and a long time elapsed before he
rose to his feet, hitched his rope over his shoulder and made
his way down the road. With the renewal of physical activity
his mental lethargy departed, and soon he was whistling
blithely. After the manifold dangers through which he had
passed, the possibility of being recognised, denounced and
burnt as a sorcerer scarcely bothered him. It was nearly
a year since he had been in the hands of the authorities at
Cashel, and he felt that the passage of time must have made him
less readily recognisable—at least, he would not still be in the
forefront of men's minds. So he went on his way, passing
without fear the mud and wickerwork cottages before which
naked children played and tumbled, while dogs ran round
importantly. He even shouted a greeting to the women
sitting in the doorways polishing cheap ornaments of bone

and bronze. He looked with affection on the evidences of human activity, the carefully woven thorn fence enclosing the field, the wooden plank across the stream, and the heaped peat won from a neighbouring bog. He stopped for a while to watch from a distance a group of men by the side of a lake busy at work on the framework on a coracle, bending the strong wattles and covering them with hide. Evening came as he proceeded, and with it came rustling showers of rain. Mists drifted across the plain, parting from time to time to let the weakened evening sunlight pick out some scene of faery-land unreality. The road was stony, and he began to become very footsore. He halted at sunset, and seated himself in the shelter of the ditch. His rope quickly procured him his supper, and he began to eat with relish. He had finished his meal and had a beaker balanced on his nose draining the dregs of the ale when he heard a lonely sound some distance down the road. A quavering voice was raised in lamentation, and the words came clearly to his ears :

" Woe to Fursey ! "

He dropped the beaker and sat paralysed. He listened to the pad of approaching footsteps, and heard the voice once more. It began with a series of staccato groans, then rose in a melancholy wail until it attained a high pitch, where it remained.

" Woe to Fursey ! " it announced. " There is a chattering in the sky, and when I listen I hear voices. I hear voices in the earth and voices in the winds. And all the voices that I hear, have but the one burden : ' Woe to Fursey ! ' "

Fursey blinked incredulously, then he dropped on his hands and knees and, crawling forward a couple of paces, raised his head over the edge of the ditch. He peered cautiously in the direction from which these alarming words proceeded. A strange-looking character in fluttering rags was approaching with a lengthy stride down the centre of the road. His head was bare, and he was plentifully supplied with grizzled whiskers. As he came by Fursey's hiding place, he raised a skinny arm high over his head and gave vent to another moan.

" Woe to Fursey ! " he repeated in heartbroken tones.

As he passed by and continued down the road, Fursey watched him from over the edge of the ditch like a rabbit looking out of a burrow. When he had gone some distance, Fursey scrambled to his feet and ran down the road after him. The stranger proceeded with a long, springy stride, but Fursey caught up before long and patiently trotted alongside. It was some minutes before the old gentleman noticed his presence. When he did become aware of the small man running beside him, anxiously attempting to attract his attention, he halted and looked at Fursey enquiringly. Although the stranger was big-framed, he was meagre and bony. His watery blue eyes were benevolent, but they wandered across Fursey's face without apparent interest.

" Have you come that I may hollow out a grave for you ? " he asked.

" I have not," answered Fursey, more alarmed than ever. " What put that thought into your head ? "

" I beg your pardon," replied the stranger. " I am a Christian man, and one of the corporal works of mercy in which I habitually engage, is the burial of the dead. I thought for a moment that you were a client."

" I'm very far from dead," retorted Fursey. " I merely wish to enquire what you were shouting as you came along the road."

" I have no recollection."

" But it was only just now. You were calling out ' Woe to Fursey ' or words to that effect."

" Was I ? The name Fursey is quite unknown to me. I must have been prophesying. No doubt I was in a state of angelic possession."

" Angelic possession ? "

" I'm a rustic prophet," explained the stranger mildly. " I'm frequently moved to prophecy, particularly on Fridays and Saturdays."

" Do you think that you'll feel moved any more this evening, sir ? "

" I imagine that it's worn off now, but I can't say for certain. Why ? "

" Because my name is Fursey."

" Indeed. That's very interesting. Well, I mustn't detain you any longer. Good evening to you."

" I'm accompanying you," declared Fursey determinedly.

" Why ? "

" In the hope of hearing something more. After all, it's very alarming to hear a gentleman of your apparent piety shouting one's name on the breeze and coupling it with woe and destruction."

The old man meditated for a moment. " That never occurred to me before," he said at last. " I suppose that it may well be alarming if one has something on one's conscience. I'm sorry if I distressed you. The best thing you can do, is repent of whatever you have to repent of. Then you'll be safe."

" I can't repent just yet," Fursey blurted out. " I've an important murder on hands.

" Oh, dear me," said the rustic prophet in shocked tones, " you shouldn't do that. Don't you know it's wrong ? "

Fursey stirred uncomfortably.   " I can't help it," he faltered. " A murder is necessary to enable me to put my affairs in order. After that I expect to be happily married. Maybe I'll repent when that joyful event has taken place."

The old man shook his head disapprovingly. " I'm afraid that you are in evil case, and stand sorely in need of spiritual treatment. I'll stay with you for a little while. It may be that the spirit of prophecy will seize on me again, though I really think that it's gone for the night."

He seated himself on a bank by the wayside and allowed his pale blue eyes to travel over Fursey's person. Fursey stood stock still in front of him until the scrutiny was complete.

" Your shoes are sadly broken," remarked the prophet at last. " Oblige me by accepting mine."

" Oh no," protested Fursey, " I can't do that."

The old man removed his sandals without a word and laid them at Fursey's feet.

" Please do not deprive me of the merit I shall gain in Heaven by my charitable act," he pleaded.

Fursey stared at him, not knowing what to say. In the face of such insistence it seemed discourteous to refuse. He seated himself on the bank and taking off his broken shoes, shamefacedly assumed the stranger's footwear.

" You are most generous," he muttered.

" You have little understanding," replied the prophet mildly. " I am in fact most selfish. I have merely exchanged the perishable goods of this world for a sure reward in the next. To be unselfish in these matters one would have to give without hope of recompense. Only those who do not believe in an after-life, can be truly unselfish."

" Do you always act like this ? "

" Certainly. I have been addicted to the practice of charity ever since as a small boy I learnt that whatever I gave away, would be repaid to me in the next world a thousandfold. Only last week a wandering bandit held me up at the sword's point and robbed me of my cloak. I ran beside him for an hour-and-a-half offering him my drawers as well. He persisted in refusing them, saying that he had a pair already. At length in exasperation he turned on me and beat me sorely."

" I'm not surprised," commented Fursey. " Why do you do these things ? "

" Because I am a Christian."

" I beg your pardon, sir, but is it not the case that everyone in this country is a Christian, barring those who have adopted the professions of banditry and sorcery ? "

" No," replied the stranger. " I've walked the roads of this country for well-nigh fifty years doing good, but I've never met a Christian man other than myself."

" I've a suspicion that it's not healthy to be unique. One of these days the authorities will burn you."

The prophet shrugged his shoulders. "What's that to me? The stake would be merely the antechamber to Heaven, where a vast reward awaits me."

Fursey pondered in silence. It seemed to him that for the first time in his life he had met a really good man, and moreover a man who might be prepared to help him.

"Sir," he said at length, "if you wish to do good, you have here a Heaven-sent opportunity. You see before you a man whose misfortunes and miseries are such, that they have become an everyday part of his existence."

The rustic prophet rubbed his hands with gratification.

"Tell me more," he said. "Anything that I can do to relieve you of your misfortunes and make them my own, will fill me with the greatest satisfaction. Hold nothing back. I am afire with Christian charity."

Fursey hesitated for some moments wondering how he would begin his marvellous tale. At length, encouraged by the eager old man, he commenced in a faltering voice to relate his story. He told of his years of happy ignorance as a laybrother in the monastery of Clonmacnoise, and of how a year previously the forces of Hell had invaded the holy settlement and made his cell their headquarters, from which to sally forth to tempt the good monks from their duty. He related how every wicked wile had failed. The obstinate sanctity of the monks had been such that showers of gold, offers of kingdom, and visions of the most lively and engaging females had left them unmoved, but the discipline and good order of the monastery had been sadly disturbed; and to rid the settlement of its unwelcome visitants, it had been deemed necessary to expel Fursey, to whose person the devils had particularly attached themselves. The rustic prophet listened round-eyed, interrupting only with an occasional pious ejaculation, as he heard how Fursey, relieved of his vows, had been forced into marriage with a witch, and how, as she lay dying, she had, before he knew what was happening, breathed into him her sorcerous spirit.

"So you're a wizard," he exclaimed in horrified accents.

" Yes, but an extremely unwilling one. I'm able to fly on a broomstick and produce food by pulling on a rope. I know no other sorcery whatever. Tell me, sir, is there no way of curing a sorcerer of his affliction other than by burning him to a cinder ? You're a man who has travelled the roads of the world, and are no doubt learned in these things."

The prophet raised a claw-like hand and stroked his grizzled whiskers meditatively.

" I've never heard of any other method of treating sorcery," he said at last, " but we could try reversing the process by which you became a wizard. You could try breathing your sorcerous spirit into someone else."

Fursey shook his head despondently.

" There are few who would wish to accept such a legacy."

" Nonsense, I'll accept it. It will be a most charitable act and will put me in the very front row in Heaven."

Fursey looked at the mild-featured old man with astonishment.

" Are you not afraid that it may put you down into the other place ? "

" I've no reason to believe so, as I'll never make any use of the sorcerous powers which I'll obtain from you. All my life I've been a powerful drawer of souls. I've endowed many monasteries with the gifts acquired by my sanctity. It's unlikely that in my old age, now that passion and desire have long since ceased to trouble me, I shall be tempted to make use of such unholy powers as may attach themselves to my person. Let us lose no time, but proceed at once to the experiment."

Fursey rose joyfully to his feet and stood facing his benefactor.

" How exactly did the old witch pass her spirit to you ? " enquired the prophet.

" She simply breathed suddenly and violently into my mouth when I was not expecting such action on her part."

The old man rose to his feet and took his stand squarely on the roadway. He opened his mouth and closed his eyes tightly. Fursey, his heart beating excitedly, filled his lungs to bursting point, so anxious was he to make a good job of it and leave no trace of the sorcerous spirit in his system. Then he exhaled violently down the old man's throat. The prophet reeled and placed a trembling hand over his heart.

" How do you feel ? " Fursey enquired anxiously as he helped his companion to sit down. The old man seemed to find difficulty in speech. Tears oozed from his eyes and made a wayward course down his corrugated cheeks. His mouth remained open, and he gasped once or twice.

" I feel queer," he said at last. " My stomach seems to be on fire, and I'm conscious of turmoil in my chest, as if certain of my organs were fighting one another."

Fursey could contain his impatience no longer. He ran to a nearby tree to put the experiment to the test. He uncoiled his rope with trembling fingers and flung it over a branch. " Bread," he whispered in an agonised voice and pulled the the rope. It ran over the bough and fell to the ground at his feet, but no foodstuffs of any kind materialised.

" Hurrah ! " he shouted, " I'm cured."

" I hope it's all for the best," gasped the old man, who had risen to his feet and tottered after him.

" Of course it is," cried Fursey giving the prophet a slap on the back that nearly put him forward on his face. " Here, take this rope and throw it over one of the branches. Now, ask for wine."

The old man seemed upset, but he did as he was bid. He showed surprising agility a moment later in skipping out of the way when a gigantic beaker came crashing through the foliage. Fursey danced and capered for joy, but his benefactor, far from sharing in his good spirits, had seated himself once more on the bank, the picture of doleful foreboding. Fursey looked at him in amazement.

" What's wrong ? " he enquired. " Why don't you take the wine ? Surely you're not a teetotaller ? "

" This is a dark and sordid business," replied the prophet. " I fear that ill may come of it."

"Nonsense," rejoined Fursey. "A few more years in this wild world of sin and wrong, and then you're off to Heaven to claim your glittering reward. I don't know what you're looking so miserable about."

"I don't know what I've swallowed," groaned the old man, "but whatever it is, it has affected my system powerfully. I'm conscious of heartburn and something akin to palpitations. But apart altogether from that, I fear that I have acted somewhat precipitately in the matter. Already my rashness has betrayed me into mortal sin. I have produced alcohol by witchcraft. Oblige me by taking back your terrible gift."

"Not on your life," rejoined Fursey. "It's far safer in the keeping of a man of sterling piety like you. Drink the contents of the beaker and forget your worries."

"I'm afraid to move," whimpered the prophet, "lest perchance I fall down and die before I have confessed my sin. It is the teaching of the infallible church that a lifetime of austerity and prayer is obliterated by a final grievous sin and that nothing awaits the offender but the Pit."

"I've been walking on a tight rope over the Pit so long," replied Fursey, "that I exude brimstone through every pore. I have to leave you now as I have an important murder on hands. The best thing you can do, is trot down to the nearest monastery and devote the rest of your life to doing penance. I'm very obliged to you for your kindly act. Goodbye."

He turned and stepped out gaily along the road, his heart lighter than it had been for many a long day. He reminded himself that in future he would have to work or beg for his bread, but he felt that to be a small price to pay for his relief from the incubus of sorcery. After all, you could not pay too high a price for normality. So he continued lightly on his way until the road bent suddenly towards the mountains, and he saw high above him the great cleft which was known locally as The Gap. He hastened his steps, happy in the thought that the greater part of his journey was over. He soon came to a crossroads and realised that the road which intersected his own, was the one which led to The Gap. As he turned the corner he became suddenly aware of a hideous and unwieldy demon sitting on a stile at the side of the road. The creature was of extraordinary aspect and stature, at least ten feet in height and built in proportion. He was coal-black in hue and covered with a rough, hairy hide. His deformed head was made remarkable by a pair of eyes like burning saucers and ears that hung down nearly to the ground. He had a pair of feathered legs and was very sordid as to his habiliments. He was in every way a most deformed monster, most dreadful to behold, and the fact that he was breathing forth flaming sulphur, did not add to his attractions. Fursey was most unfavourably impressed.

" Good evening," he said hurriedly, and hastened his steps along the road.

" Just a minute, boss," said the monster hoarsely, sliding his loathsome carcase from the stile and lumbering across the road. Fursey knew that it was unlucky to encounter such apparitions, and unluckier still if they chose to follow you. He quickened his pace, but the cacodemon joined him and kept walking alongside.

" Did you hear me talking to you ? " he growled, looking down at Fursey menacingly. " I desire some conversation with you."

" I'm busy," replied Fursey nervously. " It'll have to be some other time. Go away now like a good man."

The cacodemon parted his hairy lips and disclosed a mouthful of teeth that gleamed and champed.

" I have my orders," he said doggedly. " If you won't wait to hear what I have to say to you, I'll just have to break one of your legs to prevent you proceeding further."

Fursey came to a halt and looked up at his terrible companion with foreboding.

" What is it ? " he asked faintly.

" Life is a loathsome business," said the cacodemon. " Why not end it ? "

" What's that ? " squeaked Fursey.

" Self-destruction. Why not escape from your worries and your troubles by suicide ? It's very easy."

Fursey moistened his lips, but was unable to reply.

" About thirty paces to the left," cooed the monster ingratiatingly, " there's a lovely precipice. Why not fling yourself over ? "

" Because I don't want to," gasped Fursey. " Please go away."

" Oh no," leered the cacodemon rolling a flaming eye at his victim. " I'm never going to leave you as long as you live."

He fastened a huge claw on Fursey's arm and gave him a friendly squeeze as if to emphasise his words. Fursey staggered and just managed to gain the grassy bank beside the road before his legs gave away. He seated himself quaking in every limb. The demon took his stand facing him and wagged his head roguishly.

" Don't you understand ? " he said persuasively. " I'm tempting you."

Fursey took a look at the monster's flaming jowls, shuddered and turned away his face.

" Consider your situation," continued the cacodemon quite unabashed. " You're a sorcerer whose powers benefit him nought, but are on the contrary an intolerable burden. Sooner or later you must fall into the hands of authority, from whom you can expect nothing but an uncomfortable end by fire. You have found life empty and unprofitable. Man has been unkind to you and will continue so, because you are weak and unfitted by nature for the struggle of life. Your birth into a world inhabited by the hard and the strong, was a mistake and a misfortune. You have nothing to hope for in this world. and in the next only the flaming pit of Hell awaits you. Let me lead you to the accommodating precipice to which I have already referred, and show you how easy it is."

" It would seem the height of foolishness," faltered Fursey, " to precipitate myself into Hell prematurely."

" Maybe Hell doesn't exist," was the smooth reply. " It's
certain that this world is a miserable abode.   Why hesitate to
barter your present tangible misery for the possible miseries of
another world which may not exist ? Perchance the end of all
is dreamless sleep."

" All matter clings to its present existence," argued Fursey.
" That's true even of a lifeless stone.   It resists destruction.
One has to pick up another stone to smash it."

The monster looked at Fursey with disgust and spat a sheet
of flame into the hedge.

" If you think you can blind me with science," he said
stiffly, " you're very much mistaken."

" Anyway," continued Fursey gaining courage, " you have
your facts all wrong.   I'm no longer a sorcerer, but a normal
country lad.   What makes you think that I'm so miserable ?
I have my hopes to sustain me."

The demon opened his jaws and beat his teeth together so
alarmingly that the resultant sound was like the strokes of a
hammer on an anvil.

" You're an obstinate man," he said gratingly. " Don't
you realise that I'm talking for your own good. If you're
not miserable now, you're at least going to be miserable
henceforth.   I shall never forsake you as long as you live.
How do you like that prospect ? "

" I don't like it at all," admitted Fursey.

" Well, self-destruction is the only means you have of
escaping me."

" Look here," said Fursey determinedly.   " I know that
it's the object of demons to persecute and delude mankind.
Do not imagine that you can fascinate my imagination with
your apish threats.   You may think that you're putting up a
great show with your eyes like burning saucers and your hide
like a doormat, but I'm accustomed to such manifestations.
You needn't think to impress me with your monstrous proportions or with threats to rend me in pieces.   I have suffered so
much terror and affrightment from your like during the past
year that I can gaze on the worst that Hell can produce, quite

unappalled. Oblige me by loping away now in a rapid canter.
Any negotiations that I care to enter into with the powers of
darkness, will be with the Prince of that dreadful territory
from which you have escaped. He's an old friend of mine.
Be on your way now, and don't bother me any more."

The demon seemed considerably taken aback. A stream of
black smoke issuing from either nostril, gave the impression
that he was entirely deflated.

" Is it that you want to see the Boss ? " he asked in astonishment.

" I don't discuss my affairs with underlings and callboys,"
said Fursey haughtily. " What are you in Hell anyway ? A
scullion or a stoker, I suppose."

" All right," muttered the cacodemon as he passed rapidly
into a state of condensation. " I'll call the Boss."

The outline of his giant form shivered for a moment in the
air before it disappeared.

" I've not time to wait," shouted Fursey to the empty air,
and began to march down the road. He was conscious of a
warm glow of confidence as he continued on his way. He
told himself that in order to dispel fear, all that was necessary
was to downface the danger. " I've become a man at last,"
he said to himself wonderingly, but he had not gone more than
a hundred paces when he heard a small explosion behind him.
He glanced over his shoulder and saw that Satan had appeared
on the spot where the cacodemon had stood. The Devil
looked to left and right as if searching for Fursey ; then seeing
him in the distance, came running down the road after him.

" You might have the good manners to wait for me," he
complained as he came alongside.

" I didn't send for you," replied Fursey coldly. " I want
to have nothing to do with you or your ilk."

" We'll soon see about that," said the Devil grimly. " One
of my ilk has just complained that you insulted him."

" That's right," said Fursey belligerently. " Do you want
to make anything of it ? "

The Archfiend looked surprised. His crafty eyes examined

Fursey's moonlike face for some moments. When he spoke again, he seemed to choose his words carefully.

" So at last you have rid yourself of your sorcery."

" Yes. How did you find that out ? "

" An old gentleman has just arrived in Hell. He states that his occupation was that of rustic prophet. According to what I can make out, he is of opinion that you played a very doubtful trick on him."

" Dear me, is he deceased already ? "

" He died as a result of shock shortly after you left him."

" That's too bad," commented Fursey. " I formed the opinion that he was a man of sweet and amiable nature."

" I hope you're right," said the Devil eyeing Fursey narrowly. " He created a considerable furore when he recognised his surroundings. He was still giving vent to the most uncouth language when I left. He's shouting something about filing a petition."

Fursey shook his head sadly. " He was, perhaps, a trifle too precipitate. The golden rule in life is to think twice and do nothing."

" You seem to have become suddenly endowed with wisdom," said the Devil carefully. " I observe that you are able to twist most things so that they serve your interest."

" I'm no fool," replied Fursey, sticking out his chest. " I'm well able to look after myself."

" No one suggests anything else," said the Archfiend soothingly. " I understand that you're contemplating suicide."

" I am not," said Fursey heatedly. " It seems to me that you're in an indecent hurry to get hold of me."

There was a brittle glint in the Devil's eye as he fixed his gaze on Fursey's face.

" It would be well for you to fall in with my wishes," he answered coldly. " Do you not realise that it is my intention, if you oppose me, to make your life miserable with hideous apparitions and manifestations of the most abominable character ? "

" Call them up in their dozens. I'm ready for them."

The Devil looked at him in wondrous amaze. He raised a hooked claw and thoughtfully pulled one of his pointed ears.

" Your senses are obviously in decay. How long do you think that your sanity could endure the proximity of infectious dragons and the never-ceasing bustle of demons ? Moreover, you do not seem to appreciate that it's in my power to molest you with loathsome diseases, such as involuntary twitching of the legs, for I am never without my machinery and subtle contrivances."

" Why must you always be such an unpleasant fellow ? " enquired Fursey. " No one has ever a good word to say for you. Does popularity mean nothing to you, and the good opinion of your acquaintance ? "

" It is my business to undo mankind."

" I don't care a snap of my fingers for your snares. I'm not going to commit suicide to please you or anyone else."

" Then," said the Devil grimly as he rolled up his sleeves, " I shall have to throw you over the precipice myself."

Fursey regarded him coldly.

" That would be the height of foolishness. You'll never get me then. I'll die a blessed martyr, and be carried off to Heaven to the sound of lutes."

The Devil paused and savagely shot his cuffs back into position.

" You're very glib," he snarled, " but it's only a matter of time. I'll have you in the end of all."

" I wouldn't be too certain. I've abandoned my life of wickedness. I'm no longer a man of pernicious principles."

" What's that ? " asked the Devil incredulously.

" You heard what I said. Evil is a very overrated pursuit. I never got anything out of it except kicks and beatings. I'm not going to indulge in wickedness any more. I'm going in for virtue in future."

" What you tell me causes me the greatest inquietude and alarm. Next thing you'll be trying to denounce the pact you made with me."

"What pact?" asked Fursey.

The Devil emitted a howl, and his eyes flashed lightning. "The pact which you signed in your blood selling me your soul. You swallowed the duplicate copy in my presence."

"I haven't the faintest notion what you're talking about. It's true that after I last saw you I was violently sick. Certainly, I retain no such pact about my person."

"Ah," said the Devil, "you're very clever, but the original is filed in my cabinet in Hell."

"Are you certain that you're not mixing me up with someone else? A robber captain from the County Cork, for instance."

"Look here," said the Devil violently. "Who's the Father of Lies, you or me?"

"You are," replied Fursey innocently.

"Well, kindly remember it; and don't be trying to oust me from my office. I hold an agreement for the sale of the soul of one, Fursey, in consideration of two pieces of advice."

"There's a mistake somewhere. I signed no agreement. I can neither read nor write."

"You made your mark at the bottom of it," howled the Devil indignantly.

Fursey looked at the darkening sky and the cloud drift overhead. He pursed his lips and whistled a few bars from a sprightly tune. Then he let his roving eyes return and rest carelessly on the swarthy face of the Archfiend.

"I trust," he said sweetly, "that my mark to the document in question was duly witnessed by a third party. I'm afraid that otherwise it can have no validity. Without the signature of a witness no court on earth or in Heaven would accept it as genuine in the face of my denial."

For a moment the Devil stared at Fursey, then he turned completely black. He no longer bore the slightest resemblance to a gentleman, decayed or otherwise. He stood crouched there in all his hideousness, a hunchbacked figure with pointed ears, hooves and a forked tail. Pitchy clouds rolled overhead, and darkness began to overspread the earth.

" We don't want you here," said Fursey quietly. " You would be wise to take your departure before I call a handful of children to stone you."

The Devil's countenance became contorted with a paroxysm of fury. He gave one whisk of his forked tail so that it wound for a moment around Fursey's middle, almost persuading Fursey that he was cut in half. Then in a blinding flash the Enemy of Mankind disappeared. Fursey waved a languid hand to dispel the resultant cloud of sulphurous smoke, then he turned and began to amble down the road, his hands behind his back, whistling " The Haymakers' Jig." But his confidence did not last very long ; he became sad and tired. He realised that great labours still lay ahead of him. As he climbed the rugged track that wound towards the pass, he appreciated that he might soon have hunger to contend with as well. It began to rain. Night came down, and he had to search long before he found a convenient overhanging crag, under which he crept, and rolling himself into a ball, composed himself for sleep.

Sleep did not come easily. It was cold, and there was a surprising amount of rustling and stirring on the hillside. The moon came in and out with irritating regularity as clouds scurried across the sky before the high wind which had sprung up. Fursey tossed and turned, rolling over on to his hands and knees from time to time to remove a piece of stone from the small of his back. It was past understanding how there could be so many hard, round stones in such a confined space. He grunted and wallowed and asked himself how the wind managed to blow from every quarter at the same time. No sooner had he settled himself into what promised to be a comfortable position, than the chill breeze began to play about his ankles or his neck. Then the long grasses began to tickle his ears. He hammered them flat and lying down again, slowly drifted into an uncertain sleep.

He dreamt that he was standing in a waste spot, hideous with malformed boulders and stunted bushes. It was forlorn territory, and Fursey looked about him sick with apprehension.

As his eyes accustomed themselves to the fitful light, he saw
that the blasted countryside, stretched away from where he
stood, in all directions but one ; and on that one side there was
an awful precipice. He realised that he was standing on the
very brink. Far below him a dense pall of smoke rolled about
in the abyss. In its depths thin slivers of flame, seemingly
hundreds of feet in height, wavered and stabbed the surrounding gloom, lighting for a moment the grey, billowing clouds of
smoke. A sickening smell of brimstone and burning flesh
assailed his nostrils. From the pit arose a continuous,
despairing cry, which was not one cry, but the woven screams
of a myriad human beings in unspeakable agony. As Fursey
listened shuddering, he discerned behind and beyond this
awful plaint, the never-ending crackling of human bones and
bodies, ablaze with a fire that tortured but did not consume.
He swayed, sick with terror, for he realised that he was
standing on the edge of Hell. He tore away his eyes and cast
them upwards. Worlds and universes coursed through the
heavens ; and as he gazed, he saw a host of beings like himself
as thick as snowflakes falling, ever falling from above into
the abyss.

He started from beneath the boulder fully awake. The sky
was grey in the east, and a mournful wind blew, held its
breath and sighed again, so that the tufted reeds about him,
shook their heads despairingly. He struggled to his feet
choking with terror, and made for the road. The familiar
world was about him once again, and he stared at it as if
he could never gaze his fill. He sat down by the track and
covered his face with his hands. The horror of his dream
took possession of him once more. He sat hour after hour,
alternately hiding his eyes and uncovering them to gaze at
the reality about him. What if after all he ended up in the
eternal torments of Hell ? He told himself again and again that
it could not be the case that a merciful divinity would so torture
His creatures. But he knew that as long as he lived he would
never rid himself of the beliefs and fears hammered into
his head by his teachers in his childhood. He might forget

or put aside such terrors for a little while, but he knew that they would persist in coming back from time to time to plague his sleep and waking hours, and he knew that inevitably they would forgather to press around his bed in the last awful hour when it was time for him to die.

He tried to pray, but it was no use. He realised that it would be the merest hypocrisy. He had changed. He had lost his simple faith, and he knew that it was gone for ever. Moreover, his future course of action was determined. No matter what punishment might await him, he would kill Magnus and have Maeve.

CHAPTER IX

HE stood on the ditch and peered down at the beehive hut, two hundred paces away, a hut in no way remarkable, but just like any other hut which one might find in a spot where the woods or the overhanging mountains provided shelter. Fursey fixed his eyes on it, telling himself that humble as it was, it held the woman who was superior to all other women in comeliness and kindness. It was of wickerwork, the twigs cunningly interwoven and the crevices filled with hardened mud. The conical roof was thatched with grass and rushes. Peat smoke drifted gently from the doorway : the pleasant smell came to him where he stood. In a field behind the cottage two cows moved, peacefully cropping the grass. He heard the crowing of a cock.

He looked down at his clothes. He was a sorry sight. He had torn his trousers and vest crossing a thick fence of woven thorns, and he had slipped and fallen at the edge of a bog pool.

He was conscious of the brown peat mud caked in his hair.
He climbed down from the ditch and began to consider a plan
of action.

A small boy came along the track whistling shrilly. He was
an unpleasant, grubby little fellow, who kicked the stones

along the road as he walked, and occasionally bent quickly to
pick one up and fling it at an unwary bird hopping in the
hedge. When he came to where Fursey was standing, he
halted and began to stare rudely.

" How are you, my little man ? " said Fursey, " and isn't it a glorious afternoon ? "

The boy gaped at Fursey and spat contemptuously on to the road ; but he did not deign to reply.

" Tell me," continued Fursey soothingly, " does a man called Magnus live in the little house beyond the trees ? "

The boy regarded Fursey critically.

" What will you give me if I tell you ? "

" A poor man like me has little to give except his blessing."

The boy stared at Fursey. It was obvious that he did not regard a blessing as a marketable commodity.

" Ay, he does," he admitted grudgingly.

" I want you to do something for me," continued Fursey producing the little roll of parchment on which Cuthbert had inscribed the letter of challenge. " Take this down to Magnus and hand it to him."

" What will you give me if I do ? " repeated the youth.

Fursey felt in his pockets. They were empty except for the sheathed bodkin.

" I shan't give you anything for doing it," he replied sweetly, " but if you don't do it, I'll knock your head off."

" Garn ! " exclaimed the boy contemptuously. " An old fellow like you ! "

Fursey made a move in the objectionable youth's direction. The small boy did not retreat, but bent and picked up a heavy stone. Fursey halted and the two eyed one another in silence for some moments. Then Fursey stepped back a pace.

" When you have performed the errand, I shall reward you handsomely."

The boy hesitated. " You promise ? "

" I promise."

The small boy held out his hand for the parchment, and when he had secured it, started at a run in the direction of the cottage. With the consciousness that great events had been

put in train, Fursey scrambled over the ditch and ducked
down behind a bush. Trembling, he took the poisoned
bodkin from his pocket and drew the blade from its sheath.
It glittered wickedly in the slanting sunlight. He shuddered,
pushed it back into its cover, and slipped it into his pocket.
Then he raised his head and watched with an anxious eye the
devious course which the small boy was taking. He grunted
indignantly as the youth stopped for some moments to paddle
his feet in a stream and then set off across a field in pursuit of
a rabbit ; but the urchin returned at last and circled the
fence of sharp stakes with which the hut was surrounded as a
protection against wild beasts. There was an opening through
which he could have passed with no inconvenience to himself,
but he chose rather to climb across the fence at what seemed
to be the most difficult part for such an operation. Fursey
sighed with relief as he saw the boy at last entering the doorway
of the hut.

Inside was a scene of domestic bliss. A fire blazed in the
centre of the earthen floor, and the resultant smoke filled the
interior of the hut, circulating slowly as it drifted towards the
doorway and slipped through the opening. The boy's sharp
eyes picked out at once the woman of the house standing at a
table with her sleeves rolled up as she pounded a shapeless
slab of dough into a condition more shapeless still, lifted it up,
flung it on its back, and began to beat it with her fists. Magnus
lay in a chair before the fire, his long legs stretched out on
either side as if to embrace it, his jowl on his chest, fast asleep.
The boy stood on one leg and fixed his eyes with interest on the
sword and shield which rested in a corner beside a formidable
spear.

" What do you want, Benignus ? " asked the woman
kindly.

" A message for Magnus."

" Well, you had better awaken him."

Magnus awoke with a muffled oath as he felt himself suddenly pushed. The brat was standing in front of him tendering
the tiny roll of parchment. The man yawned, rubbed his

eyes and took it from him. He examined it from every angle, finally opened it, and looked at the writing and at the back.

" This is not much good to me," he remarked. " I can't read. Where did you get it ? "

" From a queer-looking fellow up the road."

" What sort of a queer-looking fellow ? "

The boy shrugged his shoulders impatiently. " A queer-looking fellow with white hair."

" What did he look like ? "

" He looked like something that had fallen off the back of a tinker's cart," replied the boy acidly.

Magnus rubbed his head. " I'd better go and see," he muttered.

He rose, stretched himself, went out through the doorway and stood blinking in the sunlight. His roving eye rested at last on a small, plump figure peering at him from behind a bush. With a puzzled frown he strode in the stranger's direction. As he approached, the small man skipped from the shelter of the bush and hid behind another one. Magnus stopped to consider this unusual behaviour. He could see the stranger's head round the edge of the foliage and a pair of round eyes still staring at him.

" Who are you ? " he called out. " Come forth and declare yourself."

After a moment's hesitation the stranger emerged and stood in the open, one hand behind his back.

" Fursey ! " gasped Magnus. " Are you really still alive ? " and he bounded in Fursey's direction.

Fursey had expected at least a blow, and he was considerably taken aback to find his hand seized and shaken heartily. He slipped the naked bodkin into his pocket as Magnus slapped him on the back and assured him how delighted he was to see him.

" The whole countryside thinks you're dead," he exclaimed. " On the day on which the Vikings sacked Clonmacnoise, a glorious apparition of you in shining armour was seen on the hillside giving warning of the impending danger to the holy settlement. The timely vision enabled the pious inmates to seek the shelter of the round towers, and thus they were preserved from slaughter."

Fursey was too dumbfounded to reply.

"Why man," continued Magnus, scarcely pausing for breath, "you have been publicly rehabilitated, an image of you has been erected in Clonmacnoise, and the cause for your canonisation is well under way."

He seated himself on a stone and grinned at Fursey delightedly. Fursey stood opposite him, his mouth fallen open as he strove to collect his scattered wits.

"So you're not dead?" said Magnus at last.

"No," admitted Fursey, "I'm alive."

"And what are you doing in this part of the country?"

"I was passing by," stuttered Fursey, "and I thought it but courteous to call and pay my respects."

"Maeve will be delighted to see you," Magnus went on. "She told me all about you, what a harmless, poor fellow you are, and that you're a man more to be pitied than blamed; so that the bad opinion I once had of you, is entirely dispelled."

Fursey conjured up a polite smile, but from behind the smile he looked at Magnus with distaste. Magnus had become stout, his face was puffy from good cooking and a fond wife's care, his stomach pressed hard against his breeches' belt. Fursey fingered the bokin in his pocket and thought how pleasant it would be to rip Magnus to the midriff and see his entrails fall out. But in the hard school of danger Fursey had learnt how to dissemble. Black as were his thoughts, they cast no shadow across his blandly smiling countenance.

"Do you ever do an odd bit of sorcery now?" enquired Magnus giving him a fat wink, "not that your powers in that regard were ever very formidable."

"No," replied Fursey, "I'm entirely cured. I'm glad to say that I'm a normal, decent Tipperaryman once more."

" I suppose you're going back to the monastery ? "

Fursey looked at him in astonishment. " I never thought of that," he said slowly.

" It can be easily arranged," continued the soldier. " As a matter of fact I have a bit of influence with the abbot myself. We became great friends on the journey back from Britain. Come on down to the house, and we'll talk it over with Maeve. You must stay to supper anyway."

As Magnus strode ahead of him, Fursey stared at the ruddy bull-neck and broad shoulders of his host, and marvelled at the man's self-confidence. Apparently the prime necessity for success in life was a firm foundation of insensitiveness mortared well in by stupidity. Magnus entered the cottage first and stridently announced Fursey's arrival. She dropped her work at once and advanced to greet him with both hands extended.

" Is there something wrong with your eyes ? " asked Magnus solicitously.

" The peat smoke affects them," muttered Fursey, brushing away with the back of his hand the moisture which had gathered.

Maeve glanced away and dragged a stool from a corner. Fursey went stumblingly forward and seated himself. For a long time the cottage was loud with Magnus' raucous joviality, Fursey's timid replies and Maeve's silence. Once or twice when Fursey ventured to look at her, he saw that she was observing him steadily ; but when she met his eyes, she turned away her own and began to busy herself about her work. When they sat down to supper, Fursey gave a cautious account of his good fortune in encountering a man of great piety and being cured of sorcery by him. He admitted that he had been at Clonmacnoise in the flesh. He had disguised himself in a Viking's helmet and armour, and had hurried ahead of the raiders to apprise the settlement of its danger. He said nought of his sojourn among the refugee wizards in the hills.

" And what have you been doing these last ten months since the affair at Clonmacnoise ? "

" Working with a farmer here and there, making pilgrimages, and in general mending my soul."

" You must have become a man of great piety," exclaimed Magnus with admiration.

" Well, I'm better than I was," admitted Fursey modestly.

" We must really get you back to the monastery," declared Magnus.

" Yes," put in Maeve.   " It will be the best place for you."

Fursey raised his eyes to her face.

" You will be happiest there," she added quietly and turned away her head.

When the meal was over, Magnus drew two flagons of ale, and handing one to Fursey, led him out-of-doors into the mild evening sunlight.   They sat down at the base of a tree. The dreaming hills which surrounded them, the drifting smoke from distant cottages and the muttering of a nearby stream among the stones induced in them a quiet in keeping with that breathless hour of evening.   From time to time Magnus spoke, random and unfinished sentences ; occasionally he sighed for no apparent reason.   There was war in the north. It promised good and bloody fighting, and much booty.   He would like to go.   He felt that he was growing too comfortable and soft.   Sitting at home watching a woman work and eating the food which she prepared, was no life for a man.   He would like to go.   When he was old he would have plenty of time to sit warming his knees before the fire.   A homesickness came on him at times, a longing to face a fierce and bitter enemy, and to return blow for blow.   But Maeve thought that he should stay at home.   Warfare is all right for single men, she said ; a married man has his responsibilities.

Magnus heaved great sighs and buried his face in his ale-mug. He spoke another few random words.   Fursey scarcely listened.   He was thinking of the strangeness of things, of his own hatred of adventure and his longing for the quiet and safety that went with marriage and a little piece of land. He sighed too, but more gently than the windy Magnus. Then he remembered that he had sat like this under a tree in Britain and looked about him at a scene in which everything was in harmony except himself. In those days he had possessed woman and house and land, and such share of wealth as he needed. Yet he had felt himself an outsider. He had not been content : he had been a man of property sitting under a tree aware of his possessions and of the beauty of the world in which he moved ; but he had not been content. His friend the molecatcher was a philosopher and might have been able to explain these things ; but they had taken the molecatcher and hanged him from his own roof-tree.

It waxed late. Magnus rose with a grunt and led the way back to the cottage. It seemed to be accepted that Fursey would remain in the hut for the night, and after a feeble protest he consented. A bed of rushes was spread for him on the floor, and he crawled on to it muttering his thanks. Magnus and Maeve stood in the doorway of the hut until a late hour conversing in undertones. Fursey, lying on the couch, wondered what they were whispering about. He suspected that it was about himself ; and at first he strained his ears to hear, but their speech was too low, and he soon gave over the attempt. He stretched his neck on his soft pillow and reflected on the strange turn which matters had taken. Instead of quenching Magnus as he had intended, he had permitted lassitude to creep over him. His instinct now was to allow events to take whatever course they would. He told himself that he was indifferent.

He was awakened early on the following morning by a busy stir in the cottage. He was surprised that breakfast should be so early—it did not seem long after sunrise—but when the meal was finished, the reason became apparent.

" Maeve and I discussed your position last night," began Magnus. " We think that we should let the Abbot Marcus know that you are alive and with us. I'm going to set out for

Clonmacnoise this morning. I. estimate that the journey
there and back will take me three days. We think it right to
inform you of what we are doing. You may remain here
until I return. I expect that the Abbot will come back with
me."

Fursey looked at him dully, but said nothing.

" Don't you agree that we are doing the right thing ? "
asked Maeve gently.

Fursey laboriously gathered in his thoughts.

" I suppose so. Is there any danger that the abbot may
have me arrested and put on trial for sorcery ? My life has
been of little value to anyone ; still there are pleasanter ways
of terminating it than on a funeral pyre."

Maeve unaffectedly slid her hand across the table and laid
it on his. A lightning thrill shot through Fursey so that he
trembled all over. He looked up at her dumbly, and saw with
emotion that her eyes were bright with tears.

" Dear, dear Fursey," she said, " we don't believe that you
are in any danger. Ever since it was believed that your
disembodied spirit manifested itself at Clonmacnoise eight
months ago and saved the monks from destruction, your case
has been examined and argued over, and the Abbot and
community are convinced that a grievous wrong was done
you in the first place in expelling you from the monastery.
They are good men ; and the fact that you are still in the
flesh, is no reason for them to reverse their judgment. I'm
sure that they'll take you back. In any case Magnus promises
that if treachery is contemplated, he will ride ahead and give
you warning, so that you may escape to the hills."

Fursey felt that there was nothing that he could say. He
went out of the house with Magnus and helped him to saddle
his horse. The soldier was gay and whistled as he went
about his final preparations.

" I'm looking forward to this journey," he confided. " It's
good for a man to feel a horse between his legs and a sword by
his side, and to be riding out into the free air once again."

He turned to wave his hand as he rode away. Fursey returned to the cottage marvelling that anyone should rejoice at being separated from Maeve for three long days. He sat in a corner of the hut surreptitiously watching her as she went about her work. Each time he looked at her he experienced a tiny shock of surprise. Her face as it had been when he first knew her, was indelibly engraved on his mind, the face of a girl with her hair blown back by the wind, a girl with lively eyes, and one who was always laughing. That had been only a year ago, yet there was considerable change already. Her hair was more neatly kept, her gaze, though still kind, was steadier ; and there was a firm competence about her mouth which he had never noticed before. At last Maeve became embarrassed at so frequently encountering Fursey's dog-like gaze, and she indicated to him ever so gently that in the hut he was in her way. She suggested that he should go for a little walk outside, but to be sure to be back in time for the midday meal.

He rambled disconsolately in the neighbouring fields and cursed his ill-luck that he was without the love philtre. He reflected darkly on the base ingratitude of the cow who had so ill repaid his kindness to her. This would have been a glorious opportunity for the use of the love potion, a shot of it in the porridge when Maeve wasn't looking, and the woman was his. There was no doubt but that she had changed ; yet steady eyes, well-kept hair and a competent mouth were attractive to him, and he still believed her to be without peer among womankind. When he reflected that she was married to an oaf like Magnus, entirely unappreciative of her excellences, he ground his teeth impotently. The fact that Magnus had left her unguarded for three days while Fursey was in the house, was an added injury. It meant that the hearty soldier did not consider him a serious rival.

He was sitting silently at the table after the midday meal when Maeve came from the door to tell him that the small boy Benignus was enquiring for him. Fursey immediately brightened.

" That youngster is not a relation of yours or of your husband's ? " he enquired.

" No," she replied.

" Nor a friend ? "

" No."

" I formed the impression that he is a particularly offensive
little brat," said Fursey.

Maeve laughed. " I'm afraid that he is. He's a neighbour's child, and he's rather spoilt."

Fursey rose and left the hut, picking up a heavy stick
which he had noticed behind the door. The boy was waiting
outside.

" Eh, mister," he said belligerently, " you promised me
something for delivering your letter."

" I have it for you here, my little man," replied Fursey
smiling benignantly. " Let's walk up to the road, and I'll
give it to you there,"

They walked up the track, Fursey's hand resting benevolently on the boy's shoulder. When they reached the road,
Fursey tightened his grip and gave the boy a couple of
unmerciful skelps with the stick. The child fled down the road
howling for its mother, while Fursey returned to the cottage
in a state of great satisfaction. He remained in the best of
good humour for the rest of the evening.

On the afternoon of the third day there was a clatter of
hooves on the track outside : Fursey experienced a sudden
fright, but he went to the door with Maeve. Magnus was
outside helping the Abbot Marcus to alight from his horse.
Fursey stood with a sad smile upon his face looking at the
man whom he had once loved and respected so much.

" Ah, Fursey," was all that the abbot said, but he laid his
hand kindly on Fursey's shoulder. They entered the cottage
together. Some time passed in the usual commonplaces
about the weather and the crops while the abbot sipped a
bowl of milk which Maeve had placed before him. When
courtesy had been satisfied, the Abbot rose and suggested that
he and Fursey should take a little stroll. As they climbed

the track to the road Fursey noticed with sorrow that the Abbot had become bowed and old. For an hour they paced the road together. The Abbot spoke of the sense of guilt which had lain so long upon his spirit.

" As long as I have known you," he said, " I do not remember that you ever told me a lie. A year ago when you were being sorely tempted and harried by demons in your cell at Clonmacnoise, you told me of your experiences with no attempt at evasion or concealment. You did not pause to consider whether such admission on your part would perhaps prejudice me against you. When I consented to your expulsion from the monastery as a means of ridding the holy settlement of the demons which had attached themselves to your person, I did so with an uneasy conscience. We were clearly sacrificing you for the good of the community. You will appreciate how difficult it was to preserve order and good discipline while devils lurked in every dark corner saluting with cuffs and blows all who encountered them ; and when even my oldest and trustiest monks were being subjected to temptations of the lewdest character imaginable by shameless female demons dancing in and out of their cells at all hours of the day and night."

" It was hard on me all the same," said Fursey quietly.

" It was hard," admitted the Abbot, " but it was imperative to rid the settlement of its terrible visitants. And our judgment proved to be right : when you went, the demons went with you and troubled us no more. I said just now that I've never known you to tell me a lie. I'm therefore prepared to accept without further question your assurance that you have been completely cured of your sorcery. On my way hither I stopped at Cashel to inform the Bishop that you were still alive, and of your happy deliverance. He agreed, grudgingly I'll admit, that no further action should be taken against you. I observe that you are unwilling to give me a detailed account of how you have spent the last ten months, but I shall not press you on that score. I'm sufficiently convinced of the worth of your character to be

certain that those months have not been spent in evil-doing.
In short, I'm prepared to take you back into the monastery.
Your old position paring edible roots in the kitchen awaits
you.   In a year's time if you continue to give satisfaction, I
promise to consider seriously your possible promotion to the
office of Laybrother in Charge of the Poultry."

"What a little world he lives in," thought Fursey, "yet
it was once my universe."

"Well, what do you say?" queried the Abbot. "Are you
willing to return?"

"I appreciate your magnanimity," replied Fursey, "but
I can't go."

The Abbot did not speak for some minutes, but continued
to pace the road.   At last he halted and turned to look at his
companion. Fursey was grieved at the unutterable sorrow in
his eyes.

"Why?" he asked.

"Things have changed," muttered Fursey.   "I've changed.
I've seen the world, and bitter and cruel as it is, I belong
there now.   I cannot go back to the cloister."

The Abbot said nothing more ; but he looked very old and
very bowed when they helped him on to his horse an hour
later. He declined to permit anyone to accompany him,
but walked his horse slowly up the track and disappeared
around the bend without even once looking back.

Fursey sat in the darkest corner of the cottage, leaning
forward with his elbows on his knees staring at the fire. He
gazed at the playful flames, not because he was interested in
them, but because he was afraid to encounter the eyes of the
others. Magnus sat at the table with set brows oiling his
leathern shield. When that operation was completed to his
satisfaction, he began to polish his sword, grunting occasionally
as he discovered a speck of rust. In the background Maeve
clattered dishes very determinedly. She kept her back to
Fursey. At last she approached the table with a platter
in either hand.

" Move those things," she said sharply to Magnus. " Do you expect us to eat our supper off the floor ? "

Magnus raised his head and looked at her loweringly. Then with a sudden gesture of vexation he swept his armament from the table and stalked through the open doorway. He sat down on the ground outside and continued his work. Maeve, with heightened colour, began to lay the table. Fursey sat, his heart throbbing painfully, until she curtly summoned him to his meal. He shuffled over to the table and seated himself. Magnus came in a few moments later, lifted a chair and planting it very firmly, flung his huge frame on to it so that it creaked. He pushed a couple of plates aside and set his elbows firmly on the table as if to assert that he was the master of the house. The meal proceeded in silence. Fursey, who was normally a considerable trencherman, found difficulty in swallowing each mouthful. Magnus ate doggedly staring at a spot in the centre of the table. Maeve seemed to have little appetite. Fursey was afraid to lift his eyes, but her long, white hands were within his radius of vision, and he noticed that she toyed with each morsel and raised very little to her mouth. When at last she spoke, Fursey dropped his knife with the fright of suddenly hearing her voice cutting through the silence.

" I must say," she commented in a tone of icy exasperation, " that after all the trouble Magnus went to, to bring the Abbot here ; and after the hardship the Abbot himself endured in travelling such a distance at his age, it's most annoying that you should calmly refuse his offer to take you back to the monastery. What will the Abbot think, I'd like to know ? "

Fursey stared at his plate, too miserable to attempt a reply. There was a low grunt from Magnus.

" Leave me out," he growled. " I enjoyed the ride to Clonmacnoise and back."

" Why did you refuse to go ? " persisted Maeve.

Fursey raised his eyes to her face. It seemed to him that never had she looked as beautiful as now, with the pale flame of anger flushing her cheeks. He felt as if he must burst into tears. Magnus lifted a bone from his plate and cracked it between his teeth.

" Leave the man alone," he said indistinctly. " What he does with his life is his own affair, and no one else's. Maybe he doesn't like psalm-singing. I know I wouldn't."

He flung the end of the bone into the corner, and heaving himself from his chair, lumbered across to the doorway. He picked up his sword as he went and, wandering across the yard, passed through the wicket in the thorn fence. Fursey saw him crossing the field, idly cutting the heads off the thistles and nettles.

Fursey crept out of the house too the moment Maeve had turned her back. He circled the hut almost on tiptoe and, gaining the road, wandered some hundreds of paces along it, until he found a convenient bank on which to seat himself. He remained there for a long time listening dully to a care-free bird tinkling in the hedge. He knew that as far as Maeve was concerned, he had worn out his welcome in the cottage and that it was expected of him that he would take his leave. He wondered how much longer he could stay before they put him out. It was obvious that he should without further delay proceed to the quenching of Magnus. But how was he to kill Magnus without Maeve knowing it and perhaps even denouncing him to the authorities as a murderer ? The affair must be made to look like an accident. His thoughts raced ahead, and he saw himself gently comforting the widow, one manly arm about her waist as she sobbed on his shoulder, while Magnus lay in the corner looking very dignified in his martial furniture, and the neighbours thronged the cottage shaking their heads and saying what a nice fellow he had always been. But how was the affair to be made look like an accident ? One scratch of the poisoned bodkin would be enough. If only it were later in the year, he could perhaps persuade Magnus to go picking blackberries with him, and when Magnus wasn't looking, scratch him deftly with the poisoned bodkin on the thumb. But as yet it was only the month of May, and it was in the highest degree unlikely that he would be permitted to remain in the cottage until the black-berries had ripened in the autumn.   Maybe he could persuade Magnus to come for a swim, and could scratch his back as he was letting himself down some thorny bank into the water. Magnus would think it was a straying bramble that had injured him, and would think nothing of it until he found himself unexpectedly in his death throes.   It didn't seem a very good idea, but Fursey was unable to think of a better. He sighed as another difficulty came into his mind.   How would he set about winning Maeve's affections when Magnus was safely under the clover ?   Fursey had not the remotest idea as to how one set about making love.   He rose to his feet and began to pace nervously back and forward.   He realised that he must set in motion every bit of brain he had, for he was at a crossroads in his life, and his future happiness depended on his now using his share of wit to the best advantage.   Yes, he must seek instruction in the matter of engaging Maeve's affections.   But from whom ?   Why, obviously from the man who had gained them already—from Magnus.   He had been successful with Maeve.   Fursey must therefore defer quench-ing this valuable source of information until he had learnt how Maeve's maiden heart had been beguiled by her preeent husband.   He turned and walked slowly back towards the cottage, secretly pleased that the inevitable assassination had been deferred for the time being, for at the back of Fursey's mind there lurked the uneasy thought that his onset on Magnus might fail and result in the outraged Magnus killing him.

When he re-entered the hut, Maeve had a splinter of burning wood in her hand and was lighting the taper on the table. Magnus was sprawled before the fire, heavy with food or thought.   It was snug and comfortable within ;   and as Fursey's eyes accustomed themselves to the thick peat smoke, he looked appreciatively around the kitchen at one object after another, the hearth, the chairs and table, the plates and the food, and all the other furnishings of a home.   He gazed longingly at the stout walls and the door.   Outside was night and terror. Uncertain things were abroad, men and beasts, equally dangerous. But in here there was safety. He told himself that, come what might, he would obtain possession of this cottage and never wander the unfriendly roads again. He looked across at Maeve. How graceful she was as she moved lightly to and fro intent on the final tidying of the house before she laid herself down for the night. What a contrast, he thought, to her dull, thickset husband. It seemed to him that he had rarely seen an uglier piece of merchandise. He was like a bullock you'd see looking at you over a hedge, trying to assemble its thoughts and not succeeding.

" I've been thinking," said Fursey aloud ; " I've been thinking of my position here. I feel that I should not trespass any longer on your hospitality. I feel that it's time for me to leave."

Maeve turned her head. Her face was bright. " It's late now. Wait till to-morrow morning anyway."

" Thank you," Fursey replied quietly.

As he rose to go over to his bed in the corner, he saw that Magnus' eyes were fixed on him. The soldier said nothing, but rose some moments later and yawned.

Fursey slept little. It was only when he was lying on his bed that he realised how hurt he was at Maeve's ready acquiescence in his departure. The realisation that he wasn't wanted was a bitter one. He knew now that he would have to leave on the morrow, and he considered desperately whether he would go back to Cuthbert on the mountain and beg him for a love philtre. But he realised that such a course would be the merest madness. He was convinced that Cuthbert's exasperation on seeing him return would be such that powerful magic might well be set in train with deplorable results. He wondered dolefully what it would feel like to be turned into a frog and spend an uncertain life beside a stream dodging the birds, or worse still to be imprisoned for a thousand years in a bottle. The thought of such a fate affected him powerfully and his forehead became damp with sweat   He dismissed from his mind all thought of the accursed mountain and, rolling over, pressed his hot face into the pillow. In an agony of self-pity, he asked himself where he would go and what would become of him. Before long the ebb and flow of Magnus' snoring began to shake the air of the cottage. Fursey listened indignantly, his plump fist clutching the hilt of the poisoned bodkin in his pocket. As the jarring note attained a high pitch and stumbled once or twice before receding, Fursey formed a desperate resolution. On the morrow he would somehow or other kill Magnus, having first questioned him as to how he had won Maeve.

He rose very solemnly on the following morning and shaved himself with Magnus' flint razor. The master of the house was friendly, making breezy remarks on the fineness of the day, a fact which any fool could see for himself. Maeve moved about the cottage demurely. Fursey spoke little, but kept his hand in his pocket and watched Magnus closely for an opportunity to give him a surreptitious nick with the bodkin. He felt that the situation was desperate, and was quite prepared to kill Magnus and forgo previous questioning as to how a woman's affections are best won. As the breakfast neared its end he had made up his mind to drop his knife on the floor, and when under the table recovering it, to draw the bodkin and prick Magnus in the hindquarters so gently that the lethal nick would be mistaken for the action of a splinter in the chair. But before he could put the plan into execution the soldier pushed his plate away from him and, rising, stretched himself with a mighty yawn. The unpleasant fellow was constantly stretching himself as if the house was too small for him and as if he wanted to push off the roof. Fursey rose, too, and went around the table so as to be near his host. His right hand was closed tightly over the handle of the weapon in his pocket.

" I've made up a package of food for you to take with you on your journey," said Maeve to Fursey.

Magnus turned and looked over his shoulder with affected surprise.

" What journey ? " he asked.

" Fursey is leaving now."

" Nonsense," retorted Magnus. " You can't turn a man out on to the road when he hasn't made up his mind where he wants to go. Stay a week, Fursey. That will give you time to look round you. You want to stay, don't you ? "

Fursey glanced from the broad, smiling face of the soldier to the set countenance of the wife. Her lips were drawn in a thin, hard line.

" Yes," he replied softly, " it would suit me to remain for a few days more."

Magnus clapped a huge hand on his shoulder. " Then stay. I like to see a man about the house."

Maeve turned her back and went quickly to the corner, where she began moving and gathering plates. One fell from her hand and smashed itself on the floor.

Magnus moved lazily through the doorway into the fresh morning sunlight outside. Fursey trailed out after him.

" Women ! " said Magnus contemptuously, and he gave Fursey a broad wink.

CHAPTER X

DURING the ensuing days Magnus spoke little ; he seemed preoccupied, full of heavy thoughts. He was considerate and kind in his dealings with Fursey, but Maeve remained formal and polite. Fursey tried to make himself useful, he fed the hens and chatted to the cows, knowing that cows yield the most milk when kept in good humour. From time to time he seized a broom and swept the floor with such thoroughness that Magnus began to complain of the gritty quality of the porridge, and Maeve had to take the broom from Fursey and tell him that she preferred to perform that office herself. Fursey, when he was alone, shook his head and told himself that she had become a very managing kind of woman, and thereafter confined his labours

to the hens, amongst whom he became very popular. They soon realised that he always had his pockets stuffed with food, and they came tearing from all directions the moment he was sighted. He hoped vaguely that by making himself useful about the little farm he might prevail on its owners to retain him as farmboy, and that he would so gain time and could wait for a suitable opportunity to execute his fell purpose. It came into his mind from time to time that perhaps Maeve was in love with him and that her anxiety to get rid of him had its roots in feminine psychology, which, he was beginning to realise, was in the highest degree peculiar. When this possibility first struck him he made his way along the nearby stream until he found a deep pool surrounded by trees. He studied his countenance in that green mirror. It reflected a round, foolish face, thatched with prematurely white hair. He noted that his snub nose was without character, and had to admit that his general expression was far from intriguing. Whatever way he contorted his features they stared back at him with a look compounded half of astonishment and half of fright. He sighed and sadly admitted to himself that his looks were not such as to beguile a woman's heart. Still, the thought remained with him, and he often sat by himself pondering the possibility. He remembered how she had come to be affianced to Magnus. Her father had wished to re-marry, and she had felt that there was no room for two women in the one house. Magnus had been attentive and masterful, and so it had come about. Perhaps she had never really cared for Magnus at all. Much of his time Fursey spent in day dreaming. He saw himself in heroic attitudes. He imagined one of the cows going mad and coming rampaging into the cottage where Maeve, unconscious of her danger, was calmly making a pie. He heard her screams and burst in the door. In a moment he had the infuriated beast by the horns, and the two of them were in death grips on the floor. So powerfully was he taken up by his dream that he went round to the back of the house and looked over the stockade at the two cows to see whether he could detect any signs of incipient insanity, but he had to admit that they were the most harmless looking pair of browsers he had ever seen, seemingly incapable of even a bad thought.

One night as he lay on his bed with his mouth wide open watching the curious play of the firelight on the ceiling, he heard Magnus and Maeve deep in argument. She spoke rapidly and with determination, insisting that Fursey must leave the house. Magnus answered growlingly that it would be inhospitable and unchristian to turn out on to the road a man who had no means of subsistence. As Fursey held his breath and listened, the thought again struck him that perhaps Maeve was in love with him and was trying with womanish wile to keep the wool down over Magnus' eyes. Perhaps all this time she had been striving to keep her deplorable brute of a husband in ignorance of her real feelings while she waited for Fursey to do the manly thing. A wild impulse gripped him, urging him to spring out of bed and run across the floor at Magnus, brandishing the bodkin, but caution supervened. He detected a note of genuine bitterness in Maeve's voice as she persisted in her entreaty. At last he heard Magnus impatiently and wearily consenting.

" All right, all right," he said. " I'll tell him that he must go in a couple of days."

Fursey lay motionless and played with a new thought. Could it be that Maeve, cleverer than her husband, divined Fursey's tender regard and distrusted her own strength in resisting any advances which he might choose to make. This was a pleasant thought. It made him see himself as a formidable lover. He shook his head at himself for being such a sad rogue and, smiling happily, fell asleep. He slept the whole night through with a self-satisfied smirk on his chubby features. When morning came he sat up in bed, remembered the argument of the previous night and told himself coldly that he would kill Magnus that day.

He chatted affably during breakfast and announced his intention of leaving the territory on the morrow. He said

that he once more felt the itch to wander abroad, and he
understood that the scenery in the south was very remarkable.
Landowners would no doubt be glad of his services now that
the peat-saving season was at hand, and later in the year
there would be the harvest. Perhaps some farmer with a
shrewd eye for a good workman would entrust him with the
care of a flock of sheep. He had always wanted to be a
shepherd and learn to blow music through a rustic pipe. A
man of spirit, he asserted, need never be in fear of hunger.
If the worst came to the worst, he could always join some
gang of gallant bandits or offer his services as a fighting man
to some robber lord, such as The Wolf of Ballybunion.
Magnus and Maeve listened in silence to his flow of talk
until it petered out at last somewhat lamely. Magnus emitted
a windy sigh.

" We'll miss you," he said heavily.

Maeve said nothing, and Fursey plunged hurriedly into a
further account of the gay and careless life which might be
enjoyed by a man of lively mind like himself, who had no
responsibilities. He prattled on, the words stumbling over
one another, for he was embarrassed by Magnus' apparent
sincerity. When they rose from the table, he suggested
gaily to Magnus a last walk together to a lonely tarn in the
mountains a couple of miles distant from the hut. The
soldier readily consented, and they set out, Fursey full of
self-confidence and delighted with the success of his guile.
It was a grey, cheerless day. The sky was overcast as they
crossed the waste of bog and swamp and came at length to
the tarnside. Fursey chose for their seat a spot at the lake's
edge, from which the rock dropped sheer into the waters
below. He had continued to chatter amiably during their
walk, the moody Magnus scarcely answering his absurdities ;
but now as they sat with the deep, still water beneath their
feet and the awful cliffs rearing themselves above, Fursey
talked less and in a more subdued key, until at last he too
became silent. It was a lonely spot, an area of gloom, where
no birds ever sang and where winds rarely came to stir the

long grasses by the lakeside. To Fursey the tarn was familiar. He had visited it several times during the preceding week and had chosen it as a fit spot for the terrible deed which he contemplated. Both men sat motionless. Fursey had sunk his right hand deep in his pocket and fastened it over the hilt of the fatal weapon. It seemed to him that the wild beating of his heart must surely be heard by his companion. It was a relief to him when Magnus spoke.

" So you're really determined to go away to-morrow ? "

" Yes," he replied softly.

Magnus frowned down at the water.

" Well, I suppose I can't hold you against your will. But I'm sorry that you're going, and I'll certainly miss you. Apart from the fact that I like the company of men, I've come to have a great liking for you personally."

Fursey stirred uncomfortably and changed the subject.

" I'm not a man who will ever settle down for long in the one place," he declared. " Though you mightn't think it, I have a considerable dash of the adventure spirit in my system. Roads lure me, and the hope of finding adventure around the bend."

Magnus bent his heavy brows on his companion.

" You surprise me. I shouldn't have thought it."

" Oh, yes," squealed Fursey, " I love adventure. In the course of an interesting career I've bested many a dragon and noonday devil ; but, strangely enough, success with women has always evaded me. You're a man of the world. Maybe you can explain the reason for that ? "

" Women ? " responded Magnus. He spoke with difficulty as if the subject filled him with almost unutterable gloom.

" Yes," chirruped Fursey, " females, those amiable and gracious creatures who crown our lives and efforts."

" ' Crown our lives ' is right," said Magnus lugubriously ; " more efficiently than a warrior might do with a two-handed sword."

Fursey was at a loss to understand this military jargon, so he tried again, hoping to get a plain answer.

" In brief, how should one set about engaging a woman's affections ? "

For some moments Magnus did not answer, but gazed dully between his feet at the water wrinkling in between the stones.

" The matter is very recondite," he said with an effort. " I knew nothing about women when I fell in love with her ladyship beyond in the cottage, so, being a practical man, I consulted an aged female soothsayer who lived in a hole in a hill a long distance from here. She was very aged and had the reputation of knowing everything. I often doubt now whether she did. If she was so very knowledgeable, it doesn't seem to have done her much good in life. I had to climb halfway up a cliff face to get to the rockery in which she had set up residence. I found her huddled in rags and filth, gnawing a crust and trying to warm herself over a spark."

" She must have been an interesting old lady," said Fursey breathlessly. " What did she say·about love ? "

" She said that the whole matter resolved itself into a very simple formula, that every woman wants a man to be at the same time sweetheart, father, companion and child to her.'

" I see," said Fursey.

" She said that if a man designs to engage a woman's affections, he must first be masterful, then he must chase her, metaphorically of course——"

" Of course," agreed Fursey.

" ——then he must pay homage to her elusiveness. He mustn't press the chase too hard, but must seem to tire and be on the point of giving up in despair. Then he must show fresh determination and chase her again until she surrenders. After that he must never again assert his superiority in word or deed."

The light in the sky had changed, and Fursey frowned at the merry sleekness of the water.

" Did I understand you to say that the aged soothsayer held the operation to be a simple one ? "

" She did."

"It doesn't seem simple to me."

"Nor to me," agreed Magnus.

"If only I could read," said Fursey, "I'd like to have it down in writing. Did you try this simple formula with Maeve?"

"No."

"Yet you won her."

"Yes."

"Would you recommend me to plan my future conquests on those lines?"

"No, unless you're some class of an acrobat. In my opinion life is too short. I'd rather fight a battle any day. At least you know who hits you."

Fursey threw a rueful glance at his companion and began to experience great depression of spirit.

"I don't know," declared Magnus, "why a man who longs for adventure should wish to weight himself down with the heart and hand of a lady."

"I've never seen a woman swoon for love of me," confided Fursey. "I freely admit it. I feel that their coldness in my regard is a challenge to me. I suppose that's why the subject interests me—the fascination of the unachieved."

"I expect that's what's at the bottom of it," agreed Magnus, "but it's crazy. Marriage corks the adventure spirit. Thereafter we merely wait in comfort for death."

The two men sat staring gloomily at the black ooze of water.

"I wish you wouldn't go away," said Magnus suddenly. There was a huskiness in his voice which affected Fursey powerfully. "If you go I'll have no one to talk to. You can stay with us as long as you wish. You don't eat much anyway, and you can make yourself useful about the house and farm. Will you not change your mind and remain?"

Fursey said nothing. A little smile came about the corners of his mouth, half sad, half bitter. He drew the poisoned bodkin from his pocket, looked at it for a moment, and then with a flick of his wrist sent it spinning into the dark waters below.

"What was that?" asked Magnus, startled by the sudden movement.

"I've told you a host of lies," said Fursey. "I don't want to go away to-morrow. I hate adventure. I'm afraid of the roads and what may lie in wait round the corner. I'm terrified of hunger and hardship. All I want from life is a small house with strong walls to keep adventure away from me. That and something else."

He could hear Magnus' heavy breathing, but he did not raise his eyes. He sat, a pathetic little figure, crouched on the slab of rock, staring ahead of him, his two hands clasped between his knees.

"What was that you flung away?" came Magnus' voice.

"A poisoned bodkin. One scratch would have meant death. I coaxed you here this morning so as to kill you. That has been my intention all the while I was in your cottage. When I had killed you, my design was to take Maeve, who to my mind excels all other women."

He was conscious of a choking sound proceeding from his companion, but still he did not look round. He expected to feel himself seized and flung into the tarn in the wake of the bodkin, but nothing happened. When he turned his eyes at last to look at Magnus, the big soldier was staring at him round-eyed.

"Well, aren't you the frisky fellow!" gasped Magnus. "And why didn't you do it instead of throwing away your weapon?"

"I've learnt," said Fursey mournfully, "that it's no use trying to be wicked unless it's already in a man's nature to be so."

"Philosophy now, by the powers above!"

"It's a great truth," said Fursey gravely. "It took me a long time to learn it."

" And all the time you were thinking of giving me a dig with that thing ? "

" A nick would have been enough," explained Fursey. " It was smeared with a most potent poison."

" It's a good thing for you that you didn't try it," snorted Magnus. " I'd have mangled you."

" You don't seem to understand," said Fursey patiently. " You would scarcely have had time to retaliate. One scratch would have put you into paroxysms."

Magnus stared at him with unbelieving eyes ; then he gave a sudden shout of laughter.

" By God, you've more manhood than I credited you with. Aren't you the hardy rogue ? And were you really planning to murder me all the time you were eating my bread and salt ? "

" Yes," admitted Fursey sheepishly, " that was my damnable intent. Did you never suspect me ? "

" Not at all. I was convinced that you were a harmless, poor slob."

Fursey puffed out his chest, well satisfied that his manhood was vindicated.

" But," said Magnus suddenly, " if you're in love with Maeve, why didn't you carry her off when I gave you the chance ? You can't say opportunity was lacking. I gave you three days."

" You don't mean to say," said Fursey incredulously, " that you wanted her carried off ? "

" Well," admitted Magnus somewhat shamefacedly, " I had a sort of hope. After all, there was a broomstick handy behind the door."

" In other words," said Fursey stiffly, " you're telling me to my face that I'm a liar. You didn't believe me when I told you that I was cured of sorcery."

" I did indeed," replied Magnus hastily. " Please don't take it that way. Of course I believed you ; but, situated as I was, I couldn't help hoping that a little of the old magic still clung to your person, just enough to raise a broomstick into the air. I'm sorry if what I've said seems to imply a deviation from the truth on your part. I really didn't mean it that way."

Fursey stared haughtily at his companion until a sudden realisation of the turn the conversation had taken made him slide all at once from his attitude of injured pride.

" What's that ? " he gasped. " Do I understand you to say that you want to get rid of Maeve ? "

Magnus nodded dumbly.

" Why ? "

" Have you not noticed about her a sharp, shrewish look ? "

" I have not," retorted Fursey indignantly. " The most I'll admit to, is that there is in her air a certain self-sufficiency,"

Magnus shook his head gloomily. " There's more than that."

" I'll thank you to keep a civil tongue in your head when you're talking about her," said Fursey hotly. " You seem to forget that I'm in love with her."

Magnus began to stutter an apology ; then he stopped and hung his head. He glanced up at Fursey shyly. Some moments passed. Very slowly the soldier's face cleared as his mental machinery began to stir. The apologetic look made room for a look of surprise. His countenance slowly flushed and his brow darkened.

" Look here," he said angrily. " That woman is my wife, and I'm not going to listen to her being insulted."

" It's you who insulted her," snapped Fursey.

Magnus emitted a sudden roar. " What are we talking about ? You have me all confused. What right have you to be indignant about anything ? You're nothing but a stygian villain, eating my bread and all the time resolved on the incivility of prodding me with a poisoned bodkin ! "

" I see that you're determined to hurt my feelings," said Fursey. " That's all the thanks I get for saving your life."

" Saving my what ? " howled Magnus.

" Oblige me by not raising your voice. I decline to continue the discussion unless it is carried on in the key usual to gentlemen when they meet to discuss their affairs. There is nothing so vulgar as raucous howling."

" Tell me how you saved my life ? " repeated Magnus weakly.

" By not prodding you with the lethal blade, of course. Only for my laudable restraint in the matter you'd now be lying here, completely black in all probability, with a dozen vultures squatting around you in a ring. Am I to get no thanks for that ? "

" I'm sorry," said Magnus humbly. " Will you take my hand and we'll be friends."

Fursey took the soldier's proferred palm and gave it a dignified shake.

" Where did we get to in the discussion ? " asked Magnus uncertainly.

" I admitted that I loved your wife, and you on your part admitted that you wanted to get rid of her," replied Fursey primly. " We got that far and no further. You expressed surprise that I hadn't already abducted her during your misguided efforts to have me lodged in a monastery. We may as well dispose of that idea at once. I'm not prepared to attempt her abduction for two excellent reasons : Firstly, I don't think the use of force a good initial basis for a sub-sequent happy union of heart and mind ; and secondly, I don't think I'd succeed. She's a muscular woman and might inflict an injury on me. Do you think there's any possibility of her going with me voluntarily if you turned your back for a moment ? "

" No," replied Magnus dolefully. " Unfortunately she's sore assotted on me, and she thinks you're a horrible little hop-o'-my-thumb."

" Oh, does she ? " replied Fursey huffily. " If she's not careful, I'll take my affections elsewhere."

" No, don't do that;" put in Magnus hastily. " I'm sure we can come to an arrangement. I have been hoping that you would at least consent to remain in the house for a month or two, so that I'll be able to slip away to the war in the north. After all, a husband has certain obligations to his wife, and one of them is not to leave her alone and unprotected. Maeve, like all women, is subject to astounding fancies if left alone at night. She begins to be afraid that there are bandits in the cupboard and that every noise outside is a demon creeping up on the house. Women are very dependent on us."

" Are they ? " muttered Fursey.

" Yes," said Magnus, surprised. " I thought everyone knew that. Well, the position is that I've grown weary of that woman's apron strings. I can't go out and pick a quarrel with a friend in a tavern but I feel those apron strings tightening. I feel all the time that I'm being played like a fish. When I pull hard she lets out the line a little, but she never lets go. I'm sick and tired of it, and I'm determined not to spend my life sitting at her feet. You can be her pet and warm yourself before the fire for the rest of your life for all I care. I have a solution which is in the highest degree watertight. I'll go across to Britain. When we were in Britain last summer the King of Mercia felt my muscles and offered me service in his army any time I wanted it. I undertake to have a message sent home within a month to the effect that on a well-fought field my body was dug out from beneath a heap of slain and subsequently buried with martial pomp and circumstance. Maeve will fall in a swoon, and both you and she will go into mourning. In a half-year's time she'll have got used to the look of you about the house, and eventually she'll consent to marry you. I assure you that it is merely a matter of habit with women. They get used to men just the same as they get used to the furniture. Never fear, she'll accept you in the long run in spite of your looks."

Fursey was conscious of the liveliest emotion. He clutched Magnus' fist again and shook it warmly.

" It's a most brilliant idea," he said excitedly, " and it has the advantage of being highly respectable. I was always against irregular unions. After all, one has a duty to society to preserve appearances."

" You'll stay then ? ". asked Magnus eagerly, " and look after Maeve until you receive intelligence of my demise ? "

" Of course I will," responded Fursey ; " and after it, too, if she'll have me."

Magnus' honest face glowed with satisfaction as he rose and began to lead the way back towards the cottage. The peaty soil under Fursey's feet was soft and springy, the lark which soared overhead seemed to pour down its congratulations. Fursey walked with his face raised to catch every playful breeze. His whole being was suffused with a strange, uneasy feeling of happiness. As they neared the cottage he spoke in a loud whisper to his companion.

" When do you plan to leave ? "

" In a few days," muttered the second conspirator.

As they passed through the wicket in the thorn fence, Fursey began to wax nervous.

" Will you tell her now that I'm not leaving to-morrow after all ? "

" Yes, of course," replied Magnus roughly. He turned on Fursey a piercing eye as he noticed that the latter had begun to lag behind. " Don't tell me that you're afraid of a woman."

" Oh, no," lisped Fursey. " Of course not."

They ducked their heads in the low doorway and entered the cottage. Magnus kicked a chair out of his way and took his stand near the fire. Maeve seemed to sense that something was afoot. She put down a bowl of buttermilk which she held in her hand and turned to look at them across the fire. Through the drifting smoke Fursey could see that she was quite calm and self-possessed.

" We men have been talking," said Magnus. " I'm riding north to the war in a few days' time."

Maeve glanced calmly from her burly husband to Fursey quaking in the background. She said nothing. Magnus went to the corner and picked up his spear. He tested the stout ash between his great fists. When he spoke again, he avoided looking at her.

" I won't be-gone for long," he lied ; " perhaps for a few weeks. In the meantime Fursey will stay here to guard the house,"

Maeve turned and picked up the bowl of buttermilk as if nothing had happened.

" Fursey is our guest," she said quietly. " He is welcome to stay as long as he wishes."

Fursey stumbled out of the cottage in Magnus' wake, scarcely conscious of where he was going. He stood outside trembling in every limb.

" A very formidable woman," he said shakily.

Magnus' brow was set in hard, firm lines. He walked to the corner of the cottage, while Fursey trailed along in his rear. Then he weighed the spear carefully in his hand, raised and flung it so that it stuck quivering in the palisade. Two startled cows went scampering across the field.

" Mark my words," said Magnus darkly, " she's up to some devilment."

On the evening of the following day Fursey was sitting at the base of the tree, his mind blank, gazing at the sun's afterglow in the west, when Magnus emerged from the cottage and took his arm in a grip which made him squeal. The soldier led him some distance from the cottage before he spoke.

" There's a complication," he hissed.

" What ? " asked Fursey blankly, not knowing what his companion was talking about.

" She says that she's going to present me with a pledge of our love."

Fursey gawked at Magnus with his mouth open.

" Don't you understand, you clodpoll ? She's going to present me with a squawker."

" Oh," said Fursey.

" I wouldn't be surprised if it s ail on purpose. This is a woeful complication."

" I don't mind," said Fursey brightly. " I'll adopt it."

Magnus scowled at him. " Do you think that I'd entrust my child to a ninnyhammer like you ? "

He stalked away. Fursey gaped after him, and then went over and sat down once more beneath the tree.

For two days Magnus moved about morosely. Fursey tiptoed in and out of the cottage, fearful of attracting attention. The soldier, when he spoke to his wife, addressed her with a rough kindliness. Maeve paid little attention to either of them. She seemed to live in a world of her own, remote from mundane things. Fursey watched her anxiously as she sat for hours on end by the fire, smiling slightly to herself.

" She despises us both," Magnus confided to Fursey a couple of days later as he sat on the grass outside the door savagely polishing his sword. It was already dusk, but the soldier had sat there since sunset. " She hasn't told me so, but I know it. She finds herself on the level of creation, and for all she cares the two of us may go and drown ourselves. She has another allegiance now. She is complete."

Fursey could not think of anything to say.

" She knows what we have been planning," continued Magnus fiercely. " She hasn't said so, but I feel it. And the curse of the thirteen orphans on her, instead of telling the two of us what she thinks of us and blistering the hides off us as we deserve, she chooses to be soft-spoken and gentle ! Why doesn't she let fly at us ? Why ? "

" I suppose," said Fursey miserably, " it's not in her nature."

Magnus flung down his sword on the grass.

" I'm remaining here," he declared. " You'll have to go. Now and forever my legs are entangled in this house. I should have known that marriage is the end of adventure. Here, help me to gather up my weapons."

He rose and picked up sword and spear. Fursey clumsily gathered up the shield and corslet. " What are you going to do with them ? " he asked dully.

" Put them in the corner beyond the fire where the dust can gather on them."

They entered the cottage, and Magnus piled his weapons. Maeve was sitting by the fire, but she did not raise her head. Fursey looked about him, but then remembered that he had no possessions to take with him.

" Fursey is going," said Magnus.

Maeve, brooding smilingly over the fire, did not seem to hear.

" Fursey is leaving us," repeated Magnus, touching her gently on the shoulder.

" Goodbye, Fursey," she said, but even then she did not raise her head.

Fursey walked across the kitchen and out of the house. Magnus stood beside him at the door. For one moment the two defeated men looked at one another, then Fursey turned and made his way up the track. It was dusk. He did not pause, but began to plod slowly along the road which led over the hills into the unknown lands in the south. In the dim light, against the mighty backcloth of creation, the tumbled mountains and valleys over which the shadows of approaching night were gathering, he seemed a negligible figure. He was indeed a negligible figure, a small, bowed man holding his torn coat tightly about him, not only for warmth, but as if to keep from the vulgar gaze his terrors and the remnants of his dreams. And so, as he goes down the road, he is lost to view in the gathering shadows, glimpsed only for a moment at the turn of the track or against the vast night sky, just as we have managed to catch a glimpse of him through the twilight of the succeeding centuries.

Last spring I walked the road from Clonmacnoise to Cashel, and from Cashel to The Gap. Fursey and the others are still there, trampled into the earth of road and field these thousand years.